The Canadian Climate

By

Clarence Eugene Koeppe, Ph. D.

McKNIGHT & McKNIGHT
BLOOMINGTON, ILLINOIS

PRINTED AT BLOOMINGTON, ILL.

PREFACE

The purpose of this discussion is twofold: first, to show the broad features of the climate of Canada and Newfoundland as a whole; and, second, to present some of the seasonal characteristics in more detail and on a regional basis. There have been numerous brief descriptions and more or less detailed sectional treatments of the climate of these countries; but no previous attempt has been made to bring together the essential climatic features under one cover. All of the treatments which seem to be authentic have been freely drawn upon; and, wherever possible, the material has been quoted, the assumption being that these descriptions by authors, most of whom have actually experienced that about which they write, could not be improved upon by one who has not had that experience. The inestimable helpfulness of their work is hereby appreciatively acknowledged. Most of the photographic illustrations used have been generously furnished by the Natural Resources Intelligence Service of the Canadian Department of the Interior.

The data for this study have been derived from a variety of sources, among them being: the regular publications of the Canadian government; the records of explorers and scientific expeditions and missionary enterprises; the world weather records compiled under the auspices of the Smithsonian Institution; and the United States Weather Bureau publications (for data for the bordering lands of the United States and Alaska). The chief source, however, has been the original records of the Meteorological Office at Toronto. All authentic records have been used regardless of the period or the length of record. This use has been necessitated by the sparsity of stations, especially in the less inhabited portions of the country. For the same reason, almost no adjustments of short to long record stations have been attempted, the contention being that to do so would introduce more error than would a careful use of the records as they stand. In all instances involving temperature, the Fahrenheit scale has been used; precipitation has been expressed in inches; and cloudiness in per cents of the sky covered.

The number of years of record for the various stations varies widely; and there is also a variation in the lengths of record

PREFACE

for the several climatic elements of an individual station. Almost without exception, the record is ten years for all weather frequencies such as number of days with fog, hail, precipitation, thunderstorms, and gales, for relative humidity, and for the frequency of wind directions as found in the tables of the Appendix. The length of record for temperature and precipitation data is indicated for each station in connection with the tables in the Appendix. As stated before, the scarcity of climatic data for many portions of Canada necessitated using all records regardless of their length.

In the construction of maps, only the broad and general features of distribution of the various elements have been intended. There is, however, more detail shown in the more densely populated districts because of the greater number of meteorological stations and because of the greater reliability of the climatic data. Relief and distribution of land and water have been taken into account in drawing the lines; this is notably true in the case of British Columbia.

It is only through the active and willing assistance of the Staff in the Canadian Meteorological Office at Toronto that this study has been possible; special thanks is due to their climatologist, Mr. A. J. Connor, who has given much first-hand information and who has read the manuscript critically. This does not mean, however, that Mr. Connor endorses every statement made in this book, although the author has been glad to accept many of his criticisms. Dr. W. Elmer Ekblaw of the Geography Staff of Clark University has been helpful particularly in the study of Arctic Canada. To Dr. Charles F. Brooks, also of the Clark Staff, is due the author's most sincere thanks for his constant and careful attention in the preparation of the manuscript and for his many valuable suggestions. Without his friendly and encouraging council this book would not have been attempted.

CLARENCE EUGENE KOEPPE.

CONTENTS

FIG. 1—General identification map.

CHAPTER I

THE NON-ATMOSPHERIC PHYSICAL FACTORS CONTROLLING THE CLIMATE OF CANADA AND NEWFOUNDLAND

The dominions of Canada and Newfoundland comprise nearly three-fifths of the continent of North America, extending almost a quarter of the way around the world (89 degrees of longitude) and stretching from about 42 degrees north latitude to within seven degrees of the north pole. This vast region is characterized by high mountains, broad plains and great numbers of inland water bodies. It is exposed to oceans on three sides with numerous arms of the sea extending far inland. Islands surrounded by salt water make up more than one-tenth of its area. It is the intricate combination of these several factors which makes the climates of these countries so extremely varied.

The great annual range in solar radiation, consequent on the latitude of Canada, dominates the course of the seasons here. Table 1 shows the intensity of direct and diffuse radiation at various latitudes and at various seasons.[1] These values are represented graphically in Figs. 2 to 5 inclusive. At the equinoxes there is a marked increase from the north pole to about 70 degrees north latitude; then a gradual increase to about 58 degrees, followed by a rather pronounced increase again. For the summer solstice the values are high for all latitudes, the maximum being at the north pole and the minimum at latitude 65 degrees. For the winter solstice, the values show a sharp rise, starting from zero at approximately 68 degrees north latitude.

Combined with these curves are the relative lengths of path through the atmosphere at noon on each of the four dates.[2] (See

---

[1] The figures are based on those worked out by H. H. Kimball, *Monthly Weather Review*, v. 56, 1927; p. 394. This author gives two values for each latitude which he selected; one value representing conditions over the Pacific, the other over the Atlantic. The figures for the Pacific were taken in preference to those for the Atlantic as being more nearly representative of conditions over the continent because of the lower absolute humidity over the Pacific as compared with the Atlantic. This seemed advisable because water vapor greatly reduces the value of direct and diffuse solar radiation, and because no corrections were made for the water vapor content. The factor of altitude has also been neglected although, as the author states, the values of radiation for mountain stations are greater than those at sea level.

[2] The figures here are based on those worked out by Dr. Wilhelm Zenker in *Die Vertheilung der Warme auf der Erdoberfloche*, Julius Springer, Berlin, 1888; p. 30. See also R. DeC. Ward's *Climate, Considered Especially in Relation to Man*, G. P. Putnam's Sons, New York, 1918; p. 16.

also Tables 2 and 3.) These, together with the figures for the duration of sunshine as given in Tables 4 and 5, readily explain the broad features of the curves for solar radiation. To illustrate how these factors apply to specific localities, consider Winnipeg (latitude 50 degrees) which on June 21 receives only about 6% more sunlight than Fort Norman (latitude 65 degrees) ; at the equinoxes Winnipeg receives about 30% more; but on December 21 over 12 times as much. A more pronounced comparison may be made by taking the extreme northern and southern limits of the Dominion: at the summer solstice Pelee Island (latitude 42 degrees) receives about the same amount of sunlight as Cape Sheridan on Ellesmere Island (latitude 83 degrees), the 24 hours of continuous sunlight compensating for the low altitude of the sun which ranges from about 16° above the horizon at midnight to approximately 30° above

TABLE 1. DAILY TOTALS OF SOLAR RADIATION (DIRECT AND DIFFUSE) IN GRAM CALORIES RECEIVED ON A SQUARE CENTIMETER OF HORIZONTAL SURFACE ON A CLEAR DAY

Latitude	45	50	55	60	65	70	75	80	85	90
Mar. 21	570	504	443	413	403	374	322	247	142	0*
Jun. 21	848	835	824	794	789	795	815	835	860	896
Sep. 21	509	480	410	368	354	322	272	203	114	0*
Dec. 21	215	150	88	46	12	0	0	0	0	0

*Obviously, there is some radiation received on these dates because the sun is apparently above the horizon although geometrically below it; the exact values, however, are not known.

TABLE 2. ALTITUDE OF THE SUN AT NOON IN DEGREES OF ARC ABOVE THE HORIZON, ASSUMING NO ATMOSPHERE

Latitude	40	45	50	55	60	65	70	75	80	85	90
Equinoxes	50	45	40	35	30	25	20	15	10	5	0
Summer solstice	73	68	63	58	53	48	43	38	33	28	23
Winter solstice	26	21	16	11	6	1	−3	−8	−13	−18	−23

TABLE 3. RELATIVE LENGTHS OF PATH OF THE SUN'S RAYS THROUGH THE ATMOSPHERE AT NOON

Latitude	40	45	50	55	60	65	70	75	80	85	90
Equinoxes	1.30	1.43	1.56	1.77	2.00	2.41	2.92	3.8	5.7	10.8	44.7
Summer solstice	1.05	1.08	1.12	1.18	1.23	1.34	1.46	1.68	1.82	2.14	2.61
Winter solstice	2.30	2.79	3.55	5.1	5.1	8.5	21.8	....	....	....	......

the horizon at noon. Pelee Island receives sunlight for only about 15 hours on this date, yet the sun at noon is about 75° above the horizon. At the equinoxes northern Ellesmereland receives only a third as much sunlight as Pelee Island. By December 21 there is no direct sunlight for places north of the 68th parallel.

TABLE 4. DURATION OF POSSIBLE SUNSHINE IN HOURS AT VARIOUS LATITUDES

Latitude	40	45	50	55	60	65	70	75	80	85	90
21st day of
Dec.	9.3	8.7	8.1	7.2	5.7	3.3	0.0	0.0	0.0	0.0	0.0
Jan.	9.7	9.3	8.8	8.1	7.0	5.4	1.8	0.0	0.0	0.0	0.0
Feb.	10.9	10.7	10.3	10.1	9.6	9.1	8.1	6.5	0.0	0.0	0.0
Mar.	12.2	12.2	12.2	12.2	12.2	12.3	12.4	12.5	12.6	13.3	24.0
Apr.	13.5	13.7	14.1	14.4	15.0	15.8	17.1	19.5	24.0	24.0	24.0
May	14.5	14.9	15.6	16.4	17.5	19.4	24.0	24.0	24.0	24.0	24.0
Jun.	15.0	15.6	16.3	17.3	18.8	22.1	24.0	24.0	24.0	24.0	24.0
Jul.	14.6	15.1	15.7	16.5	17.7	19.6	24.0	24.0	24.0	24.0	24.0
Aug.	13.6	13.8	14.2	16.6	15.2	16.0	17.3	20.1	24.0	24.0	24.0
Sep.	12.3	12.3	12.3	12.3	12.4	12.5	12.6	12.8	13.3	14.6	24.0
Oct.	10.9	10.7	10.4	10.2	9.7	9.2	8.2	6.6	0.0	0.0	0.0
Nov.	9.8	9.4	8.9	8.2	7.1	5.6	2.2	0.0	0.0	0.0	0.0
Dec.	9.3	8.7	8.1	7.2	5.7	3.3	0.0	0.0	0.0	0.0	0.0

An adequate understanding of the climate of Canada, and particularly its northern reaches, must be based to a large degree upon the seasonal ranges in the altitude of the sun and the duration of sunshine, and the consequent range of insolation.

TABLE 5. DATES OF "SUNRISES" AND "SUNSETS" IN POLAR LATITUDES

North latitude	Date at which sun first appears above horizon	Date at which sun remains continuously above horizon	Date at which sun ceases to remain continuously above horizon	Date at which sun remains continuously below horizon
70	Jan. 18	May 17	Jul. 28	Nov. 25
75	Feb. 6	Apr. 28	Aug. 15	Nov. 6
80	Feb. 21	Apr. 13	Aug. 30	Oct. 22
85	Mar. 6	Mar. 31	Sep. 12	Oct. 8
90	Mar. 18	Mar. 18	Sep. 25	Sep. 25

Further reference to Table 4 reveals the effect of latitude upon the yearly course of the duration of sunshine, the 21st day of each month being taken to illustrate. This, as well as Table 5, takes into consideration the refractive effect of the earth's

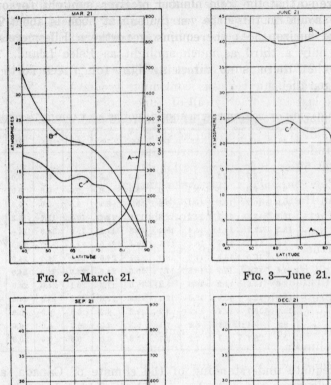

FIG. 2—March 21.

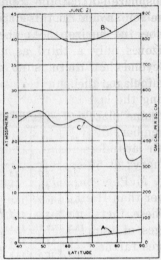

FIG. 3—June 21.

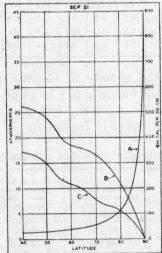

FIG. 4—September 21.

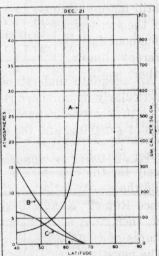

FIG. 5—December 21.

Curves showing daily totals of solar radiation (direct and diffuse) in gram calories received on a square centimeter of horizontal surface at various latitudes on the 21st day of March, June, September, and December; curve B representing conditions on a clear day and curve C representing conditions with average cloudiness for that latitude in Canada. Curve A shows the lengths of path of the sun's rays through the atmosphere, the lengths being given in "atmospheres" as indicated at the left.

atmosphere so that the total number of hours of possible sunshine for any latitude for the year will always exceed the total number of hours the sun remains geometrically below the horizon.

Beyond the 70th parallel, embracing a large part of the Arctic Archipelago, the sun remains continuously above the horizon during the last half of May, all of June and most of July; for the same places no insolation at all is received during half of November, all of December and most of January. At 60 degrees north latitude, sunshine lasts three times as long in July as in January; at 50 degrees, twice as long. To take a specific case, Fort McPherson during July has sunshine about seven hours longer than Hamilton; but in January seven hours shorter.

These facts, alone, account for the extremely high annual ranges of temperature in Arctic Canada, and for the smaller ranges farther south. Were it not for the greater thickness of the atmosphere through which the sun's rays must pass in high latitudes (Table 3), the annual ranges of temperature would be still more extreme.

If the sun were the dominant factor in regulating the climate throughout Canada, then Prince Rupert should have a markedly different climate from that of Toronto which lies 10 degrees farther south; likewise, Atlin should experience conditions somewhat more severe than Mistassini Post eight degrees farther south. As a matter of fact, the contrasts between these respective places are relatively slight in so far as temperature is concerned. Indeed, the two stations farther south experience greater extremes of temperature. At Atlin, altitude accounts largely for the extremes being smaller than at Mistassini Post; while the nearness to water accounts for the small extremes at Prince Rupert as compared with those at Toronto. It is evident, then, that some attention should be given to the physical features of Canada and Newfoundland.

The more important relief features are shown in Fig. 6. With few exceptions, all of British Columbia and Yukon Territory rise above 5000 feet. The few exceptions are along the coast and river valleys; but even along the Pacific coast, the mountains generally rise abruptly from the sea, so that the heavy precipitation is concentrated in a relatively narrow strip along the coast. On the other hand, some of the low, narrow, and confined valleys in the interior approach desert conditions

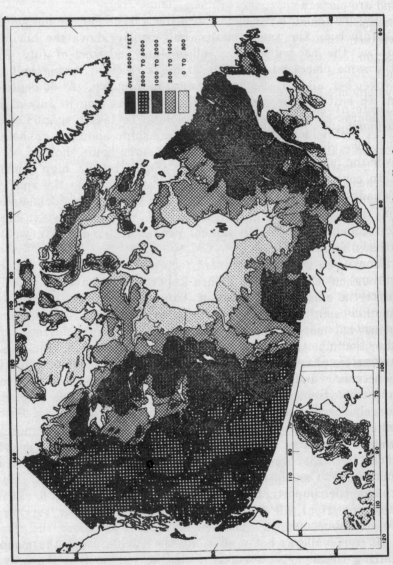

FIG. 6—Relief map of Canada and Newfoundland.

because of the mountain barriers both to the west and to the east. Several considerable areas of the western mountains are above 10,000 feet, while a few isolated peaks exceed that height and are permanently snowcapped. Thus, Mt. Robson in eastern British Columbia extends to 13,700 feet; Mt. Mystery in southwestern British Columbia, and only 24 miles from tidewater, to 13,200 feet; and Mt. Logan in southwest Yukon towers to 19,539 feet, being the highest point in Canada. This vast mountain system not only favors heavier precipitation on its windward (western) slopes, but it also acts as an effective barrier in rendering the interior of Canada drier and, usually, in preventing the cold waves of the Mackenzie district from spreading over the interior and coastal reaches of British Columbia.

In contrast to the Pacific highlands is the great interior of Canada, extending southward from the Arctic Ocean to the international boundary, and eastward from the great cordillera to the Labrador Peninsula. The whole region is marked by relatively slight relief, few parts of which exceed 2000 feet in elevation if the western piedmont is excepted. Even here the elevations seldom reach 4000 feet. Hence, this is a land where precipitation is light; where the winters are cold and the summers hot—features of a continental type of climate. The effects of water bodies are reduced to a minimum, the Great Lakes and the other numerous fresh water bodies being too small to exert any profound influence except locally. Hudson Bay, even though penetrating far south into the heart of the continent, is too cold and often too much choked with ice to act as a mitigator of extreme conditions in winter as does the Pacific, and to a lesser extent the Atlantic Ocean. On the other hand, these ice-laden waters in summer tend to keep the surrounding coasts, particularly the east coast, appreciably cooler than places farther inland. The same may be said of the Arctic Ocean, which surrounds the islands of the Archipelago; ice may be found during any month of the year, and it may be so compact some years as to hold ships firmly imprisoned throughout the summer.

It is over this vast Canadian interior of few obstructions that, during the winter months, the cold air of the far north may sweep southward, spreading over all of central Canada, reaching far south into the United States and penetrating to the Atlantic seaboard. It is over this expanse of lowland that the direct solar heating may cause temperatures to mount to 90° and even 100° in July.

Of the islands comprising the Arctic Archipelago, few have relief of special significance; although Baffin Island, the largest of these, has a ridge of mountains along the eastern coast, lofty enough to cause more precipitation than the surrounding lowlands, and high enough also to keep summer temperatures a little lower, so that numerous small glaciers may be found along the east-facing slopes. Ellesmere Island also has considerable relief, the northern portion of it certainly above 5000 feet, and lofty enough in this region of low absolute humidity to extend above the limit of appreciable precipitation.

To the southeast, covering a large part of the Labrador and Gaspe peninsulas, lies an area of moderate relief, generally not exceeding 2000 feet in elevation. Along the northern part of the Labrador coast, however, is a narrow ridge of mountains culminating in peaks above 5000 feet. There is, likewise, a small area of Gaspe which reaches above 5000 feet. The Labrador Peninsula in particular is distinctly a region of heavier precipitation and milder temperatures than that of central Canada. Altitude is of less importance here than location, for the region is thrust out seaward where the waters of the Gulf of St. Lawrence and of the Atlantic Ocean may have appreciable effect in making the summers cold and damp, but at the same time in ameliorating the severity of the winters. Newfoundland, due to the same sort of location, experiences much the same conditions; the extremes, however, are even less because of the more pronounced marine effects.

The presence of ocean waters to the east and west of Canada has a greater significance locally than any factor yet noted. The readily available moisture of the winds across these waters increases precipitation along the coasts, particularly when winds are onshore. Reference to the map of mean annual precipitation, Fig. 32, will emphasize this fact. These waters serve as heat regulators as well, bringing to the coastal stretches higher winter temperatures and lower summer temperatures than those which are experienced in the interior of the continent (note the trend of the isotherms on the maps of mean temperature for January and July, Figs. 27 and 29).

Moreover, the movements of the waters themselves should be noted. On the Atlantic side not far off the coast of Nova Scotia is the Gulf Stream which, as will be discussed in Chapter II, exerts an appreciable influence on the calmness or storminess of the Eastern parts of the United States and Canada. The cold waters of the Labrador Current likewise have their influence on the Labrador coast in summer, rendering it bleak and inhospitable. The mixing of air over these two currents makes the Grand Banks and the eastern and southern coasts of Newfoundland extremely foggy. On the Pacific side, the warm Japan Current Drift probably brings milder and rainier conditions to the coast of British Columbia than could be expected from the southerly winds alone, the mean January temperature being everywhere above freezing. Quite apart from the immediate influence of this warm water, coming with onshore winds, is the more indirect influence through the cyclonic storms of the colder months, many of which appear to have their origin over these relatively warm waters of the northern Pacific.

Thus far, only the broad features of relief have been emphasized. It is not to be presumed, however, that local topography does not play an exceedingly important part on the climate of a locality. Equally significant for small areas are the dozens of lakes, not only because of their low-lying position but also because of their great capacity for heat storage. Among these should be mentioned, in addition to the Great Lakes, Great Bear and Great Slave lakes, each larger than Lake Erie; Lakes Winnipeg, Athabaska, Mistassini, and Manitoba,. Why should Fort Good Hope in the Mackenzie River Valley have the lowest official temperature ever recorded in Canada? Why should Kamloops in the Thompson River Valley experience some of the highest temperatures ever recorded? Why should Steep Hill Falls near the eastern end of Lake Superior have the heaviest recorded snowfall in Eastern Canada? These facts must find their explanation largely in the local effects of relief and water bodies.

CHAPTER II

PRESSURE, WINDS AND STORMS

Canada exhibits only in a very broad way the general features of planetary circulation for its latitude. The size and relief of the land mass together with the relatively warm waters of the northern Pacific and the northern Atlantic in winter and their relative coolness in summer modify the general circulation, much as in Asia, although to a less degree.

In January the subpolar low pressure centers extend well south to about 60 degrees north latitude over the oceans, while the so-called horse latitude and polar high pressure belts tend to merge into one high pressure area extending from the Great Plains of the United States northwestward to the Mackenzie Delta (Fig. 7). The saddle of high pressure, or trough of low pressure, extending across the northern portions of British Columbia and the Prairie Provinces suggests the paths of numerous cyclones in their march eastward from the Aleutian low center to the North Atlantic. In years when most of the winter storms do move this far northward, the weather for that season is unusually mild.[1] Cold waves from the far north are less frequent and less severe, under such conditions. Chinooks in the Prairie Provinces are more numerous, and frequently their warming effects are carried far eastward into the borders of Manitoba.

At other times, storm centers take a more southerly course, the paths of which are indicated by the tongue of lower pressure over the Great Lakes. That is, average January pressures tend to be slightly lower along a belt extending south-southeast from southern British Columbia to Lake Superior. When storms move as far south as this or when they move from the southwestern United States northeastward toward the Great Lakes and the St. Lawrence Valley, it is then that all of Canada east of the cordillera, and central Canada in particular, experiences the intense cold which may cause temperatures to drop as low as forty and fifty degrees below zero and in extreme cases as

[1] Sir Frederic Stupart, "The Influence of Arctic Meteorology on the Climate of Canada Especially," *Problems of Polar Research,* American Geographical Society, New York, 1928; p. 49.

low as minus seventy degrees. That cold Januarys are the rule for central Canada is in accordance with the prevailing northwest winds (Fig. 7).

The almost continuous low pressure in winter keeps the west coast continuously moist during that season; and these conditions likewise obtain during much of autumn and spring, as indicated in Figs. 8 and 10. This region, however, is not particularly stormy at any season; and the same may be said for all of British Columbia, for the great mountain barrier formed by the Canadian Rockies keeps out the great masses of cold air to the east. Occasionally, this air may spill over into the interior valleys and even reach the coast; though generally, in such cases, the air is sufficiently warmed by compression and in other ways to prevent temperatures falling much below zero.

In marked contrast is the Eastern Maritime Region where the low in January is considerably deeper—a result of the meeting of storm paths from northern Canada, southern Canada, central United States and the Atlantic coast because of the prevailing contrast in temperature between the relatively warm waters of the Gulf Stream and the colder lands to the northwest. Highlands here are no considerable barrier, so the winds may blow with full force toward the lows as they gravitate toward this region. A study of Tables 6 and 7 will show how much more stormy is this region than either the interior or the Pacific Coast. Southwest Point on the island of Anticosti, exposed to winds from a westerly or southerly quarter, has a

TABLE 6. AVERAGE WIND VELOCITIES IN MILES PER HOUR FOR SELECTED STATIONS

	Jan.	Feb.	Mar.	Apr.	May	Jun.	Jul.	Aug.	Sep.	Oct.	Nov.	Dec.	Yr.
Atlin	7.4	6.6	8.4	8.3	8.2	8.1	8.2	9.0	9.0	9.8	9.9	8.6	8.5
Victoria	9.0	8.9	9.0	9.0	8.8	9.7	9.1	7.8	6.5	6.8	9.9	8.8	8.6
Kamloops	4.3	4.0	5.0	4.8	4.8	4.5	4.1	3.7	4.6	3.8	4.3	4.4	4.4
Battleford	7.2	6.6	7.9	9.2	10.1	8.6	7.7	6.9	7.3	8.1	7.3	6.7	7.8
Winnipeg	12.8	12.2	13.1	14.5	14.5	12.7	12.1	11.3	13.0	13.8	12.4	12.2	12.9
Cochrane	8.8	9.3	11.0	10.1	10.1	9.5	9.2	-9.1	10.0	9.8	10.1	9.1	9.7
Toronto	13.6	13.7	12.8	11.9	9.9	8.7	8.0	8.0	8.8	9.9	12.2	13.2	10.9
Quebec	15.0	16.1	15.3	14.4	14.4	13.2	11.6	10.7	11.5	12.4	14.0	13.9	13.5
Jones Sound	7.8	7.6	8.7	7.2	8.3	8.3	8.1	8.1	10.5	8.9	8.1	6.9	8.3
Hebron	10.5	9.2	8.9	6.9	5.8	4.9	4.3	5.4	8.1	9.2	11.6	12.8	8.1
Southwest Point	22.9	19.1	17.9	15.2	13.9	13.8	12.7	13.0	14.5	17.3	19.5	22.3	16.8
Halifax	13.8	13.2	13.7	13.3	11.5	10.1	9.5	9.6	10.1	10.0	12.8	13.4	11.9

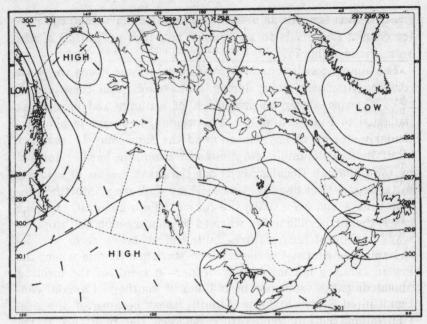

FIG. 7—Mean pressure and prevailing winds for January.

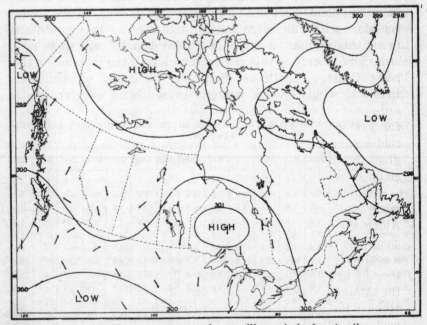

FIG. 8—Mean pressure and prevailing winds for April.

Table 7. AVERAGE NUMBER OF DAYS WITH GALES* FOR SELECTED STATIONS

	Jan.	Feb.	Mar.	Apr.	May	Jun.	Jul.	Aug.	Sep.	Oct.	Nov.	Dec.	Yr.
Atlin	0.9	1.1	0.7	0.5	0.1	0.0	0.1	0.0	0.5	0.5	0.9	0.8	6.1
Victoria	8.9	4.6	7.2	5.1	4.9	3.9	4.2	3.2	3.0	4.2	5.3	7.5	62.0
Kamloops	0.0	0.0	0.0	0.0	0.0	0.0	0.0	0.0	0.0	0.0	0.0	0.0	0.0
Battleford	0.4	0.0	0.7	0.6	1.2	0.6	0.5	0.2	0.2	0.6	0.0	0.2	5 2
Winnipeg	1.3	0.6	1.0	1.3	1.0	1.0	0.4	0.5	0.4	0.7	0.6	0.3	9.1
Port Nelson	1.4	2.1	3.2	1.7	1.0	2.2	1.7	1.2	1.8	3.0	3.8	1.8	24.9
Cochrane	0.2	0.6	0.5	0.4	0.4	0.4	0.0	0.1	0.3	0.5	0.3	0.4	4.1
Toronto	7.6	5.3	5.6	3.3	2.2	0.7	0.2	0.0	0.6	2.0	2.5	5.7	35.7
Quebec	8.9	7.6	7.7	7.6	5.7	4.1	0.9	0.8	2.5	4.5	4.6	5.9	60.8
Jones Sound	3.2	3.2	4.0	1.8	1.2	0.5	0.0	0.0	1.0	1.8	2.2	1.2	20.1
Hebron	2.6	1.3	1.1	1.4	0.1	0.8	0.0	0.3	1.8	1.9	2.6	2.3	16.2
Southwest Point	19.2	13.4	12.9	6.9	5.9	3.7	2.4	4.3	6.8	12.5	14.0	17.0	119.0
Halifax	4.6	4.3	6.4	4.1	2.4	1.0	1.0	1.0	1.0	3.1	3.6	4.1	36.6

*Wind velocities of 35 or more miles per hour over a five-minute perioa.

mean daily wind velocity in January of nearly 23 miles an hour; and is in marked contrast with Kamloops in the protected Thompson Valley of British Columbia. So far as the records can show, Kamloops has never experienced any gales (winds 35 miles per hour or over) ; Southwest Point, on the other hand, reports, on the average, 19 gales in January. In fact all points in the east report relatively high average wind velocities and from 6 to 10 or more gales a month during the winter. In British Columbia, except immediately along the coast, and in the Prairie Provinces high winds are infrequent. What few records there are available show that the far north, Jones Sound for example, is moderately stormy. Presumably the extreme cold accompanied at times by moderately high wind velocities gives the impression that this region is extremely stormy, especially in winter.

The relative positions of the two depressions in January have much to do with the temperature conditions during that month. Along the west coast, the winds follow the expected counterclockwise circulation about the center and move in general from a southerly quarter (modified to a considerable extent by relief), thereby bringing fairly mild conditions to the whole region. On the Atlantic side, the winds follow the same counter-clockwise trend. But since the centers of the cyclones lie usually to the east and slightly farther south than off the Pacific coast, the winds come from a westerly or northerly quarter, thereby mak-

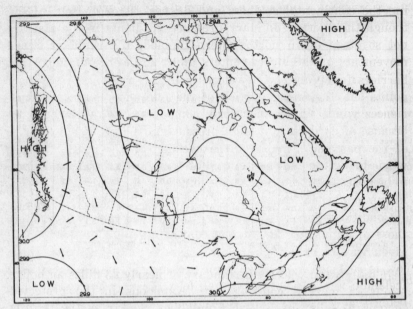

Fig. 9—Mean pressure and prevailing winds for July.

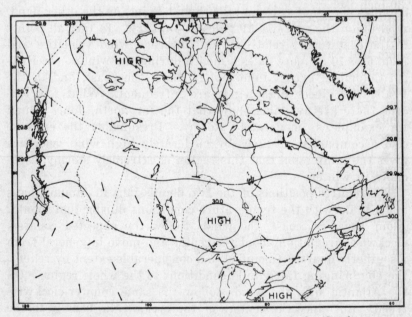

Fig. 10—Mean pressure and prevailing winds for October.

ing the continental coldness and dryness strongly felt. Even though the average January pressure gradients in the east are not so steep as in northwestern Canada, the rapid eastward movements of the storm centers and the absence of important barriers favor high wind velocities in this region. As Stupart points out, the major portion of the Labrador Peninsula experiences winds with a northerly component at all seasons, not because of exceptionally high pressure in the north but because of the passage of most of the cyclones to the south.[1] These winds bring the continental cold of winter when the winds tend to be northwest, and the marine iciness of the Labrador Current in summer when the winds are prevailingly northeast.

Conditions for July (see Fig. 9) are in decided contrast to those of January. The strong continental high pressures have given way to rather weak low pressures; the Pacific Aleutian low is replaced by a weak high pressure area; and the strong Icelandic low has only a vestige left, the only indication of it being that the pressure is lower there than either to the north or south. The subtropical high pressure belt, indicated by the 30-inch isobar, grazes only the tip of Ontario but extends farther north over the Atlantic. The cold ice-cap of Greenland brings the polar high pressure farthest south. The subtropical high belt has thrust itself far northward in the Pacific Ocean, extending well into British Columbia. Conditions are, therefore, almost the reverse of those obtaining in January. Another noteworthy distinction is the general flatness of pressure gradients everywhere on the map for July, with the attendant decreased wind velocities, except for thunder squalls.

A further study of Tables 6 and 7 shows the reduced storminess of summer. Thus Anticosti has an average wind velocity for July of little more than half of that for January, and the number of days with gales is reduced to one-eighth. Farther west, however, there is not such a great difference between winter and summer, although the west still has calmer conditions in July than does the east. The far north tends to have uniformly higher wind velocities in summer than in winter, but fewer days with gales. At this season, cyclonic storms are weaker. They move more slowly because of the weakened temperature gradients; hence, they are not so frequent. Their

---

[1] Stupart, *Problems of Polar Research*, p. 41.

paths tend to be farther north. At this season, on the Pacific coast, the winds have a westerly or northerly component most of the time; they bring the cooling influences of the water to the land immediately along the coast. The interior and south-eastern portions of Canada have winds with a westerly component, more northwest in Alberta and southwest in southern Ontario, directions which are in accordance with the pressure distribution. Hence, these regions experience the high summer temperatures characteristic of a continental climate.

In summer, pressures are affected locally by bodies of water, and these local differences in pressure likewise affect the air movements over them. Thus the cold waters of Hudson Bay, often ice-laden far into the summer, cause somewhat higher pressure with consequent onshore winds over most of the shores of the Bay. This is in direct contrast to the January conditions, when the waters of the Bay favor low pressure and winds offshore, particularly along the west shores (see Fig. 7). Likewise, in July, Lake Superior favors higher pressure with out-flowing winds.

April and October are transition months. The maps of pressure and winds for these months (Figs. 8 and 10) represent conditions only for a very short period. In these months temperatures, which largely determine pressure, are changing most rapidly. Hence, the maps are of interest in revealing to some extent what takes place during the change from winter to summer. On the whole, both maps resemble the January one, the chief difference as far as pressure is concerned being the relative weakness of the highs and lows for April and October. There are other exceptions of some importance. One is the beginning of the continental low pressure for April in the western United States. Also the tendency for low pressure over Hudson Bay and the Great Lakes becomes less pronounced on the April map. The winds for these transition months are also similar to those for January, although in April in parts of Manitoba and Saskatchewan, northwest winds seem to give way to north and northeast, due doubtless to the high pressure which persists over the snow-covered plateau of northern central Ontario. As far as records permit conclusions, winds with a northwesterly component prevail everywhere and at all seasons in the Archipelago north of 65 degrees north latitude. Exceptions to this general statement are found in certain protected

situations, particularly where the observation points are located
in fiords or confined valleys.

The relative frequency of winds from the eight cardinal points
for selected stations is shown by a system of wind roses in
Fig. 11. The map indicates a considerable variety for various
sections. It will be noticed that the winds blow more in accordance with movements of cyclones than with the planetary system of circulation, although in southern Canada there is a distinct westerly component in most of the wind roses shown.
Relief, both local and general, influences wind directions considerably in many places. The location of Dawson in the north-
south trending valley of the Yukon River causes the winds to
be either northerly or southerly at all seasons. Kamloops in
the east-west valley of the Thompson River experiences east
or west winds most of the year. Similar conditions obtain at
Vancouver. At Prince George in central British Columbia, the
trend of the Fraser Valley favors south or southwesterly winds.

In the Prairie Provinces the influence of cyclonic storms is
very pronounced, and the topographic effect is reduced to a
minimum. Here the winds pass with considerable regularity
from one direction to another. In winter and spring, the cold
northwest winds give way to east and northeast winds as a
cyclone appears over Montana; and as the center of the storm
keeps to the south on its eastward movement, the winds back
through the north to the northwest. Under such conditions,
there is little relief from the extreme cold. At other times,
however, when a cyclone starts eastward over the Alaskan Pan-
handle, the northwest winds give way to southwest or even
southeast winds, bringing in warmer air from the south or air
from the southwest which is warmed adiabatically in its descent
to the plains. Gradually the winds veer to the west and northwest as the cyclone moves southeastward, with the consequent
indraft of cold Arctic air again.

In eastern Canada, particularly in Newfoundland and the
Atlantic Provinces, the highly complex relief disturbs the normal circulation of air about cyclones. Because of this fact,
coupled with the tempering effects of the ocean waters, pronounced weather changes, as found in central Canada, are considerably reduced. As the wind roses show, most of the storms
move out the St. Lawrence Valley. To the south of the Valley,
the winds are generally southerly, changing to west and north-

Fig. 11—Wind roses showing the average annual frequency of winds from the eight cardinal points for a ten-year period. Small figures within the circles give the frequency of "calm" in per cents.

west as the following anticyclone sweeps far south in the United States. To the north of the Valley, as already mentioned in regard to Labrador, the winds blow most frequently from a northerly or westerly quarter.

Up to this point, only average conditions have been stressed. The seasonal pressure maps show only broadly the effect of land, water, relief and the effect of the movements of cyclonic storms upon the general planetary circulation of the atmosphere. Probably there is no section of the northern hemisphere whose climate is more dominated by weather attending cyclonic storms than is that of Canada and Newfoundland, largely because the countries lie in the region most frequented by these storms. Although the storms do not usually cause considerable damage on account of high wind velocities, they do vitally influence the people through the great and sudden changes of temperature which they occasion. Not only this, they sometimes cause great economic loss when an unusually late spring frost or an early autumn frost may destroy valuable crops in a few hours.

No two pressure maps for different days are ever alike; yet there are certain types of pressure distribution which give rise to similar sorts of weather. It will be the purpose of the remaining portion of this chapter to call attention to a few weather types, which will be illustrated by pressure maps, each map being for one particular set of observations, in every case taken at 8 a. m., 75th meridian time.[1]

The Cold Wave Type. This is probably the most significant type of weather in Canada and results in a very considerable drop in temperatures—perhaps as much as 70 degrees in 36 hours. The map for December 7, 1927, Fig. 12, shows the pressure conditions which gave rise to a cold wave in the Mackenzie Region and the Prairie Provinces. The chief pressure charactertistic of such a cold wave is a strong high pressure area, much elongated and extending well into the United States. An invariable adjunct is a fairly intense low pressure passing eastward or northeastward across the Central Plains of the United States. With such a distribution of pressure is a large indraft of cold air from the Arctic. The lowlands of Canada and the United States offer but little obstruction to this movement of air. Consequently the winds are strong and northwesterly over

[1] The maps are copied from the originals made by the Canadian Meteorological Service at Toronto.

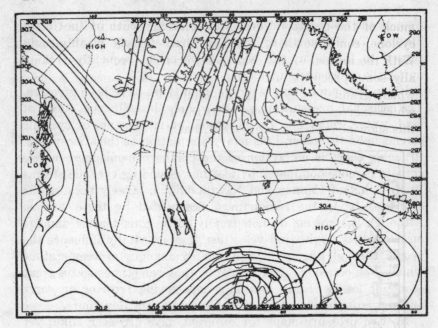

FIG. 12—Weather map 8 a. m., December 7, 1927.

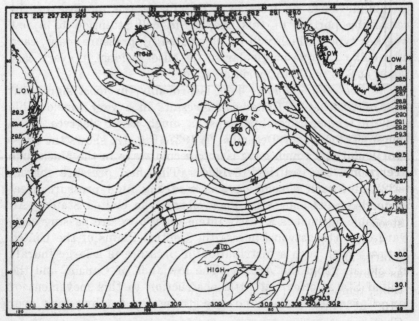

FIG. 13—Weather map 8 a. m., January 26, 1927.

much of the region. These winds, on the rear of the passing cyclone, comprise the blizzard so characteristic of this region. With the arrival of the cold front, or polar front, there is usually some precipitation, either snow or rain turning to snow, which gradually ceases as the temperature falls. The winds which increase in strength with the fall in temperature drive this snow about to such an extent that it appears as a continuous

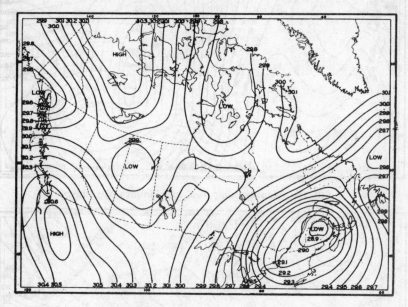

FIG. 14—Weather map 8 a. m., February 26, 1926.

snow storm. The snowfall, however, is generally light. For this particular day temperatures dropped to as low as –54° in Yukon Territory, –48° at Fort McMurray in northern Alberta, and –32° at Swift Current in southern Saskatchewan. The cold extended as far east as Port Nelson where the thermometer stood at –29°.

As the cold air moves southward and eastward, it may cover a large area in southeastern Canada and the Great Lakes region as shown by the high pressure in Fig. 13. Under such conditions, temperatures drop well below zero throughout the region: –16° at Toronto, –48° at White River, –14° as far east as Chatham, New Brunswick. To the west, conditions are relatively mild, temperatures in Alberta being well above zero.

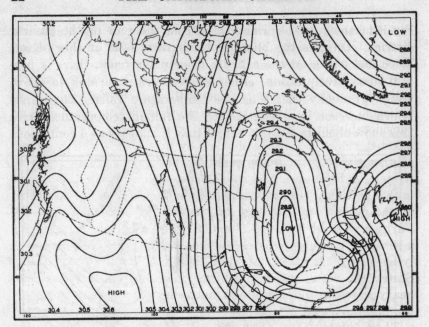

Fig. 15—Weather map 8 a. m., January 20, 1928.

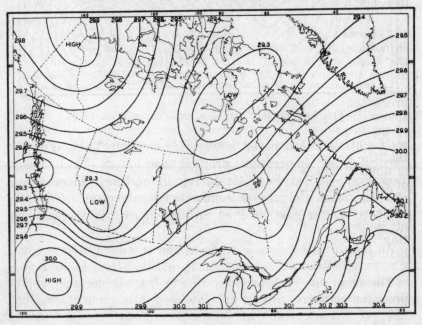

Fig. 16—Weather map 8 a. m., December 11, 1927.

Fig. 14 shows the beginning of a cold wave in the Mackenzie district. On this day, temperatures were –25° at Fort Good Hope, but above freezing in the Prairie Provinces.

Winter Storm Type. In southeastern Canada the winter storm type brings the heavy snows throughout the region. As indicated in Figs. 14 and 15, it is marked by a low pressure of considerable intensity, the center of which passes over the region affected. Such a storm is marked by high winds, shifting from southeast through south to west. Fig. 17 represents a not unusual winter condition over central Canada, which brings light snows to that section. The snows are light, not because of the weakness of the cyclone, but because of the lack of available moisture. Farther west in British Columbia, when a cyclone, or perhaps a series of cyclones, crosses the mountains, with high pressures lying over Yukon Territory and the Great Basin of the United States, the result is relatively heavy rain along the coast and heavy snows in the mountains and valleys of the interior. This type is illustrated in Fig. 16.

The Chinook Type. The Chinook as experienced particularly in Alberta is described as follows by Stupart[1]:

"The first and most obvious conclusion is that the Alberta chinook is a strong southwest or west wind which blows between the coast and Alberta when a well-marked area of low barometric pressure is passing eastward across the more northern part of the Province, and with these conditions a heavy general precipitation occurs on the outer coast line and also in a more spasmodic manner on the western slopes of the mountain ranges of the Interior. The chinook is not pronounced unless the barometric gradient be steep enough for strong winds. It is found that the temperature of the winter chinook in Southern Alberta is approximately equal to the temperature on the outer coast of British Columbia and may exceed 50° . . . . Observation does not show that a change to higher temperature on the Alberta prairies is indicated much in advance by a change occurring at Sulphur Mountain, while on the other hand cold waves setting in from the north are usually well marked on the plains before any change occurs at high levels."

The map for February 26, 1926, Fig. 14, shows the usual pressure conditions for a well developed chinook. On this day

[1] Sir Frederic Stupart, "The Chinook in Southern Alberta and Temperature Inversions at Sulphur Mountain, Banff," *Transactions, Royal Society of Canada*, Toronto, Section III, vol. 4, 1910; pp. 51-2.

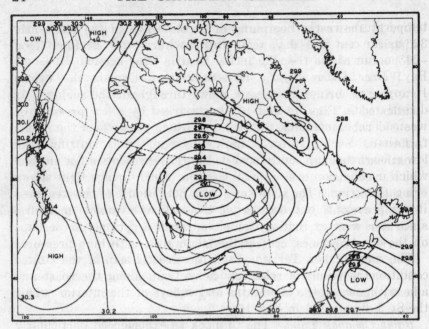

FIG. 17—Weather map 8 a. m., January 9, 1926.

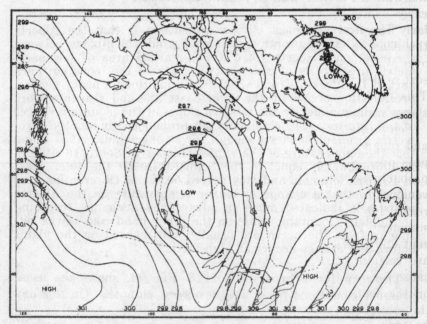

FIG. 18—Weather map 8 a. m., October 1, 1928.

temperatures reached as high as 56° at Medicine Hat and even 32° as far east as The Pas, Manitoba; while temperatures under –20° occurred in the Mackenzie district and around Hudson Bay. Fig. 17 also shows conditions which favor chinook winds. It appears, however, that the strength of the chinook varies directly with the intensity of the high pressure to the southwest. The economic aspect of the chinook lies largely in the fact that the temperature is high enough and relative humidity low enough to cause rapid melting and evaporation of the snow which usually covers the plains after a blizzard, thereby uncovering the grasses for live stock. If the chinook comes in time it may prevent the loss through starvation of thousands of cattle, since it is a common practice of ranchmen to keep their stock on the open range throughout the year.

The map for January 9, 1926, Fig. 17, also illustrates the conditions which bring mild conditions to practically all of Canada with the exception of the southeastern Archipelago and the St. Lawrence Valley, both of which have high pressure.

Pacific Coast Rainy Type. Rains on the exposed portions of the Pacific coast are of almost daily occurrence in autumn and early winter; yet there are times when the rains are particularly heavy. In such cases, a low pressure area is centered over the Alaskan Archipelago and high pressure conditions prevail over Washington and Oregon and perhaps farther inland. This sort of distribution favors southerly, and hence onshore, winds. This type is best illustrated in Figs. 14 and 18; Fig. 13 also shows similar conditions.

Fog in the Eastern Maritime Region. Aside from high winds and rough seas which accompany many of the cyclones as they pass over Newfoundland and the Atlantic Provinces, there is probably no weather condition which occasions greater inconvenience to the mariner than the dense fogs which envelop this region for days at a time, particularly in late spring and early summer. Fogs occur most frequently where the Labrador Current and Gulf Stream meet near the Grand Banks. Yet there are certain types of pressure distribution one of which may cause fogs on the east coast of Newfoundland and fair weather on the south coast; while another type may cause fogs along the south coast and fair weather along the east coast. On May 23, 1928, (see Fig. 19) all points on the east Newfoundland coast reported dense fogs. The reason is not hard to see: high pres-

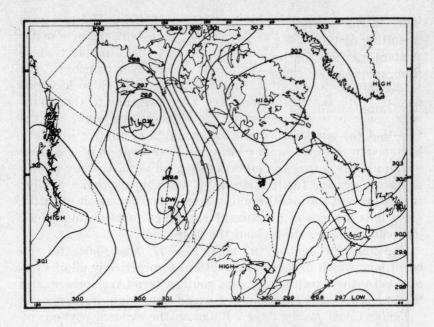

FIG. 19—Weather map 8 a. m., May 23, 1928.

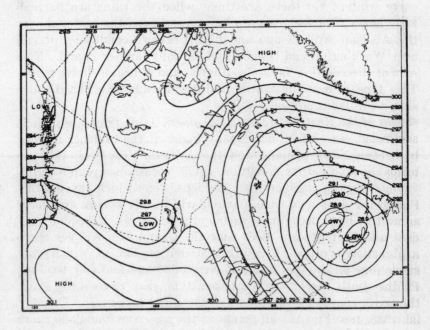

FIG. 20—Weather map 8 a. m., October 21, 1927.

sure to the northeast and low pressure to the southwest with resulting easterly winds. These winds had come from the warm waters of the Gulf Stream Drift, and upon crossing the cold Labrador waters which wash the east shores of the Island, they were quickly chilled to the dewpoint. Fig. 20 illustrates much the same conditions, although fog occurred also on the south

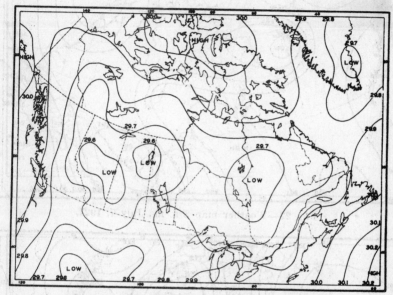

FIG. 21—Weather map 8 a. m., June 27, 1928.

shores of Newfoundland on this day because the winds were southeast and had come from the warm water. There appear to be times, however, when east and southeast winds fail to bring fog.

Fogs were somewhat more widespread on June 27, 1928, (see Fig. 21) when both the east and south shores of Newfoundland as well as those of Nova Scotia were shrouded in fog. On this date, southeast, south and southwest winds were blowing from a high pressure over the Atlantic into a low pressure trough stretching from Greenland into Quebec and on west into the Prairie Provinces. Chill waters occur between the coasts and the warm waters of the Gulf Stream. Coastal fogs almost invariably result when there is a pronounced convergence of northerly and southerly winds each saturated with moisture at their res-

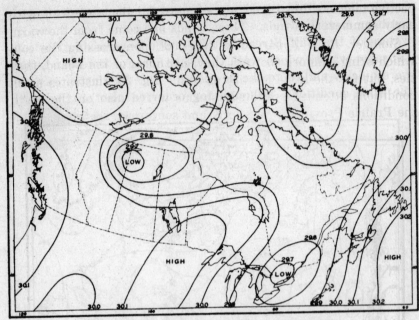

FIG. 22—Weather map 8 a. m., July 7, 1927.

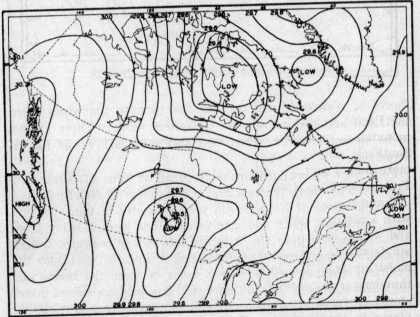

FIG. 23—Weather map 8 a. m., June 30, 1927.

pective temperatures; and they are most frequent in spring and early summer.

Summer Rain Type. The types of pressure distribution which bring summer showers vary, not only for different localities, but for the same locality as well. Fig. 22 shows pressure conditions attended by thunderstorms in British Columbia and the Prairie Provinces. Westerly and southwesterly winds from

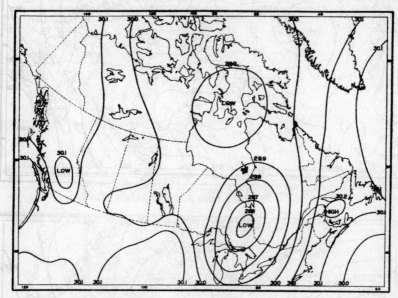

FIG. 24—Weather map 8 a. m., July 17, 1927.

the Pacific, coupled with the orographic effect of the western mountains, readily explain the showers in British Columbia. Southerly and southeasterly winds coming from warmer and more humid sections account for the showers for the Prairie Provinces. Figs. 19 and 23 show much the same conditions.

Summer showers in the Great Lakes region usually occur with a rather weak low pressure area centered over that region and with a high pressure to the west or southwest. The cooler air from the northwest causing instability of the warm and moist air from the south in front of the cyclone gives rise to thunderstorms which may yield heavy rains locally. Such a storm occurred on July 17, 1927, (see Fig. 24) when several places in the peninsula of Ontario received an inch of rain,

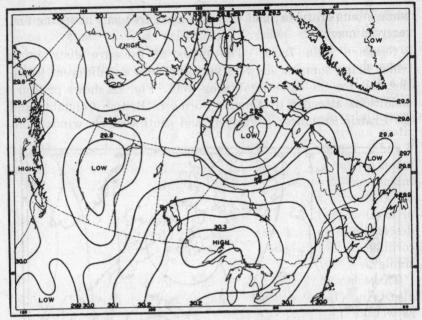

Fig. 25—Weather map 8 a. m., July 25, 1926.

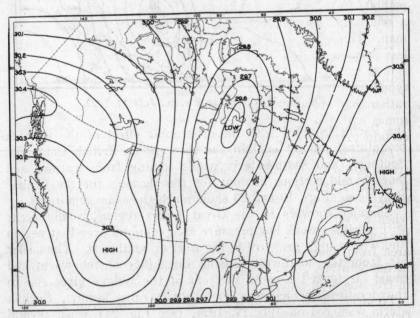

Fig. 26—Weather map 8 a. m., August 23, 1928.

while White River, a short distance northeast of Lake Superior, received over four inches. Fig. 22 also shows a similar type of pressure distribution with similar results. In both of these cases, showers of moderate intensity occurred from a few hours to a day later in the Atlantic Provinces and Newfoundland.

Summer Hot Wave Type. Temperatures of 85° and 90° and even higher are not infrequent in certain parts of Yukon Territory and in the Mackenzie Valley. Such was the case on July 6 and 7, 1927, (see Fig. 22). These warm waves seem to result when a portion of the North Pacific high pressure extends far inland and joins a high pressure over the Arctic Ocean. This, together with a low pressure to the southeast, causes southerly or southwesterly winds taking on foehn characteristics as they descend into the valleys northeast of the coast ranges and the cordillera. Conditions on July 25, 1926, (see Fig. 25) were very similar.

This last mentioned pressure and wind distribution (Fig. 25) also brings hot and dry weather to most of British Columbia as well as the Prairie Provinces. On this particular day maximum temperatures were well above 90° at most observation points. In the southern portions of these provinces, winds with a southerly component prevail under conditions shown on the map. This type of pressure is usual for the season: a more or less permanent high pressure area to the west, with a succession of weak lows coming in from the northwest. The hot wave type in southern and eastern Canada is marked by high pressure rather than low (Fig. 23). Relief from the hot southwest winds comes with the showers which the cyclone to the west is almost certain to yield.

Frost Type in the Wheat Belt. It is not uncommon for August frosts to do considerable damage to the wheat crop, especially if temperatures below freezing persist for five or six hours or longer. This was the case on August 22, 1929, (see Fig. 26) when a cyclone which moved southeastward from Alberta into the central United States was followed by a large high pressure area from the northwest favoring cold, clear weather. A drop in temperature of as much as 40 degrees in 18 hours resulted in freezing temperatures at several points in Saskatchewan.

Tropical Hurricane Type. Occasionally in September and October, tropical cyclones which proceed up the Atlantic coast of the United States continue to be intense, assuming the characteristics of extra-tropical cyclones as they move northward. Under favorable conditions they may move far north into Baffin Bay. The hurricane which first appeared on the United States weather maps over Cuba on October 17, 1927, had on October 21 reached the Gulf of St. Lawrence (see Fig. 20), causing fogs, heavy rains, and strong gales to a large part of the eastern maritime country.

In this discussion of weather types, no claim is made that the map shown represents the only pressure distribution which could yield the special type of weather for which it is used; neither has any attempt been made to exhaust the weather type possibilities. The problem is complex. The aim has been, therefore, to mention only a few significant weather types and to select one or more actual weather maps as illustrative of each type.

CHAPTER III

SUNSHINE AND TEMPERATURE

Any mean annual sea-level isothermal chart of the world will show that most of Canada, with the exception of the Pacific coast, is slightly cooler than the average for its latitude. The size of the land mass helps to reduce the temperatures in winter; the ice-filled Arctic waters including Hudson Bay and Davis Strait prevent summer temperatures over a large area of northern and eastern Canada from reaching as high as the size of the land mass would normally indicate. The west coast is under the marine control; hence this region has higher temperatures for the year than the average for its latitude. The so-called Maritime Provinces are under both the land and water control; and they experience, therefore, mean annual temperatures not far from the average for their latitude. The latitudinal factor then is considerably affected by land, ice, and water. If the world isothermal charts were to show actual temperatures instead of those reduced to sea level, then the latitudinal control would become still weaker by comparison.

The intensity and duration of sunshine are, however, the fundamental factors in any climate. The average temperature for any place must always vary directly with the insolation. Consequently, in order to have an adequate understanding of the daily, seasonal and annual course of temperature over Canada and Newfoundland, it is necessary to point out again a few significant facts regarding sunshine—its intensity and duration in the several seasons, and the effect of average cloudiness upon it.

In Table 8 are shown the full day values of solar radiation for the equinoxes and solstices at various latitudes, corrected in each case for the mean cloudiness for that season and latitude. These insolation values are shown graphically by curve C in Figs. 2 and 5. At each season the value become greater with decreasing latitude, although on both March 21 and June 21 there is considerable deviation from a smooth transition from latitude to latitude as is shown by the irregularity of the curves

33

TABLE 8. DAILY TOTALS OF SOLAR RADIATION (DIRECT AND DIFFUSE) IN GRAM CALORIES RECEIVED ON A SQUARE CENTIMETER OF HORIZONTAL SURFACE. THE VALUES HERE ARE THOSE OF TABLE 1 CORRECTED FOR MEAN CLOUDINESS*

Latitude	45	50	55	60	65	70	75	80	85	90
Mar. 21	342	313	266	269	279	247	232	161	87	0
Jun. 21	508	518	469	468	489	462	440	451	327	341
Sep. 21	326	303	242	217	198	158	131	114	51	0
Dec. 21	112	88	53	29	8	0	0	0	0	0

*For method of correction see: "Amount of Solar Radiation That Reaches the Surface of the Earth on the Land and on the Sea, and Methods by Which It Is Measured," by H. H. Kimball, *Monthly Weather Review*, v. 56, 1928; p. 395.

(Figs. 2 to 5 inclusive). Particularly noteworthy is the fact that at no time does any latitude receive more than two-thirds of the solar radiation which it might receive if there were no clouds, and generally it receives only about one-half the possible.

Closely correlated with these values of solar radiation are the monthly figures for total number of hours of sunshine and the per cent of possible, Table 9, although there are no dependable sunshine records north of the 64th parallel. For the year, southern parts of Alberta and Saskatchewan have the most sunshine; obviously, Swede Creek, the most northerly of stations reporting sunshine figures, has the least. During the month of lowest sun, there are only two localities which show an average of as much as three hours of sunshine a day, southern Alberta and the interior of New Brunswick.[1] The Pacific coast receives not more than one and one-half hours a day on the average; and a little beyond the arctic circle none is received.

Conditions are in substantial contrast in June when the region about the arctic circle shows nearly as much sunshine as the southwestern section of the Prairie Provinces, the sunniest region in the country. July, however, being a less cloudy month than June, shows as much as 340 hours of sunshine in southern Alberta; this figure, 70% of the possible, averages 11 hours of sunshine per day for the month. The Pacific coast is likewise sunny during the summer, the average being from eight to nine hours a day. The Lakes region is slightly less sunny, averaging about eight hours per day, while the maritime region probably averages not much more than seven hours per day.

[1] It should be noted that the usual heliometer fails to record sunshine when the sun is near the horizon.

TABLE 9. AVERAGE NUMBER OF HOURS OF SUNSHINE AND PER CENT OF POSSIBLE RECEIVED EACH MONTH AT SELECTED STATIONS

	Jan.	Feb.	Mar.	Apr.	May	Jun.	Jul.	Aug.	Sep.	Oct.	Nov.	Dec.	Yr.
Swede Creek	6	64	154	216	238	268	264	202	114	70	13	0	1609
	3	26	42	49	42	44	44	34	29	23	7	0	
Vancouver	46	76	138	178	228	230	282	250	179	111	55	40	1813
	17	27	38	43	50	48	58	56	48	33	20	16	
Kamloops	63	100	168	201	245	258	313	271	204	143	74	51	2091
	24	36	46	49	51	53	64	61	54	43	28	21	
Fort Vermilion	68	114	172	218	268	270	293	261	184	132	67	62	2109
	31	44	47	51	52	50	54	55	48	42	29	32	
Lethbridge	101	121	172	212	241	283	340	301	210	164	122	102	2369
	38	43	47	51	51	58	70	68	56	49	45	40	
The Pas	78	127	171	219	244	236	291	247	169	107	70	72	1931
	31	47	47	52	.50	46	57	54	44	33	27	32	
Winnipeg	102	132	168	204	251	250	288	259	177	129	85	77	2122
	38	47	46	50	53	52	59	58	47	43	32	31	
Kapuskasing	88	104	144	175	221	244	237	193	144	92	45	53	1740
	33	37	39	42	46	50	49	40	39	28	16	21	
Toronto	78	108	155	189	226	264	285	254	204	150	84	66	2063
	27	37	42	47	50	56	61	59	55	43	29	24	
Ste. Anne de la Pocatierre	91	104	149	173	220	216	247	232	173	105	79	73	1862
	33	36	40	42	43	46	52	53	46	31	28	28	
Fredericton	111	126	153	176	206	219	233	219	176	149	93	95	1956
	40	44	42	43	45	47	49	50	47	44	33	36	
Charlottetown	97	118	136	139	220	217	223	233	185	136	73	56	1833
	35	41	37	34	47	46	47	53	49	40	26	21	

For most of Canada, January is the coldest month, although extreme minimum temperatures occur probably as often in February as in January. The map of mean January temperature is shown in Fig. 27. Probably the most significant feature is the fact that all of the Pacific coast of Canada has a mean temperature above 30°—and above freezing in most parts. In striking contrast to this is the east coast where temperatures for the same latitude vary from 20° down to zero or lower. The gradient on the west coast, from Prince Rupert to Vancouver, is only 0.7 of a degree per degree of latitude, while on the east coast, from Hebron to St. Johns, it is 2.7 degrees per degree of latitude, about the same as found on the east coast of the United States from Maine to Florida.[1] The obvious explanation lies in the fact of relatively warm ocean waters with a small

[1] R. DeC. Ward, *The Climates of the United States*, Ginn & Co., Boston, 1925, p. 81.

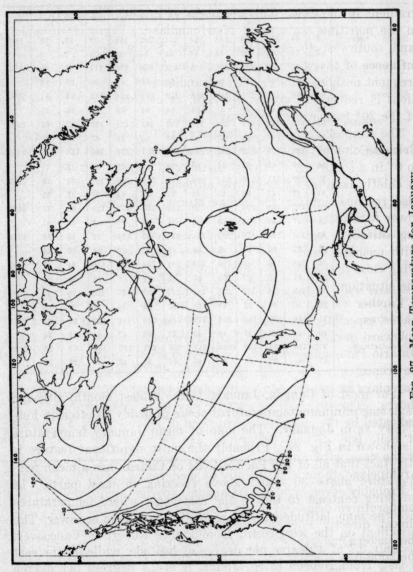

Fig. 27—Mean Temperature for January.

latitudinal gradient at sea and prevailing onshore winds in the
west; and offshore winds from a continent with a marked
gradient in the east. This steepness of gradient is due in part
to the maritime warmth of Newfoundland. From Newfoundland southwest to Cape Sable, Nova Scotia, because of the
influence of the warmer waters of the Atlantic with the rather
frequent onshore winds on Newfoundland in January, the gradient is reduced to practically zero, as evidenced by the trend
of the 20° isotherm on the map.

The steepest gradients in January are found in northwestern
British Columbia where the temperature drops from about 32°
to 0° in a southwest-northeast distance of about 100 miles. This
is chiefly because of exposure, although increasing altitude is
also responsible; for the temperatures continue to drop still
lower with increasing distance from the coast and with decreasing altitude. Again, the relatively warm waters of the Pacific
with onshore winds, and the barrier effect of the mountains
lying close to the coast, keeping out the arctic cold, must explain
the situation.

Further effects of water bodies are shown over the Great
Lakes, especially Huron, where the 20° isotherm extends sharply
poleward over the water and equatorward over the land in the
Ontario Peninsula. Also, the relative warmth of the Gulf of St.
Lawrence causes a decided loop in the 10° isotherm. Hudson
Bay plays an important role in raising temperatures on the east
shores. The influence of Baffin Bay and Labrador waters is
indicated by the sharp poleward bend of all the isotherms north
of Belle Isle. Where the waters are frozen at this season, as
is the case with interior lakes and most of the waters of the
Archipelago, there is practically no moderating effect noticeable.

Probably seven-eighths of Canada experiences mean January
temperatures below zero. In the west, the zero isotherm runs
almost directly northwest-southeast, following rather closely
the eastern margin of the Rocky Mountain piedmont, roughly
the 2000-foot contour; east of Manitoba, it runs almost due east
and west. The higher temperatures to the southwest, even
though the elevation is greater, result from the frequent southwest chinooks which occur in this month. It is to the south of
the 0° isotherm in the east that more than seventy per cent
of the population is found; also it is only to the south of this

isotherm that mixed agriculture can be practiced profitably in eastern Canada.

A large area of the Arctic Prairie has a mean January temperature under –30°. It extends from Chesterfield Inlet westward to the Mackenzie; the northward limits are indefinite, although it is probable that the –30° isotherm would be closed a little farther north after embracing most of the Arctic islands.

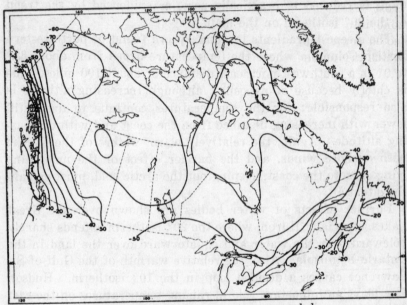

FIG. 28—Lowest temperatures recorded.

Fort Norman, in the Mackenzie Valley, has the lowest official and *long-term* January mean of any station, –32.2°. Stupart, however, is inclined to the opinion that the territory north of Chesterfield Inlet on the northwestern side of Hudson Bay, with a reported mean January temperature of –35°, is the coldest area in the northern part of the western hemisphere, with the possible exception of the ice-covered dome of Greenland.[1]

The depth to which frost penetrates and the depth of thaw vary greatly from season to season even at the same place. In speaking of the depth of frost in the Mackenzie and Yukon districts, Kindle has this to say[2]: "Mr. Harris, who is in charge of the government farm at Simpson states that his well entered

[1] Stupart, *Problems of Polar Research*, p. 39.
[2] E. M. Kindle, *Canada North of Fifty-six Degrees*, Dept. of the Int., Ottawa, 1928, p. 70.

frozen ground at a depth of about 5 feet and passed out of
frost at about 40 feet. A frost limit of 40 feet is in sharp contrast with conditions prevailing in the Yukon valley and the
Nome district in Alaska. Near Nome a shaft 120 feet deep did
not penetrate below perpetual frost. Cleveland Abbe states
that 'there is only one instance on record where excavation in
this northwestern region has gone below the zone of perpetual
frost.' This is a Klondike shaft which passed through the frost
zone into flowing water at about 220 feet." Lefroy has collected some data on the subject of frost penetration, some of
which are presented in Table 10.[1]

TABLE 10. AVERAGE DEPTH OF FROST AND THAW

	Depth of frost feet	Depth of thaw feet
Fort McPherson	52.0	3.5
Fort Norman	45.0	
Fort Rae	11.5	4.0
Fort Simpson	17.0	11.0
Great Bear Lake		1.8
York Factory	19.8	2.3
Edmonton	7.5	
Yorkton	5.0	
Indian Head	12.5	

The part of Canada which has never reported temperatures
below zero comprises a very narrow strip along the western
edge of Vancouver Island and the southern portion of the
Queen Charlotte Islands (Fig. 28). The city of Vancouver is
the only station on the mainland which has never reported a
temperature as low as zero. The extent to which temperatures
may drop, however, increases very rapidly with increase in distance inland, the gradient being as much as 50 degrees in 200
miles. The fact that the isotherms in British Columbia trend
northwest-southeast, that is, parallel with the coast, shows the
effect of the Pacific. The steep gradient also shows how quickly
the moderating marine influence disappears. In eastern British
Columbia the continental influence is strongly manifest, for
minimum temperatures of $-50°$ and lower have been reported
from here. In southeastern Canada and in Newfoundland the
oceanic effect is only moderately felt, for there are few places

[1] J. H. Lefroy, *Proc. of the Royal Geogr. Soc.*, v. 8, 1886, pp. 740-746.

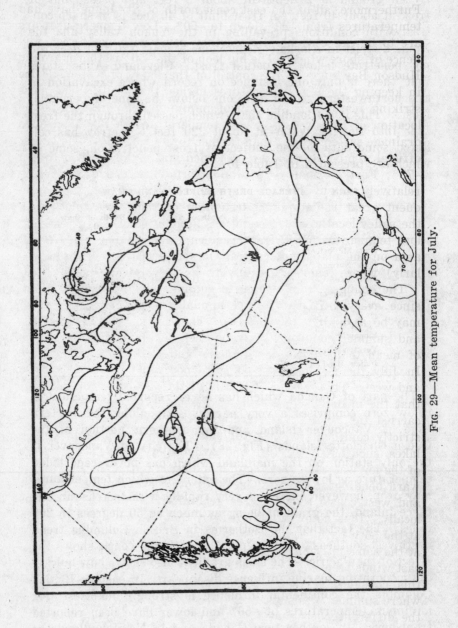

FIG. 29.—Mean temperature for July.

which have not experienced temperatures lower than –20°. Furthermore, all of the east coast north of St. Johns have had temperatures from –20° down to –50°. Low temperatures are are to be expected here, since they come with northwest, and hence offshore winds. The big loop of the –50° isotherm around Hudson Bay suggests the control of that body of water and ice in keeping the air temperatures higher than –50°. The most striking feature on the map of minimum temperatures is the location of the area of lowest temperatures in the Mackenzie drainage system rather than farther to the northeast. The lowest official temperatures ever recorded are: Fort Good Hope, –79°; Fort Norman, –72°; and Fort Vermilion, –76°. The relatively long winter nights with clear skies and the consequent great radiation and retention of the dense cold air in the valley locations of the stations account for these excessively low temperatures. In southeastern Canada, there is a small area on the plateau of central Ontario (White River, particularly) where temperatures as low as –60° have been recorded.

The changes from winter to summer are necessarily rapid, since everywhere in Canada annual ranges of temperatures may be as high as 80 degrees. The contrast between winter and summer conditions may be seen by comparing the maps of mean temperature for January and July, Figs. 27 and 29. In July the isotherms trend more north and south than east and west. This is true especially of the 60° isotherm, showing that the moderate conditions of the northern plains states are carried far north to the arctic circle. The influence here is strictly continental except for small areas around some of the lakes, such as Great Bear and Athabaska. The cooling effect of the icy waters of the Arctic is indicated by the distinct southward bending of the 40° and 60° isotherms. On both the east and west coasts temperatures generally run below 60°, except locally. It is noteworthy, however, that the mean temperature at the 55th parallel on the west coast is 10 degrees higher than at the same latitude on the east coast. The tendency for northeast winds from the ice-laden Labrador Current readily explains this considerable difference. Farther south in Nova Scotia where summer winds are prevailingly from a southerly quarter, the difference between west and east coasts is much reduced. Gradients for July along these coasts are in marked contrast to those for January: on the west coast, 1.4 degrees per degree of latitude (January 0.7 degree) ; on the east coast only 1.1 degrees per degree of latitude (January 2.7 degrees). Winds on the west coast in summer are light and trend parallel with the coast; the marine influence, therefore, is much reduced. Along Labrador and Newfoundland the winds are considerably stronger and more frequently onshore, thereby favoring greater uniformity in temperature. From St. Johns to Halifax the

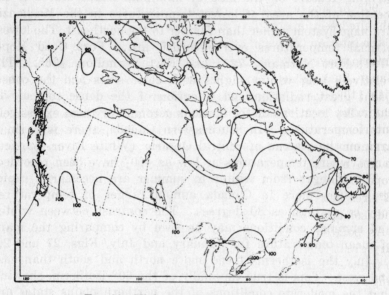

FIG. 30—Highest temperatures recorded.

gradient for July is 1.9 degrees per degree of latitude (in January, practically zero). Thus, the southern coasts of Newfoundland and Nova Scotia are very much like the Pacific coast in both January and July, in so far as the influence of the sea on latitudinal temperature gradients is concerned. The effect of relief on temperature in both winter and summer is very pronounced. This fact is clearly shown by the diversity of isotherms in southern British Columbia, Figs. 27 and 29.

So far as recorded observations can show, practically all of continental Canada has at one time or another experienced temperatures of 80° or more. Reference to Fig. 30 will reveal this fact, for the 80° isotherm hugs the Arctic coast rather closely. Temperatures always lower than 80° certainly should be expected in the Archipelago except possibly in very well protected and otherwise favored situations. The highest official temperature reported in the Archipelago was 77° at Ponds Inlet in the northern part of Baffin Island. Sverdrup, during his four years in southern Ellesmere Island, did not record anything higher than 56° (July 9, 1902).[1] A maximum of 63° was reported at Etah during the four years of the Crocker Land Expedition.[2] Fully two-fifths of Canada has had temperatures of 90° or above; and a very large part of the more thickly inhabited sections of the Prairie Provinces, together with some of the interior valleys of British Columbia and much of southern Ontario, have recorded temperatures above 100°. Cannington Manor, Saskatchewan and Griffin Lake, British Columbia, each with 110°, seem to hold the Canadian record for the extreme maximum temperature. The cooling effect of Lakes Erie and Ontario and of the Bay of Fundy is indicated by the fact that maximum temperatures in exposed parts of those regions rarely go above 100° and 90° respectively. Dawson and Fort Good Hope, both near the arctic circle, have had maxima of 95° and 93°, respectively. This is due to their long hours of sunshine and isolation from marine effects.

As pointed out earlier, the mean annual ranges in Canada vary greatly, from a marine range of 18.9 degrees at Clayoquot on the west coast of Vancouver Island to an extreme continental range of 93.4 degrees at Fort Norman in the Mackenzie Valley. Tables 11 to 14 inclusive show the mean annual ranges of temperatures for certain stations in the same latitude and for certain stations from north to south both in the interior and along the east coast. The continental and marine effects are brought out particularly in Tables 11 and 12; the effect of latitude is clearly indicated in Table 14. Altitude tends to reduce annual ranges, as indicated by Tables 12 and 13; of all the interior stations given in these tables, Banff, the station with the greatest altitude, shows the lowest range, 43.4 degrees. Calgary farther to the southward and situated on the piedmont at 3389 feet elevation has a mean annual range of 48.7 degrees; and Medicine Hat still farther to the southeast at 2144 feet has 56.6 degrees range.

[1] *Report of the Second Norwegian Arctic Expedition in the "Fram,"* 1898-1902, T. O. Brogger, Kristiania, v. 1, p. 107.

[2] D. B. MacMillan, *Etah and Beyond*, Houghton Mifflin Co., Boston, 1927, p. 274.

TABLE 11. TEMPERATURE DATA FOR SELECTED STATIONS NEAR THE 55TH PARALLEL FROM WEST TO EAST

	Alt.	Jan. Mean	Jul. Mean	Ann. Range	Jan. Range	Jul. Range	Jan. Ex. R.	Jul. Ex. R.	Yr. Ex. R
Massett	30	35.3	57.8	22.5	12	15	62	44	86
Fort Vermilion	950	−14.3	60.0	74.3	24	29	124	72	174
Churchill	55	−20.2	55.5	75.7	16	26	89	66	145
Hebron	60	−5.7	47.1	52.8	7	9	80	62	129

TABLE 12. TEMPERATURE DATA FOR SELECTED STATIONS NEAR THE 50TH PARALLEL FROM WEST TO EAST

	Alt.	Jan. Mean	Jul. Mean	Ann. Range	Jan. Range	Jul. Range	Jan. Ex. R.	Jul. Ex. R.	Yr. Ex. R.
Vancouver	136	35.6	63.3	27.7	8	20	54	48	90
Kamloops	1245	21.8	69.8	48.0	12	27	87	61	134
Banff	4521	13.4	56.8	43.4	18	29	98	65	147
Qu Appelle	2115	−0.4	63.5	63.9	18	24	98	72	152
Mistassini Post	1255	−5.8	60.4	66.2	24	22	95	71	151
Harrington Harbour	30	8.3	53.5	45.2	19	11	84	43	125

TABLE 13. TEMPERATURE DATA FOR SELECTED STATIONS IN THE MACKENZIE VALLEY AND THE PRAIRIE PROVINCES, EXTENDING FROM NORTHWEST TO SOUTHEAST

	Alt.	Jan. Mean	Jul. Mean	Ann. Range	Jan. Range	Jul. Range	Jan. Ex. R.	Jul. Ex. R.	Yr. Ex. R
Herschel Island	10	−22.0	44.1	66.1	13	13	71	40	121
Fort McPherson	150	−25.2	58.5	83.7	15	20	105	57	157
Fort Simpson	427	−19.3	60.3	74.9	16	22	94	56	149
Hay River	529	−17.0	60.0	77.0	18	23	109	62	158
Fort Chipewyan	714	−12.7	59.4	72.1	18	20	103	70	153
Fort McMurray	840	−9.9	62.0	71.9	21	29	115	73	170
Prince Albert	1432	−4.7	62.7	67.4	22	24	121	62	166
Winnipeg	760	−4.3	66.2	70.5	21	24	88	62	149

TABLE 14. TEMPERATURE DATA FOR SELECTED STATIONS ON THE EAST COAST, EXTENDING FROM NORTH TO SOUTH

	Alt.	Jan. Mean	Jul. Mean	Ann. Range	Jan. Range	Jul. Range	Jan. Ex. R.	Jul. Ex. R.	Yr. Ex. R.
Jones Sound	15	−33.2	40.0	73.2	12	11	65	26	116
Ponds Inlet	13	−28.4	42.4	70.8	11	14	58	49	129
Lake Harbour	48	−13.7	44.2	57.9	13	14	72	43	119
Hebron	60	−5.7	47.1	52.8	7	9	80	62	129
St. Johns	160	23.4	59.1	35.7	14	18	78	56	109
Halifax	88	23.0	64.8	41.8	17	19	81	59	127

Mean daily ranges for January are highest in strictly continental situations, being generally 18 degrees or more; and lowest where the water bodies are to windward, usually under 10 degrees. July mean daily ranges are almost always higher than those of January, particularly where there is a change from marine to more continental influences from January to July, as at Kamloops. In the far north, however, there is little difference between January and July, as shown by the figures for Herschel Island and Jones Sound for examples.

The highest extreme monthly ranges (the difference between the highest and lowest temperatures ever recorded) occur in winter. The nearer the station lies to a body of water, the lower is its extreme range of temperature (compare Vancouver, Kamloops and Qu Appelle). The greatest ranges occur in Alberta and Saskatchewan, where the large and sudden changes in temperatures come with the shift from southerly or southwesterly winds to northwesterly, coincident with the passage of a cyclone. The greatest absolute annual ranges occur in general where the mean January temperatures are lowest, viz., in the Mackenzie watershed, the record being 174 degrees for Fort Vermilion. The lowest absolute annual ranges are found along the Pacific coast, and amount to only about one-half that for Fort Vermilion, probably the lowest being 86 degrees at Massett.

One of the most difficult and uncertain situations which the Canadian farmer needs to face is that dealing with frost and the frost-free period. This is true particularly for farmers in northern Ontario and Quebec and in the Prairie Provinces. Throughout each of these sections (except the southern tip of Alberta and the maritime portion of Quebec) and all the region to the north, frost may be expected in any month. In the Prairie Provinces, a late spring frost may necessitate resowing the entire wheat area affected; if the frost comes too late to permit resowing, it may seriously reduce the yield. Quite as damaging are the early autumn frosts which may come while the wheat is still in the milk stage, resulting in a soft and inferior grade of grain which must be sold at a lower price. Figure 31 shows the average length of the frost-free period, and the dates of the latest spring and earliest autumn frost. It will be seen that the frost-free period in the southern portions of Alberta, Saskatchewan and Manitoba averages from three to three and one-half months. In the middle portions of these

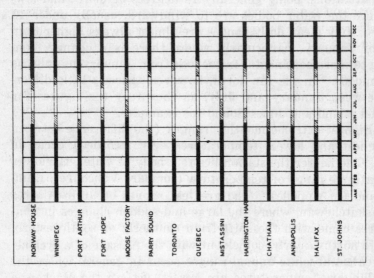

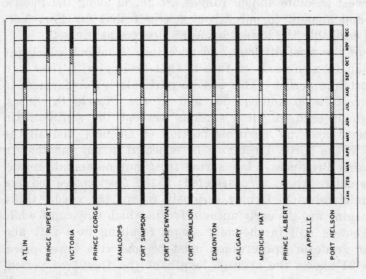

FIG. 31—Frost data for selected stations. The average lengths of the frost-free period are shown by the clear and obliquely-shaded portions of the bars. The dates of the last frost in spring and of the first frost in fall are indicated by the left and right margins, respectively, of the clear portions of the bars.

provinces, the season is only three months long; while in the northern portions it averages less than two months. Still farther north, on Great Slave Lake, the waters of which act as a heat reservoir in the autumn, a broken record of 22 years, shows the frost-free period to average 78 days. As would be expected in the Pacific coast region, the interior valleys of southern British Columbia, the Lower Lakes region, and the eastern maritime region, the frost-free periods are longest, varying from four or five months to as much as seven and one-half months, the latter being at Victoria.

In spite of the uncertainty of the frost-free period north of the 50th parallel (except in the Prairie Provinces where the 55th parallel may be chosen instead, because of the ability of cereals to endure temperatures as low as 30° for a short time without any apparent harm), certain more-resistant vegetables and some cereals may be grown with success in one out of every three, four or five years. According to Stupart, a line from Fort Simpson drawn southeastward to Fort Albany on James Bay would roughly represent the northern limit of land where agriculture might be moderately successful in a fair percentage of years.[1] Agriculture on a commercially successful scale in a region where the frost-free period is under 80 or 90 days, must remain a precarious undertaking, until new or hardier varieties of vegetables and cereals are found.[2]

[1] Op. cit., p. 41.

[2] S. C. Lee, "Some Phases of the Climate of Manitoba in Relation to Agriculture," *Bulletin of the American Meteorological Society*, v. 3, 1922, p. 36.

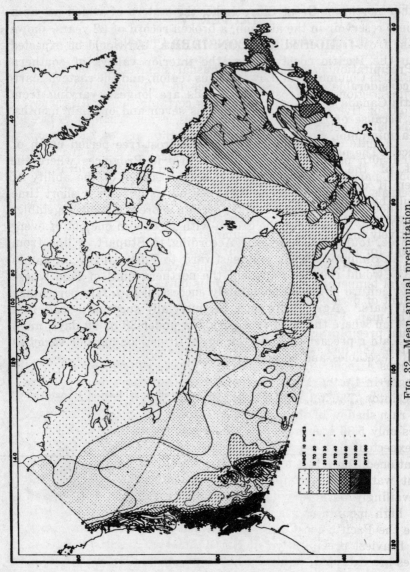

FIG. 32—Mean annual precipitation.

CHAPTER IV

MOISTURE CONSIDERATIONS

Precipitation is a factor of unusual significance as well as of considerable economic importance in Canadian climate. In arctic Canada the annual amount is certainly under 10 inches; but because of the lower temperatures, evaporation is reduced to a minimum, and consequently droughts are of rare occurrence. The permanently frozen ground within a few inches or feet of the surface also prevents underground drainage. Even if droughts were frequent here, the economic aspects would be of little moment at present. Farther south, as in the Thompson and middle Fraser valleys, where temperatures are relatively high, especially in summer, 10 inches of rain is insufficient for most agricultural purposes. Irrigation, therefore, is necessary. Hence, in respect to the availability of water, the general temperature of any station is quite as significant as the amount of precipitation.

The map, Fig. 32, shows the broader features of the mean annual precipitation. The amounts vary from a high of approximately 185 inches at Surf Inlet on the west coast to a low of perhaps 4 inches (3.88 inches in a three-year record) at Fort Conger in the northeastern portion of Ellesmere Island. Yet, at Clinton, 350 miles southeast of Surf Inlet, and situated in the rain shadow of the coast ranges, the total precipitation averages only 5.86 inches a year. This condition is one that would be expected when position and relief are considered. As already mentioned, the effect of the Pacific waters as a source of abundant water vapor, coupled with frequent cyclonic storms, the prevailingly onshore winds, especially in fall and winter, and the high mountains rising abruptly from the sea, combine to give the Pacific coast with its seaward-facing mountain slopes, the heaviest precipitation in North America if trade wind latitudes are excepted. Only those places situated beyond the bend of a fiord or in some other leeward position, or on low lying islands, receive less than 100 inches. The whole Pacific coast is marked by at least 60 inches.

49

The barrier effect of high relief is clearly shown on the east side of Vancouver Island and on the opposite mainland, where the annual amounts are greatly reduced: 59 inches at Vancouver, and only 30 inches at Victoria. To the east of the crest of the coast ranges, there is a rapid falling off, so that, for a large portion of interior British Columbia (except for a few mountains high enough to cause more frequent condensation), the total precipitation is generally under 30 inches with a considerable area showing less than 20 inches. Farther to the eastward, on the west slopes of the high Canadian Rockies, the amounts are increased again to 40 and 60 inches. The whole of British Columbia offers an exceedingly difficult problem in the construction of a precipitation map which will show all the irregularities that certainly do exist there. In the northern part of the province, the isohyets are more regular, not so much because of less complexity of relief, but largely because of insufficient data. It is a noteworthy fact here, however, that there is a very rapid decrease in precipitation with increase in distance from the coast: Juneau, Alaska, receives about 80 inches, while less than 100 miles to the northeast, at Atlin, the amount is only 11 inches—and this in spite of the fact that Atlin is at an altitude of over 2200 feet. A mountain range from 5,000 to 10,000 feet elevation intervenes.

Over the great interior of Canada, the mean annual precipitation, except on a few isolated heights, is under 20 inches; and a considerable portion has less than 15 inches. This is to be expected in the subarctic regions where temperatures are generally too low to permit much water vapor. In southern Alberta and Saskatchewan, the subarid area results more from the lack of available moisture: the great distance from the Arctic Ocean, Hudson Bay, and the Gulf of Mexico, and the intervening barrier of the cordillera, all prevent vapor from being imported in large quantities. Occasionally, when southerly winds persist for several days, as they do at times in summer, fairly copious showers occur in the form of local thunderstorms. At several places in this region, the precipitation is as low as 13 inches.

With progress eastward, precipitation is found to be greater, all of southeastern Canada having more than 20 inches. Here relief is not so pronounced as in British Columbia, so that the isohyets do not take such irregular courses. It is still true, however, that the more numerous the stations, the more patchy the distribution of precipitation appears to be. The fact that it is heavier here than farther west and north is the result of a combination of two factors: the merging over the Great Lakes and St. Lawrence Valley of cyclonic paths, with the consequent greater frequency of these storms; and the nearness to the Atlantic waters, resulting in greater availability of moisture. Under favorable conditions with southerly or southwesterly winds prevailing for several days, considerable moisture may come in from the Gulf of Mexico. In this case as well as in a similar one with respect to Alberta and Saskatchewan, it is probable that only a part of the rain, falling from the resulting thunderstorms, comes directly from vapor taken from Gulf waters; much of the vapor undoubtedly is picked up by evaporation from the more humid region to the south. The effects of the Great Lakes is clearly shown by the denser shading on the east sides of the Lakes. In southeastern Ontario there are several areas of distinctly lighter precipitation, to be explained in most cases by higher lands to windward—particularly true for the Ottawa River Valley and the region northwest of Toronto. The differences are not so great as the map seems to indicate, for most of the stations in these "islands" of lighter precipitation show amounts just under 30 inches, while most of the surrounding ones have just over 30 inches.

In the middle St. Lawrence Valley, there is a marked increase in precipitation, especially on the east slopes where there is a gradual rise in elevation to the highlands of the international boundary. Those portions of Newfoundland and the Atlantic Provinces which are exposed to the warm damp winds off the Atlantic stand out clearly as areas of heavier precipitation— at least 40 inches, and in many places, over 50 inches.

The poleward trend of the isohyets along the Labrador and Baffinland coasts is very marked. It is possible, however, that the lines should bend poleward only over the mountains, and then turn southward again along the coast. This appears to be the trend along the northern Labrador coast, where Hebron, situated only 60 feet above tide and some distance from the mountains farther back, shows only 19.3 inches of precipitation. It is practically certain, nevertheless, that the amounts are greater everywhere just back from the coast, a condition to be expected where marine and orographic influences may be combined.

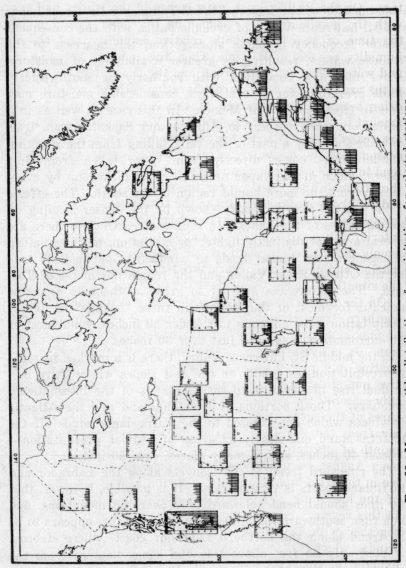

FIG. 33—Mean monthly distribution of precipitation for selected stations.

The time of year of maximum and minimum precipitation varies with the prominence of the marine and continental factors. On the Pacific coast, most comes in the winter half-year, with the maximum in November or December (see Fig. 33), the time of year when both relative humidity and absolute humidity are high, the time when the contrast between land and water temperature is great, and the time when the cyclonic paths are on their southward migration. Here, summer is the drier season, although even at this season the rainfall may amount to over 4 inches a month. At Victoria, July and August are really dry; at Vancouver, only moderately so. It is at this season that the cyclonic control is weak; winds are light and tend to parallel the coast; and even when the winds are onshore, they furnish little moisture for the warm lands, unless the altitude of the mountains can make the temperatures over the land lower than those over the water. On the plateaus and in the interior valleys of British Columbia, the precipitation is fairly evenly distributed throughout the year, partaking of both the marine and continental characteristics. In general the higher the situation, the more abundant the precipitation at all seasons.

On the east slopes of the Rockies, as well as over all of the southern Prairie Provinces, May, June and July are the months of maximum rainfall, a characteristically continental distribution. It is during these months that the combination of great heating and most available moisture together with high relative humidities render convection relatively easy. It is also at this season that there is the greatest contrast between temperatures of the surface and the free air, favoring a high ascent of air from the surface. Farther north in these provinces the month of maximum rainfall tends to be delayed until July or even August, because the persistence of the snow cover and of ice in the lakes and rivers late in spring greatly retards heating of the lower air. Winter is the season of light precipitation in this region. Low temperatures and low absolute humidities together with the drying northwest (or southwest—chinook) winds, which prevail throughout the region at this season, explain the condition.

With the eastward approach to the region of greatest cyclonic activity, the precipitation again becomes about equally divided between the winter and summer half years. Here the summer convectional showers are nearly equalled by the winter rains

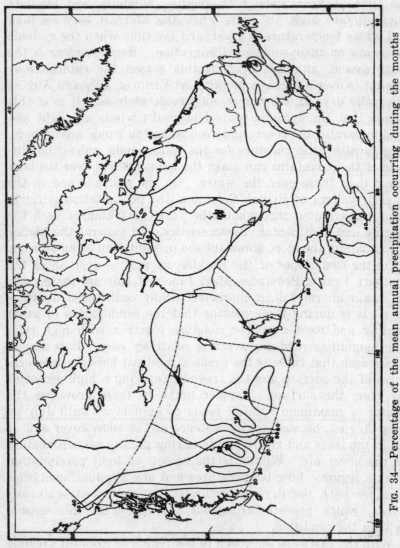

Fig. 34.—Percentage of the mean annual precipitation occurring during the months of May to August, inclusive.

and snows. In Nova Scotia and Newfoundland, where the marine influence is strong, winter again shows the heaviest precipitation.

In Arctic and subarctic Canada, the records are too fragmentary to permit definite conclusions regarding the seasonal distribution. Furthermore, the great difficulty experienced in measuring the constantly shifting snow must certainly throw some inaccuracies into the record of precipitation. Hence, only broad and general deductions can be made. It is, however, a well-known fact that snowfall in these portions of Canada is extremely light. It is evident, therefore, that much of the precipitation comes in the form of rain. Summer and autumn should be the seasons of heaviest precipitation because at those seasons there is the greatest available moisture. Furthermore, in autumn the lands are rapidly cooling, so the surrounding water bodies are warmer than the lands. A reference again to Fig. 33 shows that summer and autumn have the heaviest precipitation, and that this condition is especially marked in Labrador and Baffin Island. In the Mackenzie and Yukon basins the same is true, although the difference between the summer and autumn amounts is less marked.

To the Canadian farmer, the time of year when he may expect precipitation is of more import than the annual amount. The prominence of wheat growing on the prairies and plains of western Canada is a direct result of seasonal rainfall distribution. The map, Fig. 34, shows the percentage of the mean annual precipitation which occurs from May to August inclusive. Throughout the wheat growing region, it will be noticed that at least one-half of the total occurs in these four months; that in a large area of the more recently developed wheat lands, the percentage is around 60; and that there is one area of perhaps 10,000 square miles which receives more than 70% during these four months. The actual amount of rain received at Swift Current from May to August is about 9 inches. This amount is only 1 inch less than that received during the same period at Winnipeg; and only 3 inches less than that at Port Dover on Lake Erie or in the well-known Annapolis Valley of Nova Scotia. Less than 200 miles to the west, on the western slopes of the Selkirks, this percentage is reduced to less than 20. It increases again in the interior valley and plateau section of British Columbia, and then drops to less than 20 along the

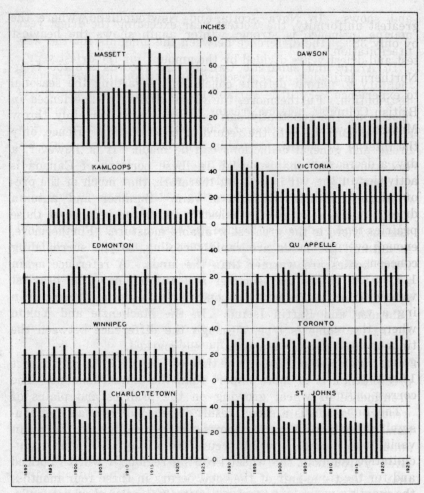

FIG. 35—Distribution of the total annual precipitation for the 36-year period, 1890-1925, for selected stations.

Pacific coast. In the eastern maritime region, the percentage is everywhere under 40; the same is true for the east shores of Hudson Bay. All of Arctic Canada apparently receives more than 40%, but less than 50%, during the same period.

As far as the annual amount of precipitation is concerned, for most places in Canada and Newfoundland the variation from year to year is not unusually great. Fig. 35 shows the annual distribution for selected stations. The Great Lakes and St. Lawrence regions as represented by Toronto show the greatest uniformity, the wettest year exceeding the driest year by only 38% (the difference between the amounts for the wettest and driest years divided by the amount for the driest year). Northern latitudes, as represented by Dawson, likewise appear to experience very little variability. The maritime sections of British Columbia present greater variations from year to year: Massett shows a variation of 136% and Victoria of 147%. In the interior of British Columbia, where even wettest years are dry, a decrease of a few inches means much to the agricultural activities in the valleys. Kamloops may be considered typical of interior valley stations; here the wettest year exceeded the driest by 145%. The very large annual variations on the prairies tend to decrease toward the east, yet remain still great enough everywhere to give the farmer and rancher considerable concern; at Edmonton the variation is 155%; at Qu Appelle, 115%; and at Winnipeg, 97%. In the Atlantic Provinces, the variability becomes more marked again, Charlottetown showing a variation of 205%. But at St. Johns, Newfoundland, where the marine and storm factors exert a strong and continuous control, the variation amounts to only 55%. All foregoing figures are based on available records for the period 1890-1925. The variations over a longer period are, of course, correspondingly greater.

The annual variation in precipitation is, however, of less significance from an agricultural standpoint than the monthly variations. Table 15 shows the maximum and minimum precipitation for each month for the same stations used in Fig. 35 and for the same period. In most cases it will be observed that the monthly variations are very large, and much larger in summer than in winter.

Probably the most unsatisfactory element of climate with which we have to deal is snowfall. This is true especially for Canada. Under the most favorable conditions, it is difficult to make accurate measurements of the amount of snowfall. It is rendered doubly difficult in regions where the snowfall is light and where the winds are strong, removing snow from some places and piling it high in others. Furthermore, measurements of snowfall are rarely comparable, considering Canada as a whole. In the far north, during the coldest part of the year, snow comes in the form of tiny, needle-like crystals which form

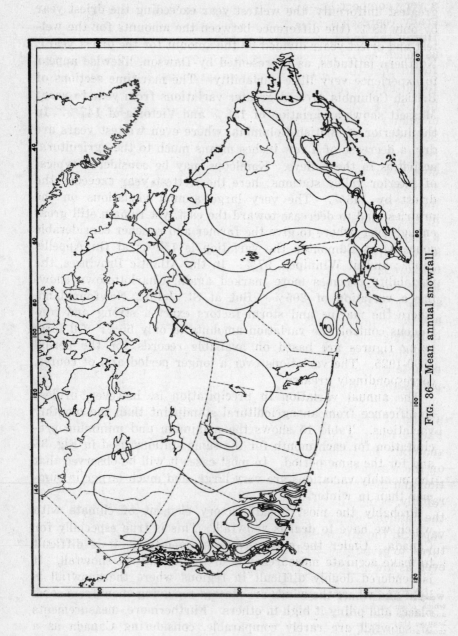

Fig. 36—Mean annual snowfall.

a very compact layer on the ground, so that 3 to 5 inches generally represents 1 inch of water. On the east shore of Lake Huron the snow is often exceedingly fluffy, requiring possibly as much as 18 inches to produce one inch of rain.[1] Cornish found that the upper two inches of snow in wave formations found near Winnipeg with a temperature of 10° had a specific gravity of 0.38 (approximately 1 inch of water from 2.5 inches of snow) ; and that the surface snow at Glacier House in the Selkirks had a specific gravity of 0.106 or not far from the ratio of 1 to 10 as used under all conditions by the Canadian Meteorological Service.[2] In southern Ontario where the average snowfall is about the same as that in the Yukon Valley, most of the year finds the surface relatively free from snow, although in the Yukon the snow cover usually lasts all winter. Hence, a map of mean annual snowfall such as that shown in Fig. 36, shows only one thing: the sum of the various measurements of of snowfall made at the end of each snowstorm or at certain hours during the occurrence of the snowfall; it does not necessarily give any indication of the amount of snow on the ground nor the weight or water equivalent of the snow. To that extent is the map satisfactory or unsatisfactory.

Obviously enough, the region of heaviest snowfall is in the mountain districts of British Columbia where most of the points above 4000 feet report more than 100 inches. At Glacier, on the west slopes of the Selkirks, the average amount reaches a total of 415 inches or nearly 35 feet. Immediately along the Pacific coast, winter temperatures are too high to permit much snowfall, the amount being as low as 15 inches at Clayoquot on the west coast of Vancouver Island. With increase in elevation and the consequent drop in temperatures, snowfall increases rapidly, being 100 inches and over on most of the summits. In the interior valleys the decreased altitude and reduced water vapor in the air combine, in spite of the relatively low temperatures, to give this region an average snowfall of under 40 inches, even as low as 25 inches at Clinton. It is a fact of considerable

---

[1] A letter to the author from Cyrus H. Eshleman, Official in charge of the U. S. Weather Bureau Office, Ludington, Mich., states that at times the light, fluffy snows which often persist for several days at Ludington (on the east shore of Lake Michigan) and similar localities may have a water content of less than 1 to 20. It is reasonable to assume that conditions on the east shores of Lake Huron would not differ essentially from those at Ludington.

[2] Vaughan Cornish, "On Snow-Waves and Snow-Drifts in Canada," *Geographical Journal*, v. 20, 1902, p. 158.

interest that most of the western Arctic has snowfall as low as, and doubtless lower than, the lands of the same altitude lying 10 to 20 degrees of latitude farther south; and this, in spite of the much longer period of winter cold. The condition is readily explained, however, by the fact that at such low temperatures as exist in this region, the amount of water vapor in saturated air is exceedingly small. Thus, in January at Fort Norman, the absolute humidity of saturated air is, on the average, only one-eighth of that at Toronto. The same explanation applies in part to the lighter snowfall on the prairies as compared with that in the Great Lakes region. The difference in this case is due more particularly to the distance from an available source of moisture for the prairies.

As already indicated, snows of a light and fluffy character occur on the leeward shores of Lakes Huron and Superior; in fact, the greatest snowfall in eastern Canada (nearly 150 inches), occurs at Steep Hill Falls at the eastern end of Lake Superior. The heavier snowfall of these areas is in part the result of winds blowing from a westerly quadrant, and hence from the relatively warm water to the higher and colder land, particularly in December and January.[1] To the same extent this explanation holds for the small section of heavier snowfall near the northeastern shore of Lake Ontario. A particularly significant feature for eastern Canada is the fact that snowfall is higher along the coast than in the interior. Thus, the lines of equal snowfall tend to run north and south, even as they do in western Canada. The numerous glaciers along the seaward facing mountain slopes of the east Baffinland coast bear visible evidence of this heavier snowfall. The frequent winter depressions which move across Labrador, causing east and northeast winds as they approach, bring exceptionally deep snows to the Hudson Straits region as well as to the whole Labrador Peninsula.

Snowfall is even more variable from year to year than is rainfall. In general it may be said that the lighter the snow-fall, the greater the variability. Thus, in the Prairie Provinces, the maximum snowfall for any winter month is usually four times the average; in the eastern maritime region, however, the

---

[1] C. L. Mitchell has found that snow occurs with a west wind as far as 10 to 20 miles back from the eastern shore of Lake Michigan, when fair weather prevails on the western coast. See *Monthly Weather Review*, v. 49, 1921, pp. 502-3.

greatest is only about two and one-half to three times the average.

The average number of days in a year on which measurable precipitation (0.01 inch or more) occurs varies in general with the total amount of precipitation (Fig. 37). Thus, along the wet Pacific coast as well as along the coast of Nova Scotia and southern Newfoundland, the number of days averages more

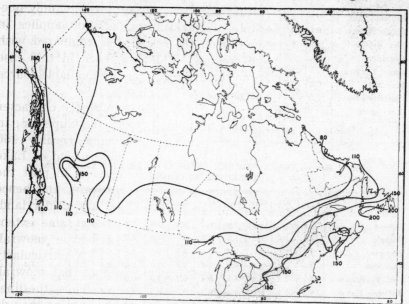

FIG. 37—Average number of days per year with .01 inch or more of precipitation.

than 150—and in places more than 200. But in most of Alberta, Saskatchewan and Manitoba, the average ranges from about 70 to 100 days (the lowest being 66 at Fort Vermilion and the highest 127 at Banff). At least two-thirds of the Dominion probably has fewer than 80 days with precipitation.

The number of days on which any rain (trace or more of liquid precipitation) falls and the number of days on which any snow falls, have a somewhat different sort of distribution from that of days with precipitation. These differences are indicated in Tables 15 and 16. In the former case, the maritime portions of Canada as well as the Great Lakes region show a relatively much greater number than the interior of the country. Conversely, the number of days on which any snow

TABLE 15. AVERAGE NUMBER OF DAYS WITH ANY RAIN FOR SELECTED STATIONS

	Jan.	Feb.	Mar.	Apr.	May	Jun.	Jul.	Aug.	Sep.	Oct.	Nov.	Dec.	Yr.
Dawson	0.0	0.0	0.0	1.7	7.0	11.7	10.3	10.9	9.8	2.7	0.0	0.0	54.6
Massett	11.2	11.0	9.4	13.7	12.0	14.4	12.7	14.7	17.2	20.4	17.1	16.4	170.2
Victoria	16.7	12.2	14.9	12.3	6.7	7.1	4.3	5.2	8.4	13.8	18.2	20.0	139.8
Kamloops	0.6	2.3	3.4	6.3	7.1	8.6	6.1	7.7	6.3	6.1	4.7	3.1	62.3
Fort Vermilion	0.0	0.0	0.1	1.7	4.8	5.3	9.1	7.5	6.2	4.2	0.3	0.0	39.2
Medicine Hat	0.2	0.4	1.0	4.3	5.8	7.6	6.3	5.2	4.7	3.2	0.6	0.0	39.3
Prince Albert	0.1	0.2	0.5	2.9	7.0	12.0	10.5	10.8	6.7	4.1	0.9	0.5	56.2
Port Nelson	0.0	0.0	0.1	0.7	3.2	8.9	8.9	11.8	10.3	3.9	0.4	0.1	48.3
Winnipeg	0.2	0.2	1.2	5.3	7.2	10.6	9.4	10.3	10.1	5.8	2.5	0.3	63.1
Moose Factory	7.2	0.5	1.5	4.8	13.5	13.5	15.2	13.2	17.5	10.8	3.0	7.2	107.9
Toronto	3.9	3.8	7.5	7.6	12.2	12.4	10.3	9.8	11.1	12.0	9.2	0.8	110.1
Charlottetown	3.5	2.7	5.1	7.1	10.6	10.7	10.9	11.6	10.9	11.6	9.7	5.0	99.4
Harrington Harbour	1.0	0.4	2.9	5.8	7.0	7.7	7.9	7.9	6.8	6.0	5.6	1.6	60.6
St. Johns	6.4	6.3	8.4	13.5	14.1	12.1	13.4	12.2	14.2	16.6	13.3	8.7	139.2

TABLE 16. AVERAGE NUMBER OF DAYS WITH ANY SNOW FOR SELECTED STATIONS

	Jan.	Feb.	Mar.	Apr.	May	Jun.	Jul.	Aug.	Sep.	Oct.	Nov.	Dec.	Yr.
Dawson	8.9	7.2	6.0	2.3	1.4	0.0	0.0	0.1	0.6	5.5	10.6	9.5	52.1
Massett	5.7	1.8	2.0	1.2	0.0	0.0	0.0	0.0	0.0	5.1	1.4	2.3	14.5
Victoria	3.0	3.2	1.5	0.2	0.0	0.0	0.0	0.0	0.0	0.0	0.6	2.1	10.6
Kamloops	8.0	4.3	2.9	0.3	0.0	0.0	0.0	0.0	0.0	0.7	3.0	7.4	26.6
Fort Vermilion	5.7	2.9	4.3	1.5	0.4	0.1	0.0	0.0	0.0	1.0	3.5	3.8	23.2
Medicine Hat	8.5	7.2	8.0	3.1	0.1	0.0	0.0	0.0	0.6	1.9	3.9	7.2	40.5
Prince Albert	9.1	4.8	7.4	4.0	1.1	0.0	0.0	0.0	0.3	2.2	6.4	7.1	42,4
Port Nelson	5.8	6.1	6.8	5.6	2.0	1.7	0.1	0.1	1.5	7.3	9.1	7.4	53.5
Winnipeg	8.4	7.3	7.0	2.9	0.6	0.0	0.0	0.0	0.1	3.7	6.1	8.2	44.3
Moose Factory	12.2	8.5	13.7	6.8	5.5	0.0	0.0	0.0	0.0	4.2	13.5	16.3	80.7
Toronto	13.4	11.7	7.6	2.9	0.6	0.0	0.0	0.0	0.1	0.8	4.4	10.8	52.3
Charlottetown	9.3	7.1	7.2	4.5	0.3	0.0	0.0	0.0	0.0	0.6	4.3	5.0	38.3
Harrington Harbour	8.1	6.7	6.1	2.9	1.0	0.0	0.0	0.0	0.1	0.5	3.8	6.5	35.7
St. Johns	10.1	7.2	5.6	2.3	0.8	0.0	0.0	0.0	0.0	0.2	2.8	7.1	36.1

falls is greater in the interior. These facts, of course, are closely related to temperature conditions.

The map of average annual cloudiness (Fig. 38) compares very well with that of average number of days with precipitation. The districts having a strong marine control, viz., the Pacific coast, Hudson Bay, and the eastern maritime country, show the most cloudy weather, the average percentage of cloudiness in these districts being from 60% to 70% and over. A large area in which the average cloudiness is under 50% extends from the Arctic southward to the southern limits of Saskatchewan and Manitoba; this shows distinctly the tendency for clearer skies in continental climates. The monthly course of cloudiness is indicated for a few places in Table 17. In most places summer has slightly clearer skies than winter; and,

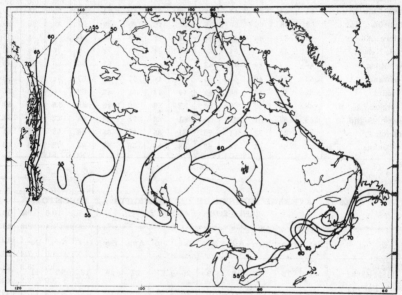

FIG. 38—Mean annual cloudiness in per cents of the sky covered.

except for strictly marine situations, autumn is clearer than spring. The average number of clear nights (nights clear enough for the observation of auroras) has been determined for Toronto and York Factory; the averages are shown in Table 18.[1] If the data are dependable it will be observed that at Toronto there are twice as many clear nights in midsummer as in midwinter. At York Factory the influence of Hudson Bay is seen for all seasons except autumn, the winds at this season being offshore.

The data on humidity for all but a few stations in the warmer portions of Canada are extremely meager, especially for the

[1] A. W. Greely, "Chronological List of Auroras Observed from 1870 to 1879," in the Appendix to *Professional Papers of the Signal Service, No. 3*, Washington, Oct. 1881.

TABLE 17. MEAN MONTHLY CLOUDINESS IN PER CENTS OF SKY COVERED

	Jan.	Feb.	Mar.	Apr.	May	Jun.	Jul.	Aug.	Sep.	Oct.	Nov.	Dec.	Yr.
Dawson	55	53	41	50	58	61	62	61	67	69	70	59	59
Prince Rupert	74	76	74	70	70	71	74	70	66	74	76	74	72
Victoria	75	72	64	59	49	47	34	34	43	60	73	76	57
Kamloops	56	52	54	56	54	54	42	46	41	48	62	62	52
Fort Good Hope	44	44	38	44	46	42	43	51	63	64	53	41	48
Fort Chipewyan	51	47	50	43	46	50	44	45	54	54	56	54	50
Medicine Hat	59	58	64	60	56	52	38	45	50	53	49	56	53
Prince Albert	40	37	48	44	50	52	42	48	48	50	43	43	45
Port Nelson	52	46	42	64	68	68	64	63	72	78	76	56	62
Winnipeg	46	47	49	48	42	48	42	41	51	56	60	53	49
Cochrane	54	49	49	55	56	48	48	52	60	67	74	64	56
Toronto	65	61	55	55	51	49	44	42	47	52	69	73	55
Chatham, N. B.	48	48	53	60	56	55	56	50	46	48	55	54	52
Jones Sound	19	37	31	47	56	61	63	78	69	65	32	28	49
Hebron	49	49	53	61	70	67	65	67	65	66	63	55	61
St. Johns	68	66	65	74	69	58	58	56	57	64	72	74	65

TABLE 18. AVERAGE NUMBER OF CLEAR NIGHTS AT TORONTO
AND YORK FACTORY

	Jan.	Feb.	Mar.	Apr.	May	Jun.	Jul.	Aug.	Sep.	Oct.	Nov.	Dec.	Yr.
Toronto (1853-1880)	11	13	16	17	19	20	21	22	20	16	12	11	198
York Factory (1874-1880)	23	20	22	20	19	22	22	23	17	13	15	15	231

TABLE 19. MEAN RELATIVE HUMIDITY IN PER CENTS. OBSERVATIONS
TAKEN AT 8 A. M., 2 P. M., AND 8 P. M.

	Jan.	Feb.	Mar.	Apr.	May	Jun.	Jul.	Aug.	Sep.	Oct.	Nov.	Dec.	Yr.
Victoria	85	83	78	74	72	73	75	78	79	85	87	86	80
Kamloops	75	73	70	58	56	57	56	60	64	71	78	74	66
Edmonton	82	78	75	66	61	68	70	75	72	70	77	81	73
Winnipeg	88	81	77	71	62	68	69	73	78	78	80	83	76
Toronto	75	74	70	65	63	66	66	69	74	76	77	77	71
St. John, N. B.	74	74	75	74	72	78	83	82	81	77	77	78	77
Southwest Point	93	90	93	91	84	87	92	91	91	91	95	96	91
Jones Sound	84	83	82	80	80	80	82	84	83	82	82	83	82
Hebron	82	79	85	87	80	84	85	82	75	76	81	79	81

months having a large proportion of, the days below freezing. A few averages of relative humidity have been worked out and may be found in Table 19. With the exception of St. John, New Brunswick, summer has lower relative humidity than winter. The difference between these two seasons is greater, as would be expected, in places having light precipitation in summer and heavy (or moderate) precipitation in winter. Victoria and Kamloops illustrate this condition. Southwest Point on the island of Anticosti is the most humid station of those shown, the average for December being 96%. Kamloops and Edmonton are the driest, the respective percentages being 61 (May) and 56 (July).

It is only in the Prairie Provinces and the region of the Great Lakes that thunderstorms may be said to be frequent; but even here the total number in a year does not exceed 25 (compare with portions of the Gulf States having 80 and 90). Southeast Canada and the Mackenzie district report from five to ten a year. The Pacific coast is a region of remarkably few, considering the great amount of rainfall received. Thunderstorms, as mentioned in Chapter II (see Fig. 22), come chiefly in the warmest months and during or at the conclusion of a prolonged hot period when convection is strong and when colder air comes in on the rear of a passing low pressure area. In Table 20 are listed a few representative stations showing the

TABLE 20. AVERAGE NUMBER OF DAYS WITH THUNDERSTORMS

	Jan.	Feb.	Mar.	Apr.	May	Jun.	Jul.	Aug.	Sep.	Oct.	Nov.	Dec.	Yr.
Atlin						0.7	1.1	0.4					2.2
Victoria	0.1						1.2	0.8	0.2		0.1	0.1	2.5
Kamloops							1.0						1.0
Fort Good Hope		0.1			0.5	2.4	4.4	1.8	0.2				9.4
Fort Vermilion				0.1	0.3	1.5	1.5	1.2	0.5				5.1
Medicine Hat				0.2	1.2	3.9	5.9	2.8	1.0				15.0
Prince Albert					0.7	2.6	3.9	3.9	0.7				11.8
Port Nelson					0.1	1.2	0.9	1.0	0.3	0.1			3.6
Winnipeg			0.1	0.4	2.6	4.5	5.0	4.2	2.4	0.1	0.1		19.4
Moose Factory				0.1	0.2	0.4	0.7	0.5	0.2				2.1
Toronto		0.3	0.5	2.0	2.5	5.1	5.2	5.7	3.1	0.7	0.1		25.2
Chatham, N. B.	0.1	0.1			0.5	1.6	2.5	1.7	0.4				6.9
Harrington Harbour						0.2	0.3	1.2	0.4	0.1			2.2
St. Johns						0.4	0.4	0.6	0.2	0.1			1.7

TABLE 21. AVERAGE NUMBER OF DAYS WITH HAIL

	Jan.	Feb.	Mar.	Apr.	May	Jun.	Jul.	Aug.	Sep.	Oct.	Nov.	Dec.	Yr.
Atlin					0.1	0.1		0.1					0.3
Victoria	0.2	0.3	0.4	0.3	0.3		0.1			0.1	0.1	0.1	1.9
Kamloops	0.2	0.1	0.5	0.6	0.2			0.1		0.2	0.1		2.0
Fort Good Hope		0.1		0.1	0.4	0.7	0.3	0.1	0.3	0.2	0.2		2.4
Fort Vermilion						0.4	0.5	0.3					1.2
Medicine Hat			0.1	0.2	0.2	0.2	0.1			0.1			0.9
Prince Albert				0.1	0.3	0.4	0.1	0.4					1.3
Port Nelson				0.1	0.2	0.4	0.1	0.1	0.1				1.0
Winnipeg	0.1		0.1	0.3	0.4	0.4	0.1	0.3	0.2	0.1			2.0
Moose Factory		0.1			0.1								0.2
Toronto		0.1	0.4	0.1	0.2	0.2	0.2	0.1		0.2	0.1		1.6
Harrington Harbour		0.1		0.1	0.2	0.1		0.1					0.6
Chatham, N. B.	0.1				0.1	0.2	0.1			0.1	0.1		0.7
St. Johns													0.0

number of days with thunderstorms. Hail is a relatively infrequent phenomenon in Canada. It is, however, closely associated with thunderstorms; and the greater the number of days with thunderstorms, the greater the number of days with hail. The frequency of hail is shown in Table 21.

One other feature of Canadian climate, and one that is peculiarly characteristic of the Grand Banks, is fog. Some mention has already been made in Chapter II of the conditions favoring fogs (see Figs. 19 and 21). The frequency of fogs is shown in Table 22. In the interior fogs most often occur where stations are located in valleys or near bodies of water; plateau stations seldom experience them. Fogs are most frequent on the Atlantic coast, because there conditions which favor fogs are almost always present. These conditions are: a pressure gradient which will carry air from warm waters across cold waters or onto cold land. The cold Labrador Current and the warm Gulf Stream are always present; the continuous procession of cyclones over the region supplies the other factor. On the west coast, fogs are less frequent because the contrast between land and water temperatures near the shore is not great. Fogs also form at much higher elevations, and then they are designated, by those below, as clouds.

Only the very broad features of the climate of Canada and Newfoundland have been discussed up to this point; and even

TABLE 22. AVERAGE NUMBER OF DAYS WITH FOGS

	Jan.	Feb.	Mar.	Apr.	May	Jun.	Jul.	Aug.	Sep.	Oct.	Nov.	Dec.	Yr.
Atlin	1.1	0.3		0.1						0.2	0.4	0.7	2.8
Vancouver	2.2	2.5	0.3	0.3	0.1			0.1	1.9	5.6	4.6	2.6	20.2
Kamloops	0.8	0.2	0.1						0.2				1.3
Fort Good Hope	0.3		0.3	0.4	0.2		0.2	0.5	0.9	0.6	0.5		3.9
Fort Vermilion	0.9	0.4				0.1		0.2	0.8	0.8	0.4	0.5	4.1
Medicine Hat	1.1			1.0		0.1	0.1		0.2	0.1	0.3	0.1	3.0
Prince Albert	0.2	0.2	0.2	0.1	0.2	0.2	0.4	0.5	1.0	0.3	0.5	0.2	4.0
Port Nelson				0.3	1.5	0.8	0.4	0.9	0.8	0.1		1.0	5.8
Winnipeg	1.2	0.6	0.3	0.3	0.2	0.1	0.4	0.2	1.4	0.8	1.9	0.3	7.7
Moose Factory				0.1	0.2	0.4		0.8	0.2	0.3	0.2	0.1	2.3
Toronto	1.5	2.1	2.2	1.4	2.7	1.0	0.5	0.6	0.7	2.3	1.4	0.9	17.3
Chatham, N. B.	0.1	0.2	0.1	0.1	0.1	0.4	0.3	0.3	0.7	0.4	0.8	0.4	3.9
Harrington Harbour	0.1	0.1	0.3	2.0	2.2	5.3	4.0	5.0	3.5	0.3		0.1	22.9
St. Johns	3.8	2.0	3.8	6.3	4.3	3.1	5.5	3.5	2.6	1.8	3.8	3.8	40.8

these have been treated with no finality of judgment. A country so vast in area, so varied in relief and other physical conditions, and possessing so few meteorological stations in the great expanse north of the 50th or 55th parallel, necessarily offers an exceedingly complex problem. To discuss all the facts of climate with equal detail for both the southern populous areas and the far north is not possible with data available. Hence, Arctic Canada has not received so full a discussion as the size and importance of it would warrant. The purpose of the discussion thus far has been merely to point out certain fundamental aspects of the climate upon which could be based the more intensive study of local climates which follows in the succeeding chapters.

CHAPTER V

BRITISH COLUMBIA AND YUKON TERRITORY

It is obvious that a specific description of the climate of Canada and Newfoundland must be based on several small units; but how to divide the Dominions into practical units or regions is a serious question. Divisions made strictly according to physiography or vegetation are not climatic regions; and divisions based strictly on climatic considerations frequently divide an otherwise natural region into two or more units. The divisions adopted for use in this and succeeding chapters are determined by convenience rather than by any one geographic condition; relief, vegetation, location, and land utilization as well as climate have been considered in making the divisions. Hence, they can not be called climatic regions; rather, they are broadly geographic or natural regions.

Four major regions are recognized and the climate of each is considered in a separate chapter. The regions are: British Columbia and Yukon Territory; the Continental Interior; Eastern Canada and Newfoundland; and the Archipelago and Arctic Prairies. Each of the first three major regions is further divided into four or more subregions or nuclei with broad, indeterminate transition zones surrounding them. It will be observed, as the discussion proceeds, that these subregions are to some extent climatic; that is, the climatic characteristics of each are very similar; the differences are in degree rather than in kind.

The first major region mentioned, British Columbia and Yukon Territory, is one of exceedingly diverse relief, elevations ranging from sea level to nearly 20,000 feet. Mountain and plateau, and marine and continental climates are all represented in varying degrees. The marine control is dominant immediately along the coast or in the broader valleys, such as the lower Fraser, leading back from the coast; but this marine control gives way rapidly to the continental or the altitude control with increasing distance from the sea. Yet, the continental influence is not nearly so strong in this region as in the great continental interior. The great latitudinal extent, about 22 degrees, means a considerable difference of climate between the extreme northern and southern limits. It is this great complexity of land and water, relief and altitude, which makes for a greater diver-

ILLUS. 1—Cool, sunny and frostless summers makes apple growing profitable in the southeastern part of Vancouver Island.

sity of climate in this region than in any of the other three. On the whole, the climate may be considered as fairly uniform from year to year, and as generally dependable.

THE PACIFIC COAST AND LOWER FRASER VALLEY

This subregion is rather narrowly confined to the Pacific islands, to the immediate coast with its seaward-facing slopes and to that portion of the open lower Fraser Valley which extends in an east-west direction—a distance of perhaps 80 miles. Although all of the island of Vancouver is included, the climate on the leeward slopes of its mountains is more like that of the Harrison Lake district 50 miles inland from the city of Vancouver. The waters on the east and south sides of the island are wide enough, however, to keep the whole area dominantly under the marine control. The relief here is more

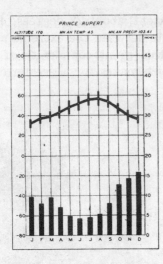
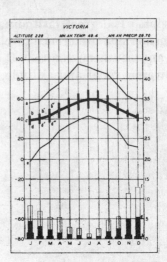
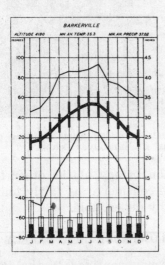
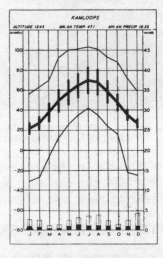

FIG. 39—Temperature and precipitation charts for Prince Rupert, Victoria, Barkerville, and Kamloops. The charts in this figure as well as those in Figs. 41, 42, 44, 47, 48, 49, 50, 52, 53, 54, and 55, are to be interpreted as follows, using the Victoria Chart as an example: curve *a* shows the highest temperatures ever observed and curve *e* shows the lowest temperatures ever observed. Mean temperatures are indicated by the heavy curve *c*. The upper extremities of the vertical bars (*b*, *b' b''*, etc.) and the lower extremities (*d*, *d'*, *d''*, etc.) represent respectively the mean maximum and mean minimum temperatures; while the bars themselves (*bd*, *b'd'*, etc.) show mean daily ranges of temperature. The maximum precipitation in any month is to be read from the top of the vertical bar as indicated at *f*; the mean precipitation is to be read from the top of the black bar as indicated at *g*; and the minimum precipitation is to be read from the top of the broad bases as indicated at *h*.

significant in its effect upon precipitation than upon temperature.

Extremes of temperature as experienced in other parts of Canada are unknown in this region. At no place along the coast do mean monthly temperatures ever drop below 32°, nor exceed 65°. Even at Victoria where the summer months are for the most part clear and sunny, the highest monthly mean does not reach 60°. Where the altitude factor becomes pronounced, the general level of temperatures is lower, although the ranges are no greater. Hence, the winters may be characterized by relatively high temperatures for the latitude and the summers by relatively low temperatures. Massett, near the 54th parallel, enjoys winters as mild as those of Washington, D. C., and its summers are as cool as the winters of Jacksonville, Florida. Victoria is even milder and is as warm in winter as Richmond, Virginia; while its summers are as cool as the winters of St. Petersburg, Florida. Everywhere, October is warmer than April.

The daily ranges of temperature are on the average relatively low at all seasons, but lower in winter than summer, the range in the various months tending to vary inversely with the mean cloudiness. At Victoria, the mean daily range in winter is only 8 degrees; but in summer, when clouds are few, the range is about 17 degrees. At no place in this province do mean daily ranges exceed 20 degrees in any month. Annual ranges are likewise small, from less than 20 degrees to no more than 30 degrees.

Extremely high temperatures and extremely low temperatures in winter are rare; seldom being above 90° or below 0°, except far back from the coast. The highest temperature to be expected on the average in January is about 50°; in July or August, about 73° at Massett, and 85° at Vancouver. The lowest to be expected in January is about 15°; in July, about 45°. Extreme temperatures, like ranges, become greater with increase in distance from the coast. Thus Agassiz gets warmer in summer and colder in winter than most coastal situations; but the mean temperature for the year is about the same.

The marine influence is fully as striking in its effect upon precipitation as upon temperature. Late fall and early winter are everywhere the rainiest seasons, and late spring and summer, the least rainy. The rainiest month has at least three and one-half times as much rain as the driest; at Victoria on the leeward side of the mountains of Vancouver as well as those of northwest Washington, November receives more than 14 times as much as July. For places exposed to the ocean influences, the precipitation is never less than 35 inches in any year—it may exceed 200 inches in some years. Denison states[1]:

ILLUS. 2—Strawberries in carload lots are shipped to eastern markets from the vicinity of Victoria, B. C.

"In connection with heavy precipitation in this province [British Columbia], it appears that at Henderson Lake on the the west coast of Vancouver Island, where we now have a station, the annual precipitation was 228 inches in 1923, with 79 inches in December, and in 1924 the yearly total was 281 inches. It is probable that owing to peculiar local conditions this station may prove to be the wettest spot not only in this Province but on the North Pacific Coast."

The total precipitation at this station for the years 1925, 1926, and 1927 was 256 inches, 274 inches, and 272 inches, respectively, making the mean annual for the five-year period 262 inches. On the lee sides of Vancouver Island in some years the amount may be as low as 20 inches. Precipitation is, however, sufficient in most months. All forms of vegetation flourish in this cool, humid climate. In only a small section of southeastern Vancouver Island are the summers usually too

[1] F. Napier Denison, "The Climate of British Columbia," *Monthly Weather Review*, Washington, vol. 53, 1925, p. 354.

dry for ordinary agricultural purposes without some artificial method of keeping the soil moist. Snowfall rarely exceeds a total of 40 inches except in the higher situations; at Victoria the average annual snowfall does not exceed 15 inches.

In general, this whole subregion is characterized by a large number of rainy days—from 150 per year in the south and on less exposed situations to more than 200 on the Queen Charlotte Islands. Since most of the precipitation comes in the winter half-year, it is evident that that season is exceedingly dull, cloudy and humid. Juneau, Alaska, and Tatoosh Island, Washington, may be considered as fairly representative of the extreme northern and southern limits of Canada's Pacific coast. In Table 23 are given the percentage frequencies of both sum-

TABLE 23. PERCENTAGE FREQUENCIES OF WEATHER TYPES[1]

	Juneau, Alaska	Tatoosh, Wash.	Kamloops	Atlin	Barkerville	Dawson
			Summer			
Hot			54			
Moderate	84	95	45	69	55	91
Cool	16	4		31	44	8
Fair	86	63	75	75	45	58
Windy	8		5	1	5	
Hot; Rainy			7			
Hot; Fair; Quiet			47			1
Moderate; Rainy	45	34	16	14	24	39
Moderate; Fair; Windy		8		3	1	4
Moderate; Fair; Quiet	39	53	28	51	30	48
Cool; Rainy	14	2		10	30	3
Cool; Fair; Windy				1		1
Cool; Fair; Quiet	2	2		20	14	4
			Winter			
Cool	40	96	8	7	8	
Cold	60	3	92	93	92	100
Fair	35	31	75	72	53	69
Windy	3	18		12	9	6
Cool; Rainy	33	67	8	3	4	
Cool; Fair; Windy		16		3	1	
Cool; Fair; Quiet	7	13	26	1	3	
Cold; Snowy; Quiet	20		17	21	38	28
Cold; Fair; Windy	2	1		6	4	4
Cold; Fair; Quiet	26	1	48	62	45	66
Cold; Snowy; Windy	1			3	3	2

[1] The figures in this Table, as well as those in Tables 25 and 26, were taken from an article by G. F. Howe, "Summer and Winter Weather of Selected Cities in North America," *Monthly Weather Review*, v. 53, 1925, pp. 427-30.

mer and winter weather types. At Juneau, a third of the winter days are cool and rainy and about a quarter are cold, fair and quiet; at Tatoosh, two-thirds are cool and rainy. In summer, throughout the whole region, the weather is predominantly either moderate and rainy, or moderate, fair and quiet. Fogs are most frequent during the winter season at Vancouver, the average being four each month. Quite the opposite is true,

ILLUS. 3—Moderate, moist winters and relatively dry summers favor large wheat (and straw) yields on the level stretches of eastern Vancouver.

however, at Prince Rupert where most of the fogs occur from June to October. Victoria, likewise, has nine of its fifteen average annual fogs occurring in August to October. Thunderstorms are rare, the north coast experiencing on the average only one a year, Victoria less than three, Vancouver only six. Even though numerous cyclonic storms pass over this region, the valley locations of most of the stations favor fairly calm weather at all seasons. Victoria is an exception to this rule; its low-lying situation with the smooth expanse of water to all quarters except the northwest, favors higher wind velocities, with an average of two or three gales a month in winter. Wherever coasts are wide and flat, particularly at Vancouver and in the lower Fraser Valley, the sea breeze is of almost daily occurrence.

A new arrival at Victoria finds climatic conditions essentially different from those at almost any other place.

"If he arrives in July or August, the warmest months of the year, he finds a mean temperature of 60° Fahrenheit and a rainfall of less than an inch per month. If he arrives in January or February, our coldest months, he finds a temperature of 40° and a rainfall of less than three inches a month. There

ILLUS. 4—The cool and constantly moist lower slopes of the seaward-facing mountains of British Columbia (including Vancouver Island) produce thick stands of immense trees, Douglas fir predominating.

may be a light fall of snow, but it soon passes away. In July or August he finds the grass brown and dry; in January and February it is green everywhere."[1]

The southeastern portion of Vancouver Island is particularly well adapted to the production of small fruits, especially strawberries, blackberries and currants. Strawberries are produced

[1] A. W. McCurdy, "Factors Which Modify the Climate of Victoria," *National Geographic Magazine*, vol. 18, 1907, p. 345.

in sufficient quantities to call for carload shipments to the east. Probably the most important agricultural section of British Columbia is the lower Fraser Valley where the abundant rainfall and long growing season favor the growing of tree fruits as well as small fruits, both being exceedingly profitable crops in this section. Farther north along the coastal

ILLUS. 5—The interior valleys of British Columbia are really dry, as the semi-barren slopes of the mountains here show.

stretches of British Columbia and Vancouver Island the summers are too cool and the ripening or maturing season too rainy to permit profitable agricultural pursuits on a large scale.

THE INTERIOR VALLEYS OF SOUTHERN BRITISH COLUMBIA

The western part of this subregion is frequently referred to as the dry belt, because the rainfall during the frost-free period is insufficient for agricultural purposes except grazing. If this subregion is limited more broadly to those areas where the mean annual precipitation is under 30 inches, then it takes on a most peculiar shape, conforming almost completely to the drainage systems of the region. It is, therefore, confined to relatively narrow strips along those streams whose beds do not exceed 2000 feet elevation. Most of these valleys are characterized by terraces or benches, the lower ones cultivated and irrigated (where necessary), the upper ones used largely for grazing. The most important of these valleys are: the middle Fraser with its Lillooet and Thompson branches; the Okanagan;

the middle Columbia; and the West Kootenay. From a climatic standpoint the city of Kamloops is fairly typical of the whole province. It is situated at the junction of the North and South Thompson rivers at approximately 1250 feet above the sea.

In general, the climate of this district may be considered a transition between that dominated by the marine control on

ILLUS. 6—To avoid the late spring frosts which result from the drainage of cold air into the lowlands, the apple orchards of the lower Okanagan Valley of British Columbia occupy the benches which are situated well above the valley bottoms.

the west and the extreme continental type to the east. Temperatures here are higher in summer and lower in winter than those on the Pacific coast. Both daily and annual ranges of temperature are much greater. April is appreciably warmer than October. But, as on the coast, the summers are decidedly less cloudy and therefore sunnier than the winters; the difference, however, is more striking in the interior than along the coast—not excepting even southeastern Vancouver Island. The annual course of precipitation takes on the characteristics of both marine and continental climates. In the western part of the region, the annual precipitation is fairly evenly divided between the winter and summer half-years. At Kamloops, the summer half has almost a third more than the winter half. Places having a distinct western exposure have a greater percentage of winter rain than those with no pronounced exposure. Even as far east as Cranbrook in the East Kootenay district

(450 miles east of the Pacific Ocean) nearly two-thirds of the total precipitation falls in the winter half-year. A detailed map of the mean annual precipitation for southern British Columbia is shown in Fig. 40. There is no other region in Canada where the distribution of rainfall and snowfall is more irregular. The valleys and ridges stand out as prominently on this map as on a topographic map. This is partly due to

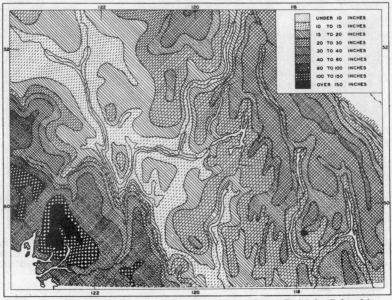

FIG. 40—Mean annual precipitation for southern British Columbia.

the fact that relief was followed in determining the trend of the isohyets, particularly where the precipitation data were few or lacking. Yet, the lines are entirely in accord with what the records of the many and well-distributed stations show. Because of the normally small amount of rainfall in the irrigated districts in summer, droughts in that season are not of much significance except to the grazing industry. More serious is a diminution in the winter and spring precipitation, thereby causing a decrease in the water available for irrigation in summer. The lowest mean annual rainfall for any station in the province is 5.86 inches at Clinton in a north-south tributary valley of the Thompson River and in the rain-shadow of a considerable mountain range to the west. The amount of snow in any average year is light, ranging from 20 to 40 inches for stations under 2000 feet elevation.

Over most of this subregion temperatures below zero may be expected every year during each of the three winter months. On the other hand, temperatures as high as 45° or 50° may also be expected during the same period. The lowest temperature recorded during 33 years at Kamloops was –31°, although

ILLUS. 7—Cherries from orchards like these in the irrigated portions of the West Kootenay district won the gold medal at the San Francisco Exposition.

one January the temperature dropped no lower than 20°. The lowest on record for the whole province appears to be –49° at Princeton in the Okanogan district. Every month, except June, July, and August, has had temperatures below freezing. Temperatures as high as 95° may be expected in every July. Kamloops once reported 103°; Griffin Lake, 110°. From the standpoint of temperature, the district around Kamloops in January is very similar to that of southern Iowa; in July it corresponds very well to Central New York.

Most of the subregion is characterized by calm weather with relatively few rainy days. In summer almost half the days are characterized as hot, fair, and quiet; in winter, as cold, fair, and quiet (Table 23). Average monthly wind velocities do not exceed three miles an hour (compare with Southwest Point on Anticosti Island where the average in January is nearly 23). High winds and thunderstorms are rarities. The relative humidity is always moderate, ranging from 50% to 80%.

ILLUS. 8—Relatively long summers, sunny skies, and freedom from winds and storms make favorable conditions for tobacco growing in some of the lower valleys of the British Columbian interior. This photograph was taken in the lower Thompson Valley.

The dry chinook is fully as characteristic of this region and quite as important to the ranchers, as in Alberta. One writer describes the chinook phenomenon for the lower Thompson as follows[1]:

"After having a cold snap of zero weather, with a foot of snow, on the flats and hillsides—bright clear weather—there comes a change; heavy dark clouds loom up from the west and southwest, accompanied by a very strong wind—at times one might call it a gale. No matter what the temperature previous to this change (40° below zero, or anything), within a few minutes the air becomes balmy as spring—by contrast it seems hot. I have known the thermometer to rise 59° in five minutes. When we have this wind, one can read in the daily papers of shipping disasters and storms off the Vanucouver Island and Washington coasts. Heavy rain and snow [occur] west of the Cascade Mountains, but I find no account of the temperature being so high west of the Cascade Mountains as with us.

[1] R. T. Grassham, "The 'Dry' Chinook in British Columbia," Monthly Weather Review, v. 35, 1907, p. 176.

"As to the dryness, our house lies in the valley. The Cariboo wagon road is some feet above the house, and the ground rises at an angle of 30° to the first hill, then in a series of benches to timber. The curious phenomenon [may be noted] of having one foot of snow as it were sucked up from off the ground (the ground being frozen to the depth of several inches). In three or four hours not a vestige of snow may remain, and yet not a trickle of water crosses the road. As the ground is frozen, therefore the idea of absorption in the ground is untenable; the water does not run off.

*   *   *   *   *   *

"We are much interested in these same chinook winds. This winter I have been at Keithley Creek managing an estate. On the flat the snow was 5 feet deep; on the Bonaparte the snow was 18 inches to 2 feet deep; and all cattle had to be fed—a serious item with a big band of cattle. Usually we need only to feed range cattle once in seven years, our fenced-up winter pastures being fully sufficient, except for a few sick cattle. So when we have a heavy fall of snow and zero weather our sole ambition is for a chinook; and there is no doubt whatever when it does come—we never forget the accompanying atmospheric conditions with us at the ranch, or on the seacoast."

A resident of Kamloops writes as follows regarding the climate of that district[1]:

"The conditions which exist here are practically the same throughout the entire dry belt. The seasons do not vary materially from year to year. We are as a rule relatively free from extremes of heat or cold. Such a thing as a blizzard is really unknown in this vicinity. We have no gales of any intensity; a snow or rain storm is seldom accompanied by violent wind. Rain in the winter is of very rare occurrence. Kamloops is famous as a health resort; it is the seat of a large tuberculosis sanatorium.

"The winters of 1925-26 and 1926-27 were both abnormal; in the former we had no winter at all, the thermometer seldom going lower than in an ordinary fall; in the latter we had a heavy fall of snow in the early part of November, the snow continuing through the entire winter until the following March —a most unusual winter—with the temperatures falling to —25°. Ordinarily there is not much snow or cold weather before the middle of December, with temperatures ranging from 12° to 20°. Occasionally, the thermometer will drop to —10° or maybe —20°, a condition which does not last for more than a few days. The annual rainfall averages about 6 inches and snow from 25 to 35 inches—total precipitation from 8 to 10 inches.

[1] (Mrs.) E. E. Palmer (From a letter to the author, dated November, 1928).

ILLUS. 9—The scant precipitation in the interior valleys of British Columbia necessitates some form of irrigation for most agricultural activities other than dairying.

"The agricultural products include fruits, vegetables, hay, grain, and live stock. The wonderful irrigation system throughout the country supplies the ranches and farms with all the water needed. This, with the even temperatures, early springs, late falls, and moderate snowfall insure ideal conditions for successful farming."

In the upper (which is also usually the northern) portions of the interior valleys, only the hardier varieties of apples and other tree fruits can be raised profitably; consequently, mixed- and truck-farming pay better than fruit-growing because of the greater frost risk on the bottomlands. If the benches could be irrigated, fruit-growing there would become highly profitable because such situations are less susceptible to late spring frosts. In the lower and southern sections of the valleys, less hardy fruits are grown, even on the bottom lands, with considerable success. Here, late spring frosts are a less important problem than that of available water for irrigation. The abundant sunshine and the fairly uniform and moderate temperatures of summer make most of this region, where irrigation may be practised, particularly adapted to a variety of agricultural industries, not the least important of which is tobacco-growing.

THE MOUNTAINS AND PLATEAUS OF BRITISH COLUMBIA AND ALBERTA

This subregion comprises probably nine-tenths of the area of British Columbia. It includes all of the country which is not exposed directly to the Pacific influences and which has an elevation above 2000 feet. On the whole, the region is sparsely populated; and most of the population is scattered along the river valleys of the middle and southern sections, particularly along the railway lines. Consequently, the meteorological data are few, often fragmentary, and not well distributed.

The region is by no means a unit from the climatic standpoint. Conditions vary markedly with change in latitude and with change in altitude. Hence, the wide latitudinal range of more than ten degrees and the altitudinal range of from 2,000 to 10,000 or more feet clearly indicate the extent of these varying conditions. It is difficult, therefore, to make a broad characterization of the climate which should apply equally well to all parts of the area. Yet, in general, it may be stated that the region takes on the characteristics of mountain and plateau and that, like the lower portions of the southern valleys, it is a transition zone between the extreme marine and continental types of the coast and the interior. The variations from south to north and from low to high elevations are, again like those of the valleys, differences in degree rather than in kind. Everywhere in this subregion, the winters are long, cold, and moderately quiet; the summers are short, moderately cool, and quiet (Table 23). The transition seasons of spring and fall are quickly passed over. October is slightly warmer than April, except in northeastern British Columbia on the east facing slopes of the Rockies. Changes in temperature from one day to the next are not extreme. They are less in the high situations than in the valleys; they are everywhere much less in winter than in summer. Precipitation is generally light except where mountains rise high above the surrounding valleys or plateaus. Between a third and a half of the moisture comes

ILLUS. 10—The light, fluffy snow, falling during calm weather, frequently collects on tree stumps to form huge snow mushrooms weighing as much as a ton. The one here pictured occurred in the Selkirks of British Columbia.

in the form of snow. At elevations above 4000 feet, snow may occur in every month except July.

Atlin, at 2240 feet elevation, is typical of the northern interior at the same altitude. It is hemmed in on all sides by mountains rising to 5000 feet or higher which reduce the precipitation to less than 11 inches, about equally distributed between the summer and winter half-years. As at coastal stations, November is the month of maximum precipitation, although July, September, October, and December have about the same amount. The minimum occurs in May. For the most part, precipitation is dependable, there being no month on record which has received less than 0.05 inch; and the variation in the annual amount from the normal has not been as much as 40% either above or below.

Fluctuations in temperature at Atlin indicate a stronger continental control than do the variations in precipitation, the annual range of temperature being about 54 degrees (compare with 25 degrees at Prince Rupert and 55 degrees at

Edmonton). July, the warmest month with a mean of only
53°, places Atlin very near the limit of tree growth and hence
very near to a polar type of climate (50° for the warmest
month). Because of altitude, large areas throughout this portion of British Columbia are devoid of tree growth. Indeed,
permanently snow-capped mountains with their attendant glaciers are common wherever the altitudes reach 10,000 feet.
Winters may be exceedingly severe at times, while at other
times they may be comparatively mild in this northern sector,
the variation from the normal of –2° being as much as 17
or 18 degrees—an extreme variation of 35 degrees. On the
other hand, summer mean temperatures vary only slightly.
The lowest temperature to be expected in any year is about
–25°, although –58° has been recorded. There was one January, however, when the minimum temperature dropped no
lower than 7°; and there are few Januarys in which the
temperature does not, on one day at least, go above freezing.
Frost has been experienced in every month; yet, the average
frost-free period is slightly over two months in length. In
about half the years, 75° has been recorded, while the absolute
highest is 86°.

Fogs to the extent of about three a year occur, mostly in
winter; while an average of two thunderstorms a year may be
expected during June, July, and August. The fact that hail
rarely occurs is an indication that the thunderstorms are not
very violent. About one day in four or five has measurable
precipitation; days with snow are more frequent than days
with rain. Broadly speaking the Atlin district may be said to
have clear, cool and moderately quiet and uniform weather in
summer; in winter, conditions are severe in most years,
although storminess is not generally a characteristic. The
cultivation of crops aside from a few vegetables is a hazardous
undertaking. At present the chief attraction of this northern
plateau district lies in its delightfully clear, cool and dry summers and in its natural beauty.

Little is known of large portions of northeastern British
Columbia. The principal routes of travel lie in the Liard,
Peace, and Fort Nelson river valleys; and there are vast
stretches of land over which man rarely travels. The meteorological records are few and incomplete, that of Hudsons Hope
(nine years) being one of the best. From these fragmentary

records and from the reports of travellers and of the relatively few settlers the more general characteristics of the climate of the district may be determined. From the fact that temperature extremes are greater than on the plateaus to the west but less than on the plains to the east, it may be said that this piedmont area has a transition type of climate between that of the former district where the altitude control dominates and that of the latter where the continental control is more pronounced. For the most part, the climate resembles that of northern Alberta or the middle Mackenzie Valley, except that conditions are not so extreme. The winters are only moderately cold; the summers are cool. The mean daily ranges of temperature, however, are large—equaling and even exceeding those of strictly continental situations. The chinook winds are important in keeping average temperatures in winter higher here than in places of the same latitude farther east, and in causing the high ranges in temperature during that season.

The average precipitation of 15 to 20 inches is abundant for the latitude; and with the exception of July and April, the months of greatest and least precipitation, the amounts are fairly evenly distributed throughout the year. Snowfall is much heavier here than on the plains, and it usually comes during nine months of the year. The whole district, except the higher mountain slopes, is thickly forested.

From a climatic standpoint the higher and more northerly parts of this district offer little incentive to its permanent occupancy by man. Yet, farther to the south in the Peace River area, there appear to be opportunities for successful agriculture. An official bulletin of the Provincial Government of British Columbia, emphasizes this point[1]:

"The climate is moderate considering the latitude, the air being pure and bracing—in winter, clear and crisp; in summer, dry and balmy. Extremes of temperature, sudden changes, and severe storms are rare. Rigours of climate need not be feared, but houses should be substantially built. Summer mean temperature is about 58°; winter mean about 1°. The winters, though not mild, are dry with clear skies, little snowfall, and moderate winds. From time to time the chinook winds work through the mountain passes from the Pacific, bringing milder weather. The thermometer on rare occasions drops as low as

[1] *Peace River Country*, Bulletin No. 25, Bureau of Provincial Information, Victoria, British Columbia, 1928, pp. 6-7.

50° below zero, but does not, as a rule, remain there long. Blizzards are unknown. The average snowfall is 6½ feet, but except in bush lands this is dissipated to a great extent during the winter through the influence of the chinooks. Spring comes early and quickly; ice breaks on the water in late April or early May.

"The summers have long, warm days followed by refreshingly cool evenings and nights. In the midsummer weeks there is practically no night, but a gentle and gradual transition from daylight to twilight and then to sunrise. Seeding is usually under way in mid-April, and growth never halts during the summer nights. The rainy season generally sets in about the end of May or early in June and lasts intermittently for two or three weeks, as a rule providing all the moisture necessary to carry the seed along to maturity. The occasional shower thereafter is all that is required to fill and ripen the grain.

"September and October are usually pleasant months, the days being warm in September but the nights getting cooler. October brings heavier frosts, ice forming late in the month of November, though ploughing has continued in some years late into November. Fairly mild weather up to Christmas is not uncommon. Summer frosts occur but do not affect the crops as much as they did during early days in Manitoba. Much of the damage done by frost in former years was due in great degree to lack of proper farm machinery and consequent delay in seeding. Much time was lost in this way when every hour of a very limited seeding season has a definite value.

"Experience in northern Alberta has shown that early ripening strains of wheat mature along the upper Peace in 110 to 115 days and in Fort Vermilion district in 95 to 100 days. Lower altitude and longer hours of sunshine offset shorter growing seasons. Barley, oats, and vegetables also mature more quickly. Climatic conditions on the whole favour the growing of cereals and vegetables throughout the greater part of the Peace River country."

The interior of British Columbia is a vast plateau region from 2000 to 5000 feet in elevation, with mountains of considerable height fringing it on all sides. The effect of altitude is seen in both the course of temperature and precipitation. That is, the annual ranges of temperature decrease with increase in altitude, and the time of maximum rainfall tends to be delayed accordingly. The effect of the Pacific, however, is fully as pronounced here as in the interior valleys to the south. Prince George at approximately 2000 feet elevation may be considered as fairly typical of a valley location; and Barkerville at twice that altitude is probably typical of the plateau proper. Both places show moderate ranges of temperature, Prince George with 47° having considerably the higher. Both indicate that fall is slightly warmer than spring —a characteristic of mountain as well as of marine climates. Prince George is colder in winter and warmer in summer than Barkerville; the mean daily ranges of temperature average about 30% higher at the former. Greater absolute extremes

ILLUS. 11—The westward-facing slopes of the Canadian Rockies during the winter are often shrouded in a thick mantle of snow. The difficulties of transportation are manifest.

of temperature have been recorded at Prince George. Presumably places at still higher altitudes would show even fewer extremes than does Barkerville.

The average precipitation in the valley is less than half that on the plateau. The maximum for Prince George comes in August; that for Barkerville in September. At both stations the amounts are fairly evenly distributed throughout the twelve months; although spring tends to have slightly lighter precipitation. The rainfall and snowfall are much more dependable on the plateau, where the number of days with precipitation, 174, is just twice that in the valley. Fogs are unknown at Barkerville; and thunderstorms are very infrequent, averaging less than two per year.

In general, the climate of the whole district of middle British Columbia may be described as cold and fair with little wind during about half the days of the year. The frequent cyclones which cross this section from the Pacific are apparently too shallow to affect the region materially as far as storminess is concerned. Nearly half the days of each month have rain or snow; and the number of snowy days in each year is nearly as large as the number of rainy days. The chinook is quite as prominent a feature of the climate in the central part of this province as in the southern part; and its effect is shown in the relatively high mean temperatures of winter (14° to 18°), although minimum temperatures have dropped to as low as −48° on the plateau and −56° in the valley. Half the years may have extremes as low as −15° on the former, and probably five to ten degrees colder than that in the latter. More than half the years have extreme absolute temperatures above freezing in January; but no place shows a record of higher than 50° for that month. The highest temperatures of the year have reached 90° and 95°; but these are rare; normally, (that is, in more than half the years) nothing higher than 85° is to be expected. Frosts are likely every month on the plateau, although the average frost-free period lasts nearly two months there and fully two months or even longer in the valleys.

Certain forms of agriculture are practiced in this district in spite of the hazard of frost, and apparently with considerable success. An official bulletin of the Provincial Government of British Columbia has this to say regarding the climate and the agricultural possibilities of the valley sections of the region[1]:

"Snow usually begins to fall in November, but in many years there is not sufficient for good sleighing until late in January. It lies until the latter part of April. Winter may be said to begin in November and end in April, but apart from an exceptionally cold wave, lasting usually from ten to twelve days, it is a winter of bright sunshiny days and clear cold nights. Though the meteorological records show records of extremely low temperatures occuring in January, the mean average for the month, 18° in 1918 and 25° in 1919, shows a very moderate winter month on the whole. Snow varies in depth from 2 to 3 feet, but there is a great difference in the amount of snowfall in localities separated from each other by very short distances.

"Under present conditions—that is, with so little land actually cleared and cultivated—summer frosts are to be expected; but for the last two years they have done practically

[1] *Central and Western Portions, Fort George Land Recording Division*, Bulletin No. 35, Department of Lands, Victoria, B. C., 1921, p. 7.

ILLUS. 12—The abundant precipitation, coupled with the great height of the mountains, favors numerous glaciers in the higher situations of British Columbia. Mt. Assiniboine towers to 11,860 feet.

no damage. So far, the main crops raised are potatoes and other vegetables, and I have yet to learn of a case where these crops were actually destroyed or even very badly damaged from effects of frost. Although the length of the season between time of planting and harvesting is of short duration, the length of the daylight period, together with the amount of sunshine, is so great it has been found sufficient to bring to maturity all the crops."

Of the mountains of southern British Columbia, the Selkirks and Coast Range are very similar with reference to the seasonal distribution of precipitation. The Rockies, as represented by Banff, situated on the east slope of the province of Alberta, are essentially different in this regard. In other words, the western slopes of all the mountains, wherever high enough, take on something of the marine characteristics. Their leeward slopes, however, have more the characteristics of the region lying immediately to the east. As indicated, the similarities refer more to moisture than to thermal conditions. Since it has already been pointed out that the Pacific-facing slopes of the Coast Ranges experience approximately the same conditions as the immediate coast, the difference being that resulting from difference in altitude, attention will be centered on the mountains of southeastern British Columbia and along the southern portion of the boundary between that province and Alberta.

The Selkirks may be considered as distinct from the Canadian Rockies, the two ranges being separated by the upper Columbia and Kootenay rivers. Both systems have distinctly mountain conditions of temperature, i. e., moderate annual ranges of temperature; and the greater the altitude, the smaller the range. Thus, Golden at 2000 feet and situated in the depression between the two ranges has an annual range of 51 degrees with a January mean of 10°; Glacier at 4100 feet has a range 10 degrees less with the January mean nearly five degrees higher. Banff at 4500 feet and with an eastern exposure has a range seven degrees lower than Golden. The mountain valleys here, therefore, are seen to have greater extremes of temperature than the mountains themselves. The records of below –20° or above 90° at Glacier are probably unknown on the west slopes of the Selkirks at the altitude of Glacier. The combined influence of the winds from the Pacific and of altitude serve to moderate winter conditions decidedly and summer conditions considerably. On the other hand, places situated like Golden may experience extremes as low as –50° and as high as 95°. Conditions at Banff are even more extreme because of the strong continental control. Here the chinook is important in producing higher mean winter temperatures than might otherwise be expected; to some extent the same is true at Glacier and Golden. Banff has had temperatures as high as 50° in January, some five degrees higher than Glacier. On the other hand, temperatures usually drop somewhat lower in summer at Banff.

The most noteworthy effect of western exposure is seen in the seasonal course of precipitation. Unquestionably, the winter half-year receives more than the summer, fully 125% more at Glacier—a condition which is quite the opposite in a typical mountain climate. Approximately two-thirds of the total annual precipitation comes in the form of snow, making this district the snowiest in Canada, with a mean annual of 415 inches at Glacier. In the high valleys, the regime is less pronounced, although the winter half-year is still the wetter. Both rainfall and snowfall are much reduced as a consequence both of leeward position and decreased altitude. On the east slopes of the Rockies, conditions are completely altered, the summer half receiving almost twice as much precipitation as the winter half. Likewise, the variability of rainfall and snowfall from month to month is much greater here than on the western flanks.

Because of the great amount of snow in the Selkirk region and because of the formation of snow mushrooms there, the element of snowfall takes on an added interest. Cornish made a special study of conditions there in 1901[1]:

"At the date of our visit the registered snowfall was 25 feet, and the depth of snow upon the ground was 5 feet. There was no sign of drift in the valley. According to the concurrent testimony of railway officials stationed here, most of the snow falls at or above 32° Fahrenheit, so that, although zero weather is often experienced, the snow as it falls is adhesive. I was informed also that the air is usually calm during the snow-falls . . . . I was informed by three persons that a snowfall of 12 inches in an hour is not unknown here."

The same writer states that snow mushrooms are common features of the winter landscape wherever there are tree stumps of considerable height, the eaves of the mushrooms sometimes projecting four feet beyond the pedestal. It is further stated that some of these mushrooms may weigh a ton. As in the Sierras of the United States, the heavy snows of the Canadian Rockies and Selkirks are serious handicaps to winter railway transportation.

As a whole this southern mountain district is little adapted to agricultural activities other than grazing, for frosts may be expected in every month except July, and they have occurred even in July at Banff. The growing season is, therefore, short —in most cases two months or less. The climate, however, is particularly desirable in summer because of the clear, dry air, sunny days and cool nights. It is the climate which attracts so many tourists to this district from May to October.

YUKON TERRITORY

The only justification for treating this large and diverse area as one climatic province is the fact that little is known of the climate except in the vicinity of Dawson. This lack of

[1] Cornish, op. cit., pp. 140-1.

knowledge can be easily understood when it is realized that less than 5000 people populate an area of over 206,000 square miles (equivalent to the combined areas of New England, New York, New Jersey, Pennsylvania and Ohio) ; and most of these people live in the narrow Yukon Valley.[1] The climate of the whole region must, therefore, be based largely on the records of Dawson. The difficulties of such a method are real when

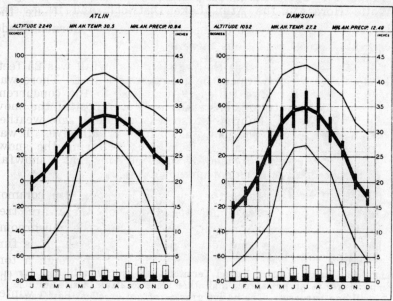

Fig. 41—Temperature and precipitation charts for Atlin and Dawson.

the great difference in altitude, in latitude, in relief, and in exposure are considered. The climate may be that of the permanently snow-capped mountains of the Brooks Range or of the northern extensions of the Rockies and Coast ranges where the temperature can only infrequently be above 32°. It may be that of the tundra or treeless sections along the Arctic coast or above the timber line of the interior mountains where the mean temperature for the warmest month must be under 50°. It may be that of the restricted and protected lowlands of the valleys of the Yukon and its tributaries where winters are long and cold but summers short and warm. The climate of the whole region is preponderantly continental, although the Arctic

[1] *The Canada Year Book, 1926*, Dominion Bureau of Statistics, Ottawa, 1927, p. 90.

waters must reduce extremes of temperature near the coast, even as they do at Herschel Island and Fort McPherson of the Mackenzie district.

Stupart points out several features regarding the climate of the Territory[1]:

"The climate of the former place [Dawson] is much more suitable for agricultural purposes than that of the latter [White Horse in the Atlin Lake District], and in general

ILLUS. 13—Large areas of Yukon Territory have sufficiently high summer temperatures to permit spruce and other trees to attain a size suitable for building purposes. The native grasses afford excellent pasturage.

the northern and eastern portions of Yukon have a warmer summer climate than have the southern portions. This is probably owing in part to the fact that southern districts are much nearer the ocean from which the westerly winds blow; while in the north the westerly winds are from the broader land area of Alaska, and the country generally is protected by mountains ranging from 5,000 to 10,000 feet. The mean summer temperature at Dawson [June, July, and August, 56.8°] is fully 5° F. higher than either at White Horse or Atlin, B. C.; and while frosts seem to be frequent at the latter places in both June and August and occur occasionally even in July, in the former both June and July are practically free from frost and it is not until about August 20 that there is much danger; and very frequently September opens with as yet no frost. After the close of August the downward trend of the Dawson tem-

[1] R. F. Stupart, "The Climate of Yukon Territory," *Monthly Weather Review*, Washington, v. 35, 1907, pp. 16-17.

perature curve is very rapid, and the winter months are probably between 15° and 20° colder than at White Horse. . . . .

"It is claimed that there is little wind at Dawson in winter, and this to a large extent is true. The cyclonic areas which enter the continent from the Pacific pass far to the southward of latitude 64° north, hence barometric gradients are not usually steep."

Regarding conditions in January, the same author states that the temperature at Dawson seldom rises above zero; that on about one day in three, it falls to –40° or lower; and that temperatures of –50° are not infrequent. The lowest on record, –68°, occurred in 1901. At Selkirk, farther up the Yukon, conditions are similar; but at White Horse, the January mean is 20 degrees higher. Here comparatively mild days occur occasionally, while extremely low temperatures are. less frequent.

"April may well be termed the first spring month, as there are few days on which the thermometer does not rise above 32° F., and 50° F. is occasionally recorded. The average mean of the month is 28° F., and in some years the temperature does not fall to zero. The precipitation is usually in the form of snow, but rain sometimes falls. In this month the average temperature is very approximately the same throughout the Yukon. . . . . The average date of the last frost is the 19th [of May].

"The ice on the Yukon at Dawson usually breaks up between the 15th and 20th [of May], but not until a fortnight or three weeks later on Lake Laberge [upper Yukon Valley]. The season is now farther advanced in the north than in the south, and it is not until the end of August or early September that the mean temperature in the north is again as low as at White Horse or Tagish.

"June is a perfect summer month, and with practically no darkness, and with nearly twenty hours of bright sunshine on fair days, vegetation advances very rapidly. Frost, while not unknown in this month, is quite unusual. . . . . July weather in Dawson is quite fairly comparable with that in the same month in southern Alberta, and with the longer days growth is probably more rapid in the former locality than in the latter. . . . . There are very few days on record when the temperature did not reach 60° F., and 70° F. is reached on the average twenty days in the month; 80° F. is reached on six days and there are a few instances of 90° F. [the highest ever recorded, 95°].

". . . . The month [August] opens warm, but a very decided downward trend of the temperature curve occurs after about the 15th, and there seems to be decided danger of frost after the 20th. It is still early autumn when the temperature of Dawson drops below that of White Horse and the southern

Yukon generally; and the difference, as has been shown, becomes more and more pronounced until after mid-winter. . . . . October is winter, with a mean temperature of 24.1° F., and zero readings well before its close." [1]

Dawson is occasionally subject to extremely cold weather. Thus, in December, 1917, the mean temperature was –49°, nearly 38 degrees below normal; the highest for the month

ILLUS. 14—Not every year sees such a bumper crop of potatoes along the 64th parallel. These were grown at Dawson, Yukon Territory.

was only –35°, and the lowest for the same month was –63°. In spite of such extremes, the mean daily ranges of temperatures in winter are small, amounting to less than half those of summer—a distinct contrast to the maritime district of eastern Canada. The annual ranges average nearly 82 degrees.

At the same station, three days out of 10 on the average have precipitation; August and November are the rainiest months with 11 days; April is the least rainy with less than 4. Snowy and rainy days are about equal in number during the year. Fogs occur frequently from September to February; these are presumably largely frost fogs, similar to those along the west coast of Hudson Bay. Thunderstorms average about six a year, coming mainly in June and July. Summer days are either moderate and rainy or moderate, fair and quiet; while most winter days are cold, fair and quiet or cold, snowy and quiet (Table 23).

[1] Ibid.

In spite of the widespread knowledge of the cold of the
Yukon, the general favorableness of the climate, especially in
summer, is attested by visitors:

"It would appear from a reference made to 'Dawson' by a
lady, who has wintered there (1898-9) that the climate for a
portion of the year at least is very enjoyable. The lady writes
(April 8): 'The March month of the Yukon is one of the gems
of the year. Of all that dwell in my memory, this March, spent
in the Yukon, has been incomparably the finest; from first to
last a series of still, fair, sunshiny days, each lengthening and
warming into greater geniality, until now in these last hours
the little hill encircled basin and its bit of the big Yukon river
is flooded with sunshine; the surface of the ground is soft
enough to demand the pulling off of moccasins and felt boots,
and the daylight lasts far into the evening. Scanning the past
weeks, we recall nothing of the raw winds, or rude or bluster-
ing blizzard—only a gentle, continuous mellowing from midwinter severity, and a gradual, gracious extension of warmth
and light. It seems absurd to have to come to the sub-arctic
to defy March, yet here in this windless valley of the Yukon
it has been a glorious month throughout!' "[1]

Another enthusiastic writer states:

"We have no idea of the beautiful summers of the Yukon.
. . . . The months of May, June, July, August and part of
September are regular paradises and are the finest we meet
in any part of Canada. . . . . The sun shines for a large
part of the twenty-four hours; . . . . there is continuous
daylight during the months of June and July. . . . . It is
true that ice is found only a short distance below the surface
of the ground, yet the traveller is perfectly ignorant of such a
circumstance unless it be pointed out to him. The thermometer
often registers 85° F. during the day and the evenings are
clear and cool for sleeping. Vegetation is very rapid; the
abundance of sunlight hurries things along, the heat from above
combined with the moisture from below causes rapid growth;
and consequently Dawson can boast of the finest vegetables in
the world. Her lettuce, celery, beets, carrots, cabbages, and
cauliflowers are unexcelled. As we go along the streets most
brilliant flower gardens meet us on every hand, and if we forget
ourselves a moment we would think we were in some tropical
land. But the refreshing breeze from the mountain far away
recalls us to ourselves." [2]

As already suggested, altitude is a significant factor in the
climate of the Yukon, particularly in summer. Lambert reports

¹ Alexander Begg, "Early Explorations in North-West Canada," *Scottish Geographical
Magazine*, Edinburgh, v. 15, 1899, pp. 354-5.
² F. A. McDiarmid, "The Climate of the Canadian Yukon," *Monthly Weather Review*,
Washington, v. 36, 1908, p. 178.

that in his ascent of Mt. Logan (19,539 feet high) during June, "the weather was indescribably bad, and the incessant winds, the heavy snowfall, the cold, all added to our labor."[1] He states further of his encounter with "a sudden wall of fog" which blocked out all vision, and with severe blizzards which would suddenly give way to bright sunshine. A temperature of –33° was encountered on the night of June 18-19 at approximately 19,000 feet.

As the pressure of population becomes greater in the lands to the south, the valleys of Yukon Territory should become more and more a permanent abode for the white man. Certainly, so far as present meteorological records can indicate, the climate need not offer any serious obstacles. Though the winters are severe, the almost total absence of strong winds and of storms of blizzard-like character in those portions suitable for settlement, makes the winters quite as tolerable as those of the Prairie Provinces or of northern Ontario. And there is no doubt that the average summer is really delightful.

[1] H. F. Lambert, "The Conquest of Mt. Logan," *Geographical Journal*, London, v. 68, 1926, pp. 1-26.

CHAPTER VI

THE CONTINENTAL LOWLANDS

The great continental interior of Canada, everywhere under 4000 feet in elevation and at comparatively few places above 2000 feet, makes up at least two-thirds of the Dominion. The region now under consideration comprises probably half of this total area. It extends across a latitudinal distance of nearly 30 degrees, or 2000 miles; its greatest east-west extent is almost as great. In a region so vast in areal and latitudinal expanse, it would seem that the climate must show important differences with progress north and south or east and west. As a matter of fact, however, the differences are not considerable. Everywhere the continental influence is strong. The region, therefore, is marked by cold winters and warm to hot summers with great extremes of temperature, both diurnal and annual. The winters are moderately moist to dry; summer is the season of rain. The continental control is the more pronounced because of the formidable character of the great cordilleran barrier which keeps out the ameliorating effects of the Pacific. Marine influences are felt to some extent for a short distance from the Arctic coast, around Hudson Bay and in the vicinity of the Great Lakes. In such localities, winters are less severe and summers are cooler than elsewhere. Altitude is of little significance except locally. The factor of latitude is seen in the lower temperatures in the north than in the south. Yet, in the western portion of the region hot summers are found far down the Mackenzie. Latitude for latitude temperatures in July are five to ten or more degrees higher in the west than in the east.

In this great interior, six subregions stand out as fairly distinctive: the Mackenzie Valley, the Prairies, middle Ontario and southern Quebec, the Hudson Bay plains, southern Ontario, and the St. Lawrence River Valley. It will be noticed that these subdivisions are somewhat restricted—that they do not comprise all of the great interior of Canada. Yet they are taken as nuclei of the six climatic districts because of their distinctiveness geographically and climatically. In each division the life and activities of the people differ as well as the meteorological conditions. To demarcate the six areas, however, is exceedingly difficult, for in every case they are separated by broad transitional zones. There are no sharp topographical breaks, like the Rocky Mountain crest, to make equally sharp climatic differentiations. There is no sudden change from subaridity to high humidity; from subarctic to Alleghenian, from ice-marine to continental. In places the climatic data are too few to determine a narrow dividing zone. Consequently, here as in Chapter V, no attempt is made to delineate these provinces on a map.

THE MACKENZIE VALLEY

The area included in this subregion is not confined to the valley of the main stream; it comprises a large part of the drainage basin—certainly Great Bear, Great Slave and Athabaska lakes, and the lower portions of the Liard, Peace and Athabaska tributaries. Its north-south extent is easily 1000 miles, and its greatest width is not less than half this distance. Its area, if practicable to measure it, would exceed that of the province of Ontario or of the state of Texas. The fact that the total population of the valley of the Mackenzie proper does not exceed 5000, including only 150 whites, gives some indication of the inadequacy of the meteorological records.[1]

From the data available, however, it appears that throughout this huge area the climate is, in many respects, strikingly similar. The winters are everywhere long and cold—the coldest in Canada, although perhaps not so continuously cold as parts of the Archipelago; the summers are short and decidedly warm for the latitude, an average July being much like an average January in middle Florida—fairly hot days alternating with cool to cold days, and freezing temperatures not infrequent. Precipitation is light and everywhere adequate in normal years, although twice as heavy in the south as in the north.

As already pointed out, the Mackenzie Valley is one of the coldest districts of North America as far as meteorological observations can indicate. Abbe mentions a temperature of −81° having been recorded at Fort Reliance[2]; and an unofficial

---

[1] Kindle, *Canada North of Fifty-Six Degrees*, p. 65.

[2] Cleveland Abbe, Jr., P. P. No. 45, *The Geography and Geology of Alaska*, Government Printing Office, Washington, 1906, p. 155.

temperature of –87° near Great Bear Lake has been reported.[1]
But the lowest official temperature in Canada is –79° at Fort
Good Hope.   Its location in the Mackenzie Valley with highlands on each side doubtless favors air drainage and consequent low temperatures in the lowlands.   Fort Norman, a little
farther south has, however, a January mean temperature nearly
one degree lower than Fort Good Hope.   All places in the

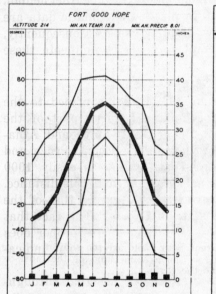
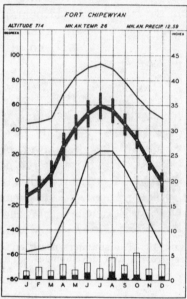

FIG. 42—Temperature and precipitation charts for Fort Good Hope
and Fort Chipewyan.

Mackenzie Valley north of Great Slave Lake have mean temperatures below zero from November to March inclusive.   From
Great Slave Lake southward to Lake Athabaska, only the three
winter months have means below zero.

If a temperature of 50° for the warmest month is taken as
the southern limit of polar climate, then Herschel Island, with
its highest mean only 44°, falls distinctly in that class.   Yet,
because of its location near the mouth of the Mackenzie, it is
brought into this discussion for comparative purposes.   In spite
of its low annual mean of 11°, this island does not experience so
intense winter cold as do the more continental situations far-

[1] Observed by Ralph Clark in 1904 according to a statement made by J. A. Blake at
Yale University, April 3, 1916.

ther south; but the cold is of long duration, even April once showing a mean below zero. All months from October to May inclusive have had minimum temperatures below zero, the lowest ever recorded being −52° in January.

In the lower Mackenzie, Fort McPherson is warmer in winter than Fort Good Hope or Fort Norman. The two latter have experienced temperatures below zero in every month except

ILLUS. 15—The summers north of Great Bear Lake are too short for large tree growth and development. This is the grazing land of the musk-ox (ovibos) and the caribou.

June, July, and August, although only the November to March means are lower than at McPherson. The influence of the Arctic waters serves to ameliorate the severity of winter cold decidedly at Herschel Island and to a considerable degree as far inland as Fort McPherson; though this influence hardly reaches as far south as Great Bear Lake.

On the other hand, places still farther up the Mackenzie are appreciably warmer in winter; the hours of sunshine at that season are longer than farther north; the intensity of insolation is greater. Fort Simpson experiences much the same winter temperatures as Fort McPherson. Hay River on Great Slave Lake and Fort Chipewyan are still milder. There is, therefore, a gradual diminution in the coldness of the winter season in proceeding to the northward as well as to the southward from the region of Great Bear Lake.

Certain winters have been exceedingly cold in this last named region, the highest temperature at Fort Good Hope in some months being as low as –18°. No part of the Mackenzie, however, has reported so severe conditions as Dawson in the Yukon, where the highest temperature recorded in December, 1917, was –35°. At Fort Chipewyan, on the contrary, there has been no month in which the thermometer did not register above zero. There has been no case on record at Fort Good Hope during which the extreme minimum of any of the three winter months has been above –42°. In fact, in every winter each month from November to April inclusive has had temperatures below zero at least once.

The lower Mackenzie at Fort Good Hope may expect temperatures of below –50° every year and of –65° in about half the years; and temperatures as high as 5° may be expected in only half of the Januarys. The expectancy or probability of severe cold here is much greater than farther up the river at Hay River, for example, where half the years will have no temperature lower than –50°, although –40° is to be expected in most years. On the other hand, above freezing weather for at least one day comes in about one January out of three. In spite of its more southerly location, Fort Vermilion has mild periods in January no more frequently than Hay River.

Chinook or foehn winds occur in the Mackenzie district even as they do on the plains of Alberta or in the valleys of British Columbia, and they serve to raise the winter mean temperatures appreciably. Fruh reports the following on foehn winds at Fort Good Hope[1]:

"Abbe. E. Petitot, who has lived for thirteen years in the Saskatchewan and Mackenzie river districts, described in his extensive meteorological notes for the years 1864-1873 the following interesting phenomenon. Every winter from the end of December to the beginning of February, there is experienced from one to three days a strong wind from the north or northwest sufficient to remove shingles from the house roofs. The thermometer rises to two or three degrees above freezing, even on the north exposures where it had formerly been at –40°. The result is a sudden thaw. The snow surface melts. . . . . People and animals experience complete lassitude and, in the open, one has the feeling as if he were in a warm bath. The wind coming out of the northwest in winter is warmer than the south wind

[1] J. Fruh, "Foehn in Fort Good Hope," *Meteorologische Zeitschrift*, v. 18, 1901, p. 36.

or the raw east wind. Petitot wonders whether an extension of the Asiatic high pressure or the formation of an ice-free polar sea is not the cause of this phenomenon.

"Evidently it cannot be considered merely as a descending wind. Yet we are unable to analyze it farther because of the imperfect cartographic work done on the mountain range lying between the lower Mackenzie and the Yukon River in Alaska."

On December 6, 1928, a west wind of chinook character swept over a considerable area of the Mackenzie Valley causing the temperature at Aklavik to rise from –5° to 54° in about six hours. This rise in temperature at Aklavik was in line with similar changes as far south as Edmonton where, on the same day, the temperature rose from 7° to 27°. Obviously, true foehn winds in this district should come from a westerly quarter, unless deflected locally by the topography, because only in that direction are the mountains high enough to permit air to be warmed greatly by compression in descent to the valley floor. Chambers states that the chinook in this region is a southwest wind.[1] Kindle adds that the chinook is stronger in the upper Liard than in Manitoba.[2]

Warm season conditions are in pronounced contrast to those of winter in most of this northwest section of Canada. Under the increasingly long days of more intense insolation from April to June the country rapidly assumes the characteristics of a Montana summer, although the daytime maxima in Montana are somewhat higher. Mean temperatures for July are generally as high as 60° or nearly so. Herschel Island is the notable exception. Fort McPherson again represents a transition, although its mean July temperature falls only slightly below that of places farther south. The icy waters of the Arctic Ocean still restrict the departure of temperatures from the freezing point, but to a less extent in summer because then the winds are prevailingly from a southern quadrant except near the coast.

Fort Chipewyan situated on the north side of Lake Athabaska is slightly cooler in July than any other station in the Mackenzie district south of Fort McPherson. Local lake breezes from a body of water which is ice-covered well into May, and therefore still relatively cold in July, explains this seeming

[1] E. J. Chambers, *The Unexploited West*, Dept. of the Int., Ottawa, 1914, p. 224.
[2] Kindle, op. cit., p. 70.

anomaly. Obviously, places similarly situated with respect to Great Bear and Great Slave lakes should show the same conditions but in a more pronounced form because of the greater size and the more northerly locations of these water bodies. On the other hand, places located thus, should show higher autumn temperatures than places removed from the lakes. This certainly is true of Fort Chipewyan, and very pronouncedly in September. In fact, every station in the province shows October to be from one to six degrees warmer than April, a characteristic of marine rather than continental climates, here owing to the slow removal of the accumulated ice and snow of winter and the slow cooling of these large water bodies in fall.

Although mean summer temperatures of that portion of the Mackenzie Valley lying between 57 and 67 degrees north latitude are about the same as those on the coast of eastern Newfoundland at 46 to 47 degrees north latitude, the extreme maximum temperatures of the summer months will run appreciably higher for the former; for temperatures as high as 93° have been recorded at Fort Good Hope, 96° at Hay River, and 98° at Fort Vermilion. For most of these northern stations, the months of May to August inclusive have shown, at some time in their records, temperatures above 80°. In each of these months the maximum has never been lower than 54°, except possibly at Aklavik or Herschel Island. Summer days are actually hot at times, and with the long hours of sunshine there is limited cooling during the night. That the Mackenzie Valley should have so much warmer summers than points east or west in the same latitude must be attributed not only to the long and relatively intense insolation through the clear dry air, but also to the low elevation of the stations reporting meteorological data, all being below an altitude of 1000 feet.

Most of the stations in the Mackenzie must expect freezing temperatures in July and August during at least half the year; although, strange to say, the middle portion of the Mackenzie generally has milder conditions than the upper, as far as minimum temperatures are concerned, the greater altitude being more than a match for the lower latitude. At Fort McPherson, a shift of wind to northeast, and a persistence of it, bring to that settlement the chill of the ice-laden Arctic, which may change balmy summer conditions in July to those resembling the approach of winter—all in less than a day. But temperatures of 90° are to be expected more frequently at Hay River than at Fort Vermilion, although the latter, in accordance with its much more southern location, occasionally experiences greater heat than any other station in the region. The records for frost and the frost-free period show that Fort Vermilion has a very short growing season, averaging only 51 days; while Hay River,

ILLUS. 16—Dense stands of small spruce are characteristic of the protected river lowlands even beyond the arctic circle. This is a forest in the Peel River Valley not far from Fort McPherson.

on the lake, is more favored with 78 days. Fort Simpson, still farther north, has a growing season almost as long, it being 76 days.

Mean daily ranges of temperature are large all year, varying from a low range of 11 degrees at Fort Chipewyan in November to a high range of 29 degrees at Fort Vermilion in July. They are everywhere higher in summer than in winter, and they vary directly with distance from water bodies. Thus the mean daily ranges for the year run as follows from north to south: Fort McPherson, 16 degrees; Fort Simpson, 19 degrees; Fort Chipewyan, 18 degrees; and Fort Vermilion, 27 degrees. The extreme monthly ranges of temperature increase in the same way; and in all cases the greatest occur in winter. As pointed out earlier, it is this Mackenzie region which has the highest absolute ranges in Canada, varying from 121 degrees at Herschel Island where the marine control is pronounced, to 174 degrees at Fort Vermilion, far removed from any large water body.

The break-up of the ice in spring occurs on the smaller streams and in the upper portions of the drainage system first, with consequent ice jams and highwater at the mouths of the tributaries. These ice jams may be piled 20 feet high and extend down to the bed of the river; a rise of 30 feet in the depth of the water is not unknown.[1] The upper Mackenzie is free from ice about the middle of May, although ice persists in Great Slave Lake from two to four weeks longer, even as late as July 5 at the east end,[2] though the average date appears to be from June 16 to July 2.[3] The lower river is open for navigation fully a month before this. Thus, navigation on the Mackenzie for steamers from Fort McMurray is determined by the ice conditions in Great Slave Lake. Ice continues in Great Bear Lake even longer than in the lakes to the south; and frequently, some ice remains in the lake all summer. On June 23, 1900, the ice was so firm that parties sledged across it.[4] Blanchet states that the wind is a more important factor than temperature or rain in causing the break-up of ice in the lakes. He adds[5]:

"The lifting action of the water flowing in from the surrounding hills loosens the ice around the lake margins, and soon open water, there and along the fissures, permits the winds to give the lossening ice fields a little play. When this condition is reached, the first heavy storm is liable to drive the ice before it. The tremendous pressure of the field piles it up on lee shores, while the grinding of the mass furthers the disruption, and the increasing open spaces permit greater movement with the shifting winds of spring. The speed at which the loose fields travel is sometimes incredible, and the momentum is irresistible. The period of drifting ice fields is entirely dependent on the winds, for the ice must break itself up to offer many surfaces to the sun and waves."

Ice begins to form on quiet pools in September, and by the middle of October, navigation on Great Slave Lake is rendered difficult especially for small craft. One year, the lake was closed to steamers as early as October 6th, and on Great Bear

---

[1] Kindle, "Arrival and Departure of Winter Conditions in the Mackenzie River Basin," *Geogr. Rev.*, v. 10, 1920, pp. 390 and 392.

[2] G. H. Blanchet, *Great Slave Lake Area, Northwest Territories*. Dept. of the Int., Ottawa, 1926, p. 42.

[3] Kindle, op. cit., p. 390.

[4] J. B. Bell, "Explorations in the Great Bear Lake Region," *Geogr. Jour.*, v. 18, 1901, p. 252.

[5] Blanchet, op. cit., pp. 42-43.

Lake, a boat was frozen in on October 4, 1919.[1] The lower
Mackenzie is open several weeks longer, navigation being possible, in average years, up to the middle of November; although
in the delta district where the current is slow, ice forms by
November 1.[2]

In most years, ice attains a thickness of six to eight feet,
being thicker on Great Bear than on Great Slave Lake.[3] River
ice does not usually reach such a great thickness because it is
much later in forming in the fall.

Throughout this climatic division, the ground never thaws
completely even in the warmest summers, except perhaps in
the cultivated lands on the southern margin.   In an average

ILLUS. 17—The accumulation of snow, due to the absence of thaws during
the long, cold winter over the wind-swept plains of the lower Mackenzie,
makes sledging inevitable and easy. This is a detachment of the Canadian
Mounted Police near Fort McPherson.

year, for all places having a mean annual temperature under
30°, the soil at considerable depths (say 10 feet or more) presumably remains unfrozen.   A. J. Connor, Climatologist of the
Canadian Meteorological Service, writes as follows[4]:

"Around Great Slave Lake, the soil seldom thaws out to a
greater depth than 8 feet and in many muskegs and marshes

[1] Kindle, op. cit., pp. 397-399.
[2] Otto Nordenskjold and Ludwig Meeking, *The Geography of Polar Regions*, American
Geogr. Soc., N. Y., 1928, p. 197.
[3] Ibid.
[4] A letter to the author, dated Toronto, May 13th, 1929.

ice remains throughout the year at a depth of about 2 feet. In descending the Mackenzie, we find the frozen soil gradually approaching the surface. At Fort Norman at the end of summer, it lies at a depth of about 6 feet. At Fort Good Hope while installing a pier to support our magnetic instruments we encountered in summer at a depth of less than 2 feet stones which became covered with a film of frost when exposed, and solidly frozen soil was encountered at three feet. Survey parties in other years gave 4 feet as the depth of frozen soil. At the mouth of the Peel two feet is the ordinary depth reported. . . . .

"It is the experience of all districts that after the moss is burned off and the soil once tilled, the summer thaw penetrates to a greatly increased depth, and land apparently barren becomes productive. . . . .

"The character of the surface, as well as the conductivity and permeability of the underlying soil, no less than the orientation of the slope, evidently play important roles in determining the diurnal and seasonal ranges of temperature at any given depth."

As in Arctic Canada, records of precipitation for the lower Mackenzie are few and unsatisfactory, chiefly because of the difficulty of measuring the snowfall which makes up a large part of the total. The record for Fort Good Hope indicates that practically all the precipitation from October to May comes in the form of snow. Both rain and snow are light throughout this whole climatic region, varying from less than 10 inches in the northern portion to perhaps 15 inches in the middle portion, and then decreasing slightly farther south where at both Fort Chipewyan and Fort Vermilion the annual amount averages 12 or 13 inches. Though the amounts are small, they are adequate in most years for all forms of agriculture practiced in the valley, because most of the precipitation comes after the time of highest sun when it is most needed. The influence of the cold Arctic waters to the north and of the ice filled lakes and snow covered lands in the interior greatly delays the time of maximum rainfall, the delay being greater where these influences are strongest and most persistent. This may be seen in the fact that Fort Good Hope has its maximum in October and November; Fort Simpson in September; Forts Chipewyan and Vermilion in July. If we were to go still farther into southern Alberta we should find the maximum in June. In most cases, the minimum occurs in February, and usually equals from a sixth to a fourth of the amount received in the month of heaviest precipitation. Precipitation then is one element in the climate of the Mackenzie district which shows little uniformity over the region as a whole.

No records are available to indicate the dependability of precipitation except in the extreme southern portion. In a broken record of 43 years at Fort Chipewyan, there has been no month without some rain or snow, although there have been occasions when the amounts were hardly measurable. On the other hand, there have been some months when very heavy rains have occurred, one July having had 9.5 inches of rain. The wettest year with 17 inches had three times as much as the driest year, showing that fluctuations are considerable. The record at Fort Vermilion shows essentially the same sort of variations. Very droughty summers and very wet summers have occurred at Forts Resolution, Providence, and Norman.

The snow cover in the middle Mackenzie begins about the 15th of November and continues to the middle of May. For the lower Mackenzie (Fort Norman), Hann states that the snow cover begins November 2-4 and lasts until May 9-25; farther up the river (Fort Simpson), the corresponding dates are November 17-30 and May 1-14.[1] In an average year, snowfall amounts to from 30 to 50 inches, being less in the more continental situations and where summer conditions prevail longer, as at Fort Vermilion. Two feet of snow in one month is not unknown at Fort Chipewyan, although the normal amount for the snowiest months, November and December, does not exceed eight or nine inches. Snow has been recorded in some part of this province every month. Five inches fell at Fort McPherson one July 2nd, and the temperature dropped to 25°; snow was also reported at Fort Good Hope on the same day.[2]

A notable feature concerning the precipitation of this region is the fact that the number of days on which measurable amounts fall is relatively small, being less than 70 in the southwest and less than 80 in most other portions. As would be expected, in the south rainy days and snowy days are in the ratio of about 3 : 2. The season of heaviest precipitation is reflected in the greater cloudiness for that season, although the average cloudiness at that time (summer) is not usually

---

[1] Julius Hann, *Handbuch der Klimatologie*, v. 3, J. Engelhorn, Stuttgart, 1911, p. 656.
[2] J. Patterson, "A Meteorological Trip to the Arctic Circle," *Jour. Royal Astro. Soc. of Canada*, v. 9, March 1915, pp. 101-120.

greater than 70%. In fact, the highest monthly percentage for the whole Mackenzie is reported as only 74% in September and October at Fort McPherson. Here, the prevailing north winds can import without much warming considerable amounts of vapor from the waters of the Delta and Arctic Ocean. For most parts of the Valley, winter, spring and early summer are remarkably clear, the average cloudiness rarely exceeding 50%. Thunderstorms with lightning and hail occasionally visit the region. Fort Vermilion reports an average of five thunderstorms a year; Fort Good Hope appears to experience them even more frequently. Patterson states that they occur as far north as Fort McPherson.[1] River and frost fogs apparently occur a few times each year, although there is no evidence that they in any wise hinder navigation.

Numerous writers emphasize the significance of the long summer days of the lower Mackenzie in their effect upon plant growth. A reference to Table 4 shows that most of June and July have almost perpetual sunshine; and, since twilight continues when the sun is as much as 18 degrees below the horizon, it is evident that there is no darkness during a long period. Even as far south as Great Slave Lake, it is said that during the time of highest sun, one can sit out all night and read. It is only because of this greater daily period of sunlight that certain forms of temperate plant life can grow and reach maturity in a land where the frost-free period is so short. The rapidity with which plants grow under favorable thermal and photometric conditions seems almost incredible.

Of native vegetation there is an abundance. Over much of the Mackenzie River Valley there are dense stands of timber, dominately spruce and poplar. Kindle writes[2]:

"Many varieties of flowers in bloom crowd the fire-cleared spaces of the lowland and the mountain slopes early in July. Among these orchids occur locally in abundance. Ripe red raspberries were seen on August 7 at Bear Mountain, which is about 80 miles south of the Arctic Circle. Blueberries were a feature of the writer's camp fare from the first week in August to the end of the summer."

Wild roses bloom as far north as the arctic circle; and wild strawberries are common south of Fort Simpson.

[1] Ibid., p. 118.
[2] Kindle, *Canada North of Fifty-Six Degrees*, p. 65.

In the region of the Mackenzie Delta, the raising of most vegetables is unsuccessful because the permanently frozen soil is so near the surface there in summer; but throughout the rest of the valley of the main stream as well as in most of the tributary valleys of the upper Mackenzie, various crops may be raised in most years. At Fort Good Hope, Kindle saw "fine-looking gardens in which potatoes were the most conspicuous vege-

ILLUS. 18—At Fort Simpson in the Mackenzie Valley, potatoes yield a fair crop in most years.

table," and he states that, at Fort Simpson, potatoes, a few of which weighed a pound each, and a turnip measuring five inches in diameter were grown.[1] He also states that on the upper Liard, barley, rye, oats, corn, potatoes and turnips mature by August if planted toward the end of May; wheat is a sure crop four out of five years; while at Fort Vermilion it failed only three years out of twenty-seven.[2] Chambers cites scores of instances of successful vegetable and cereal culture in the middle Mackenzie Valley.[3] Connor writes[4]:

[1] Ibid., p. 70.
[2] Ibid.
[3] Chambers, op. cit., pp. 223-259.
[4] Letter cited.

"At Fort Providence, where there are flat, arable lands of good quality, the Hudson's Bay Company and the Roman Catholic Mission raised quantities of farm produce, according to a report of R. G. McConnell of the Geological Surveys. He states that for nine years prior to his visit, wheat had been sown on the H. B. Co.'s ·farm and had in no year of the nine been a complete failure, although on some occasions lightly touched by summer. frost.. Sowing is usually about the 20th of May,

ILLUS. 19—The long days in the Peace River district more than compensate for the short summers, so that agriculture is proving to be a profitable industry.

ripening about three months later. As much as twenty-nine bushels have been reaped from one bushel sown. Barley was a sure crop. It ripened a week earlier than wheat. Potatoes planted 15th to 20th of May are taken up 20th September. Most garden vegetables are grown in most years without great difficulty."

It is not, however, to be supposed from all the foregoing that agricultural activities are possible on the same scale as in southern Canada. So far as known, commercial production of cereals is impossible except in the extreme southern portions of the region; and then only in the most favorable years. Under proper conditions of exposure, the cultivation of the home garden is practicable in most years as far north as Fort McPherson. Kindle is more hopeful, however; for he says that "all of the south shore of Great Slave Lake will, in the writer's opinion, be found to lie within the wheat belt." Later he adds: "There is no reason, as far as luxuriant pasture is concerned, why cattle should not be raised in the Mackenzie valley as far north as the arctic circle and even beyond."[1]

There appears to be no difference of opinion in regard to the severity of the Mackenzie winter, the mildness and delightfulness of the summers, and the inevitableness of the mosquito during the latter season. Concerning the latter, Patterson says[2]: "By June 9th the ubiquitous mosquito was at the height of his career, making life miserable for man and beast; there is no escape except by drowning or protecting yourself with mosquito netting." The following excerpt taken from Kindle's *Canada, North of Fifty-Six Degrees* undoubtedly gives a fair indication of summer conditions[3]:

"A traveller in the Mackenzie valley who sees for the first time the limestone scarps and cliffs of the Mackenzie mountains so near the Arctic zone entirely free of snow in midsummer, is apt to be surprised when he recalls the glaciers and permanent snow fields which are familiar features of the same mountains many hundreds of miles farther south. The Nahanni mountains of the Mackenzie valley, which are quite free of snow in July, are in about the same latitude as the mouth of Frobisher bay, Baffin land, where the writer has seen a ship stuck for days in the ice floes and experienced a snow storm late in July. The warm genial summer climate of the Mackenzie valley cannot fail to impress anyone who is familiar with the bleak coasts of northeastern America which lie in the same latitude. Although the middle portion of the Mackenzie valley lies in about the same latitude as Baffin land, its summer climate bears a much stronger resemblance to that of Gaspe peninsula south of the Gulf of St. Lawrence than it does to the Baffin land summer."

THE WESTERN PRAIRIES AND PLAINS

Of all the natural regions of Canada, there is probably none in which climate relates more directly to the economic activities of its people than it does in this great granary of Canada. If it were possible to. delineate this climatic division, the northern limit would be roughly a line running northwest from the northern end of Lake Winnpeg to Fort McMurray on the Athabaska River, thence west to the British Columbia border. It is not to be inferred that all this area, comprising two-fifths of

---

[1] Kindle, op. cit., pp. 71 and 72.
[2] Patterson, op. cit., p. 106.
[3] Kindle, op. cit., pp. 69-70.

Manitoba and two-thirds each of Saskatchewan and Alberta, is given over to grain culture; neither should it be assumed that all of it is under cultivation. Yet, as far as climatic conditions are concerned, this whole subregion as outlined is capable of producing cereals and other crops on a commercial scale. If the mean summer isotherm of 57° is taken as the extreme northern limit of successful wheat growing, a limit determined

ILLUS. 20—Wheat is by no means the only crop which can be grown successfully in northern and western Alberta. The long daily period of sunshine accelerated the development of these fine vegetables at Beaver Lodge, Alberta.

by Baker[1], then all of this province can reasonably be expected to produce wheat in most years, the other physical conditions being favorable. To be more conservative, the isotherm of 58° for the three summer months may be taken as the northern limit of the province under consideration. This line and the area producing wheat in appreciable quantities in 1925 are shown in Fig. 43.

In no sense can this large region be considered a unit from the standpoint of topography, vegetation or climate. The Lake Winnipeg district has the lowest elevation, being under 1000 feet. There is a gradual increase in elevation westward to the Rocky Mountains. Northward from about the 54th parallel, the elevations decrease; that is, the drainage is toward the

[1] O. E. Baker, "Agricultural Regions of North America," *Econ. Geog.*, v. 4, 1928, p. 409.

Mackenzie or Churchill rivers. South of that parallel, the drainage is in general eastward toward the lake region of Manitoba. The region is not all prairie and plain; it is broken by hilly and plateau areas and by numerous scarps. The northern part is partly under a forest cover of aspen, poplar, birch, spruce, and pine. Though the climate is strictly continental at all times, except as the chinook may modify it, there are many

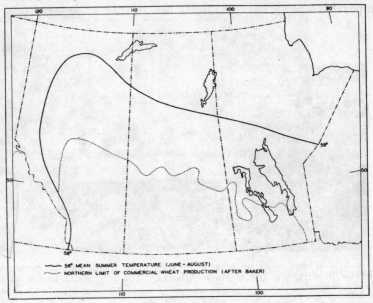

FIG. 43—Mean summer isotherm of 58° and northern limit of commercial wheat production in the Prairie Provinces.

local differences, particularly with reference to precipitation. In southeastern Alberta, conditions approach semi-aridity; on all the higher situations precipitation is heavier, and the amounts increase fairly regularly with progress eastward. Temperature conditions likewise vary locally. Winters are colder in central and eastern Alberta than in Manitoba; summers are hottest in southern Saskatchewan. Extremes, both winter and summer, tend to be less near the Rockies and toward the southeastern margin of the province (see Figs. 27-30, inclusive).

In January mean temperatures are everywhere under 20°; in two-thirds of the region, they are below 0°. The isotherm of −10° for that month marks fairly well the northern limit of the region. The average daily maximum temperature for January varies from slightly above zero in the north to about 29° in extreme southwest Alberta; while the daily minima range from approximately 4° in that section to –20° or lower along the extreme northern margins. The mean daily ranges for January are, therefore, very nearly the same over the whole province —that is, not far from 20 degrees.

With few exceptions, all parts of the province have reported temperatures of –45° or lower, the lowest probably being at

ILLUS. 21—Oats is also a crop of the Prairie Provinces, which is favored by the same climatic conditions which favor wheat growing. One may see hundreds of acres like this in traveling northeast from Calgary, Alberta.

Prince Albert where –70° was recorded one February. As indicated earlier, extreme low temperatures occur most frequently and are lowest at some distance from the western cordillera. On the other hand, the highest extreme temperatures in winter are found very near this mountain system. Thus, in January 58° has been recorded at Calgary, 56° at Medicine Hat, 50° at Qu'Appelle, and only 42° at Winnipeg—all stations in about the same latitude. Farther north, and proceeding from west to east, the temperatures run: 56° at Edmonton, 55° at Prince Albert, and 47° at Norway House. This decrease in extremes eastward is in large part due to the chinooks. Indeed, the chinook effect is seen as well in the decrease in mean January temperatures (Fig. 27). Certain years when chinooks are less pronounced, temperatures from December to February may rarely go above freezing.

A feature of prairie winters is the wide range in mean, as well as in extreme, temperatures from one year to another. For instance, the mean temperatures for the three winter months during a 30-year period at Prince Albert have varied as follows: December, from 10 degrees below zero to 17 above; January, from 19 below to 8 above; and February, from 14 below to 10 above. Fluctuations are fully as great as Winnipeg, and even more so at Edmonton. Chinook winds alone do not account for these differences; the reason lies farther back and may be found in the lack of uniformity from year to year in the paths of cyclones across the country (see Chapter II, page 10). If the kind of change in extreme temperatures from year to year at Edmonton is typical of all the prairie provinces, then Table 24 should give some idea of the average extremes which might be experienced during each of the twelve months.[1] Lower extreme minima in January are to be expected at Norway House and Prince Albert than elsewhere (except in the extreme northern portion of Alberta as at Fort Vermilion); and for the same month the highest extreme maxima should be found in Alberta along or near the piedmont.

The change from winter to summer conditions in this region is as great as, or greater than, in the Mackenzie Valley; certainly no other part of Canada has such large annual ranges of temperature as these two regions. A reference again to Tables 11-14, inclusive, proves this fact. Throughout most of the prairies and plains region, the summers are short but exceedingly warm for the latitude. In fact, one of the highest temperatures ever recorded in Canada, 110° at Cannington Manor, Sask., was reported from here. Except for a small section of the mountainous part of western Alberta, all of this region has a mean July temperature of more than 60°; very few places have means exceeding 65°. It is plain, therefore, that summer

[1] In a 46-year record at Edmonton, the highest maximum for January was 56° and the lowest maximum for the same month was 29°, the average, (56 + 29) ÷ 2, being 42.5°. The average of the whole 46 extreme maxima for January is 43.4°. Hence, a fair approximation of the average extreme maximum temperatures may be had by adding the highest and lowest and dividing by 2. Of these 46 maxima, 54% were above 43° and only 31% below 42°, thus showing that there is a tendency for maximum temperatures higher than the average to occur almost two years out of three. Similarly, the average of 98° and 78°, the highest and lowest extreme maxima in July, gives 88°, while the average of the whole 46 maxima gives 90°. In 61% of the years, the extremes were below 88°; and in only 22% of the cases were they above 88°. Hence, as far as extreme maximum temperatures are concerned, there appears to be a strong tendency toward the milder conditions: higher maxima in winter and lower maxima in summer. With minimum temperatures, there is a slight tendency for extremes lower than the average in January; but in July, minima higher than the average occur in more than six years out of seven, again revealing that in summer the moderate conditions may be expected more frequently than the extreme ones.

TABLE 24. AVERAGE EXTREME TEMPERATURES

Maxima (the sum of the highest extreme maximum and the lowest extreme maximum divided by 2).

	Jan.	Feb.	Mar.	Apr.	May	Jun.	Jul.	Aug.	Sep.	Oct.	Nov.	Dec.
Banff	34	43	50	63	75	81	86	82	74	62	48	40
Calgary	47	57	58	71	80	86	88	85	81	66	56	50
Edmonton	38	40	56	68	80	84	88	85	80	66	56	47
Fort Chipewyan	24	24	35	56	70	80	84	81	70	58	42	32
Fort Vermilion	28	32	50	62	84	88	86	81	78	68	42	32
Medicine Hat	43	50	64	69	87	95	97	93	85	80	65	54
Norway House	24	28	35	59	76	78	82	83	72	62	44	28
Prince Albert	32	38	47	66	82	85	87	85	80	72	49	37
Qu'Appelle	35	38	52	66	82	88	90	89	83	68	50	38
Winnipeg	31	33	51	70	84	90	90	92	88	73	54	26

Minima (the sum of the highest extreme minimum and the lowest extreme minimum divided by 2).

	Jan.	Feb.	Mar.	Apr.	May	Jun.	Jul.	Aug.	Sep.	Oct.	Nov.	Dec.
Banff	−26	−29	−14	4	20	28	33	35	15	9	−12	−28
Calgary	−21	−24	−10	5	22	33	37	37	20	9	−8	−20
Edmonton	−32	−33	−18	6	20	34	37	34	22	4	−16	−22
Fort Chipewyan	−37	−33	−27	−10	9	28	33	30	20	6	−12	−36
Fort Vermilion	−54	−54	−32	−11	4	26	29	30	11	−2	−20	−51
Medicine Hat	−28	−28	−14	8	22	38	42	40	28	10	−7	−23
Norway House	−50	−39	−31	−8	17	33	40	36	24	11	−15	−34
Prince Albert	−48	−41	−26	−2	18	32	40	32	23	8	−16	−35
Qu'Appelle	−32	−31	−24	1	22	34	40	36	20	5	−6	−24
Winnipeg	−36	−30	−17	6	22	32	44	38	26	13	−8	−33

conditions as typified by July are remarkably uniform. During a 30-year period, mean July temperatures varied over only 9 degrees at Edmonton, 8 degrees at Prince Albert and 11 degrees at Winnipeg. Compare these with the variations for January during the same period: 37 at Edmonton, 28 at Prince Albert, and 23 at Winnipeg. Fully a third of the province has experienced temperatures of 100° or more, and practically all of it has reported temperatures higher than 90°.

Of the seven places shown in Fig. 31, only two, Medicine Hat and Winnipeg, have been spared from frost in July. As a matter of fact frosts have been reported at least once in each of the summer months during the record. The average length of the frost-free period is quite another matter; in at least half of the years, all of July and most of June and August are free from frost throughout the entire area. In Fig. 45 is shown

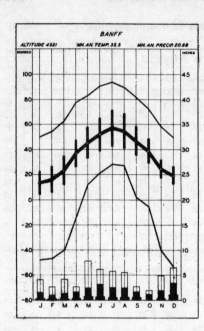

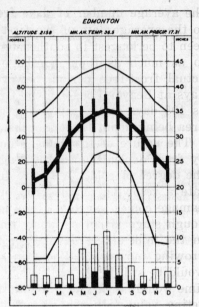

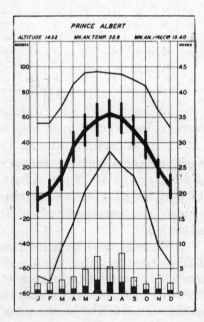

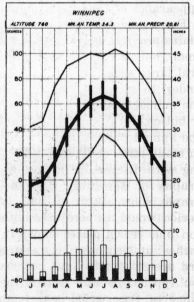

FIG. 44—Temperature and precipitation charts for Banff, Edmonton, Prince Albert and Winnipeg.

the average number of days from the average date of seeding to the average date of the first frost. This growing season is seen to be longest in southeastern Alberta, although it amounts to as much as four months over most of the region. The actual frost-free period, however, ranges from as low as 67 days at Beaver Lodge in the Grande River district to as much as 105 days at Winnipeg, the general average over the whole area being about three months.

The nature of the damage done to cereals, especially wheat, by frost depends upon the stage of maturity as well as upon the degree of cold. A severe frost in late spring may necessitate a resowing of the crop or complete abandonment if the damage comes too late. In August, "wheat frozen in the stiff dough stage is not seriously impaired but . . . . wheat frozen in the milk stage may be seriously damaged for milling and growing purposes. Wheat in some parts of Western Canada would be still in the milk stage in early August. Frost at this time would be very detrimental to the crop in yield and in marketing value. In the season of 1928 frost occurred in many areas on August 23rd. Owing to the fact that most of our wheat was well advanced the damage was not so severe as the appearance of the wheat might suggest."[1]

For a region so important agriculturally as the prairies and plains provinces, the average annual precipitation is surprisingly small, only a few places having as much as 20 inches, and several large areas in southern Alberta and Saskatchewan having under 15 inches (Fig. 32). More significant, however, than the annual amounts are the dependability and the seasonal distribution. As pointed out in Chapter IV, the fluctuations of the annual precipitation from year to year are not so great as in many other parts of Canada, the degree of variation decreasing with distance from the Rocky Mountains, as shown by the graphs for Edmonton, Qu'Appelle and Winnipeg (Fig. 35). The graphs show conditions over the period 1890-1925. A longer period would, of course, show wider ranges. Thus, at Edmonton one year the record was 28 inches, another year only 8 inches; at Medicine Hat the highest and lowest amounts on record are 22 and 7 inches; at Prince Albert, 30 and 7 inches; at Qu'Appelle, 26 and 10 inches; at Winnipeg, 27 and 14 inches. None of these takes into consideration the years since 1925.

[1] Statement prepared by A. G. O. Whiteside, Dept. of Agri., Ottawa; May 1929.

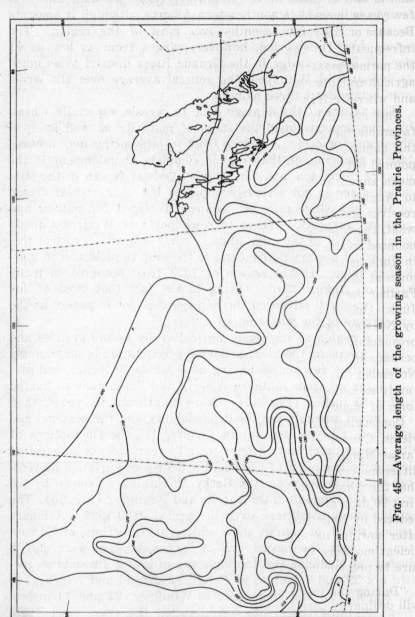

Fig. 45—Average length of the growing season in the Prairie Provinces.

Although there are months in many years when the precipitation is two to three times the normal, there are comparatively few years in which there is a month without any precipitation. Because of the relatively light amounts in all months floods are infrequent. On the other hand, even a slight diminution in the normal monthly amounts may mean serious consequences in agricultural districts where the normal rainfall is very small and where irrigation can not be practiced.

The seasonal distribution of precipitation is particularly favorable for general agriculture and even more favorable for the dominant type in this region, viz., wheat culture. As pointed out in Chapter IV, from 50% to more than 70% of the mean annual precipitation comes in the four months from May to August. September, the most important harvest month, receives less than May. The month of maximum varies somewhat, the tendency for an early summer maximum being pronounced in the south; that is, Winnipeg receives about as much in June as in July, and June is distinctly the month of maximum at Calgary, Medicine Hat, Prince Albert, and Qu'Appelle. Farther north, as at Edmonton, July receives slightly more than June. Only in the northeast section of the province, as typified by Norway House, is the month of maximum greatly delayed, presumably because of the effects of the Manitoba lakes and perhaps of Hudson Bay. Everywhere, the precipitation from November to March is extremely light, the monthly amount rarely exceeding one inch. Practically all of this comes in the form of snow.

Concerning the relation of rainfall and temperature to wheat yields, Connor has arrived at some interesting conclusions as far as Manitoba is concerned; presumably conditions would not differ materially in either Alberta or Saskatchewan.[1] He states that the wheat plant demands moisture and coolness during the first 90 days after sowing, and that the subsequent yield is most reduced by large ranges of temperature during the third month after sowing; usually there is during the first two months sufficient moisture in the soil and low enough ranges in temperature to prevent harmful evaporation. He adds:

"During the latter part of the 90-day period, however, there will ordinarily obtain midsummer weather with increased prob-

[1] A. J. Connor, *Relation of the Weather to the Yield of Wheat in Manitoba*, The Monthly Bureau of Agricultural Statistics, Ottawa, April, 1918, pp. 6-7.

ability of heat and drought, and in this regard the last part of the 90 days after sowing may be said to be a 'critical period.' If in this 'critical' time the weather be warm, dry, with great temperature range, the wheat-plants will head early and the harvest will be light, but if the cool and moist conditions continue, heading will be postponed and the yield increase. Now the average date of sowing of wheat in Manitoba since 1890 is approximately April 25, which will fix the average time of the

ILLUS. 22—Just enough rain in late spring and early summer favors the development of the wheat plant, while the drier days of late summer aid in the ripening process and permit harvesting with slight loss. Occasionally, however, an early snow temporarily halts harvesting and threshing. This farm is near Calgary, Alberta.

'critical period' as the last week of June and the first three weeks of July. Hence the variability of early July weather may be regarded as the 'critical factor' in wheat production in Manitoba."

The snowfall of the prairies is notably light, a large part of Alberta and Saskatchewan having an annual total of less than 40 inches (see Fig. 32). Fullerton Waldo comments, somewhat facetiously, as follows concerning snow and cold in Edmonton[1]:

"The street-car lines in Edmonton scarcely require snowplows —little ones no higher than the wheels may be called into service two or three times in a winter. The snow does not drift in the streets as it does in eastern cities. Neither do the people— unless it is a fire or a band or a parade or some other good reason."

[1] Fullerton Waldo, *Down the Mackenzie through the Great Lone Land*, The Macmillan Co., New York, 1923, p .7.

Available records appear to show greater differences than probably actually exist; for Battleford records only 24 inches (a 20-year average) while Prince Albert at about the same altitude and only 100 miles east receives 48 inches (a 30-year record). The difficulties in measuring snow on the plains must partially account for such a remarkable difference. Since most of the snow comes with strong winds, particularly northwest

ILLUS. 23—The amount of snowfall increases with progress eastward from the Rocky Mountain piedmont; and heavy snowfalls are not infrequent in Manitoba. In spite of this blanket of snow, the intense winter cold in this section makes certain the annual ice crop.

winds, the snow is fine, is blown about and drifted or laid in wave-like crescents by the wind, and is therefore very compact on broad open spaces. Whether measurements be taken on a surface, smooth and protected, or on one where the wind has been an important factor in laying the cover, determines somewhat their comparableness. The personal element is certainly of some consequence also.

Snowfall is here much more erratic than rainfall. It is not unusual for one month to receive five, and even ten, times as much as the average for that month. As an instance, consider Medicine Hat which one October received over two feet of snow, although the average is only one inch; in fact almost as much came in that one month as is normally received in a whole year. Such an extreme case is, however, unusual. July and August are the only months which have not, at some time in the records, had snow; and even on the northeastern margin, at Norway House, snow has occurred in July. Snow is to be expected throughout this region during every year in all months, except June, July, and August. As recently as May 8, 1929, a train on the Hudson Bay Railway northeast of The Pas was marooned for five days in snow drifts. A report from Winnipeg, dated May 14, 1929, stated that on that day a blizzard brought six inches of snow with a temperature of 30° to Calgary, and 28° but less snow to southern Saskatchewan; all points north of these were blanketed with snow.[1] Fortunately such apparently long delayed visitations of winter do very little harm.

Two very desirable features of the climate of this region are found in the large percentage of sunshine or at least the very weak tendency to overcast skies, and the comparatively small number of days with measurable precipitation (see Figs. 37 and 38). Obviously, the time of year has an important control over the sunshine; for the number of hours with the sun above the horizon on December 21st is only seven hours in the north and about eight in the south (Table 4). Yet the percentages of the possible during all of December for these two divisions are relatively high since the average cloudiness is shown to be from 45% to 55%. At the time of highest sun, June 21st, sunlight lasts from 15 hours on the southern to 18 hours on the northern margins of the region. In spite of the heavier precipitation in June, average cloudiness runs only about 5% higher. For most places July is the least cloudy, the percentage rarely being higher than 40. Indeed, as shown in Fig. 38, the Prairie Provinces and the Arctic Prairies are as free from clouds throughout the year as any other part of Canada.

Notwithstanding the fact that the Canadian prairie climate is dominately under the control of cyclones and that these storms are frequently referred to as blizzards when temperatures are below freezing, the region is remarkably free from strong winds, more so in the west than in the east. Edmonton, with an average annual wind velocity of only 5.3 miles per hour, experiences approximately twice a year winds of gale force; and, strange to say, the months when blizzards are most common and cause the greatest discomfort are not the windiest months. On the contrary, April and May have the greatest wind movement— a time when the interior of the United States is warming up

---

[1] *New York Times*, New York, May 15, 1929.

rapidly but a time when the Mackenzie Valley and the Arctic Prairies as well as northern Ontario are still under a blanket of snow and ice, thereby causing a considerable difference in pressure between the north and south. At times, however, spring conditions of pressure may be just the opposite: low pressure in the north and high pressure toward the south. In the eastern part of the region, as exemplified by Winnipeg, winds are fully twice as strong as in the west, and gales are probably three times as frequent. Like the west, however, and for the same reason, April and May bring the highest average winds speeds. The percentage frequencies of both summer and winter weather types are shown in Table 25. Moderate, fair and quiet or moderate and rainy days are the dominant types in summer; although at Medicine Hat, a large percentage of summer days is hot, fair and quiet. In winter most days are either cold, snowy and quiet or cold, fair and quiet. The low frequency of windy days in either summer or winter is significant.

Although winds are prevailingly northwest all year in Alberta, it should not be inferred that winds from other directions are infrequent. At Edmonton in February, southwest winds are almost as common as northwest. When the former, chinook, winds do start to blow, they may continue for several days. Allbright refers to one instance at Beaver Lodge in west central Alberta in 1916 when "a six-week's extreme cold spell was broken in the middle of February by a chinook, and for a week it did not freeze day or night, while the ensuing week it froze only slightly at night."[1]

Southwest winds are more frequent at some distance from the mountains than near them. For instance, at Calgary on the piedmont at 3400 feet elevation, they blow only five or six per cent of the time in winter, while at Edmonton the percentages are about 16 to 17, and at Qu'Appelle 12 to 14. Apparently, the chinook is more frequent out on the plains; that is, it appears to flow over the colder air at Edmonton, not reaching the surface until farther east. In fact, Stupart finds the chinook generally less pronounced at Banff than on the prairies and "in marked instances" less pronounced at Calgary.[2] This does not

[1] W. D. Allbright, "Some Climatic Characteristics of Central Alberta," *Bull. Am. Meteor. Soc.*, v. 3, 1922, p. 171.

[2] R. F. Stupart, "The Climate of Southwestern Alberta," *Trans. Am. Climatological Assoc.*, v. 30, 1914, p. 7.

TABLE 25. PERCENTAGE FREQUENCIES OF WEATHER TYPES IN THE CONTINENTAL INTERIOR

	Edmonton	Medicine Hat	Prince Albert	Winnipeg	Port Nelson	Port Arthur	Cochrane	White River	Parry Sound	Toronto	Quebec
Summer											
Hot	8	56	18	35	4	14	18	12	40	51	27
Moderate	85	43	79	63	51	81	73	75	59	48	72
Cool	7	1	3	2	44	4	8	13			
Fair	57	80	66	60	63	68	57	64	70	65	54
Windy	2	8	3	15	13	7	1	2		7	31
Hot; Rainy	2	5	6	11	2	4	6	4	10	17	13
Hot; Fair; Windy		6	1	6	1	1				2	3
Hot; Fair; Quiet	6	45	11	18	1	9	13	8	30	32	11
Moderate; Rainy	38	11	27	18	17	24	32	28	19	17	32
Moderate; Fair; Windy	2	2	2	9	8	5	1	2		5	10
Moderate; Fair; Quiet	45	29	51	36	26	52	40	45	40	26	29
Cool; Rainy	3	1	1		16	1	4	4			
Cool; Fair; Windy					4						
Cool; Fair; Quiet	4	1	2	1	22	3	4	28			
Winter											
Cool	10	25	1	1		5	1	2	8	30	1
Cold	90	75	99	99	100	95	99	98	92	70	99
Fair	69	75	76	73	76	74	77	52	56	53	48
Windy	3	7	1	18	21	15	7	2	12	33	45
Cool; Rainy	1	3				2	1	1	5	14	
Cool; Fair; Windy		2							4		
Cool; Fair; Quiet	9	21				3			2	12	
Cold; Snowy; Quiet	28	21	23	20	13	18	21	44	31	13	22
Cold; Fair; Windy	1	4		11	11	8	4		5	12	18
Cold; Fair; Quiet	59	49	76	62	66	62	73	52	50	26	31
Cold; Snowy; Windy	1	1	1	6	10	6	3	1	7	18	28

mean that winters are more severe in the mountains; on the contrary, severe winters on the prairies may be contemporaneous with much milder ones in the mountains.[1]

In certain winters, chinooks fail to make their appearance as frequently or as pronouncedly as usual; such winters are very severe, and the resulting hardships are trying. C. F. Sykes gives his version of a "bad winter" in Alberta, in part, as follows[2]:

[1] Ibid.
[2] C. F. Sykes, "A Bad Winter in Alberta," *Chambers Journal*, 7th series, v. 17, 1927, pp. 158-159.

"Winter had set in earlier than usual, three weeks before the shortest day. The fields were still covered with stooks, which had to be dug out of the snow—no easy task with the butt of every sheath frozen solid to the ground. A fortnight after the first storm the country lay for three days in the grip of a driving blizzard. The day preceding had been mild with a soft wind blowing out of the east, sure harbinger of bad weather. . . . .

"The morrow, however, brought an even lower temperature and stronger wind. That night the wind dropped. We awoke to find the thermometer standing a fifty-two degrees below. The steam rose in little clouds from the stables, and the smoke from the house chimneys went up so straight and far, ere spreading out into a huge mushroom-shaped growth, that it could easily have been mistaken for a natural cloud. Little pools of mists marked the spots where the cattle stood in huddled bunches, the heat from their bodies combined with their breath hanging over them exactly as mist will gather over a pool on a chilly summer's night. . . . .

"Our main bunch of horses were on pasture four miles from home when the blizzard struck. In an ordinary winter they could have been able to forage for themselves and grow fat. It was ten days before a man could be spared to see how they were doing. . . . .

"When the snow finally cleared, dead horses were to be found with manes and tails eaten off by their starving companions, lying in every sheltered corner, whither they had drifted before the winds, only to find that they had not the strength to turn around and fight their way out through the snow that had blown in behind them. . . . . Stacks of feed which, last September, looked so huge that we doubted if we could ever move them, melted like snow before the chinook. . . . .

"And then, almost as suddenly as it had commenced, the siege was raised; the snow vanished like magic, grass coming up green and fresh as fast as it had disappeared. Horses that had seemed about to die fattened over night. Feed that had gone to famine prices became worthless as it stood rotting in the fields—fields which the farmer, with the optimism that had marked him through the ages, was impatient to be preparing for another crop, just so soon as he could burn the ruin of last year's one that stood there in the way."

With progress eastward, northwest winds become somewhat less frequent, particularly in the warmer months; and even by March, winds at The Pas are prevailingly northeast, continuing from that direction through June. Winds with a southerly component are somewhat more frequent in the summer months; and those from a northeasterly quadrant occur fairly often in all months with the oncoming of a low pressure area. The relation of winds to pressure in the Prairie Provinces was discussed in Chapter II. It is well to emphasize again, however, that the movements of cyclones have a very strong control on directions of wind movement, more so in these provinces than in any other part of Canada. This fact is reflected in the annual wind roses, Fig. 11; and it is clearly shown in the tables of wind frequencies as given in the appendix.

All dwellers of the prairies and plains testify to the great number and severity of blizzards. That fewer reports come

ILLUS. 24—On the semi-arid plains of southern Alberta, the light snowfall of winter permits year-around open range grazing of sheep and cattle.

from the northern parts of the Prairie Provinces is doubtless due to the fact that fewer people live there to report them, and to the fact that the lands have a fairly dense forest cover to break the force of the wind, and therefore, to reduce the amount of snow which might be carried in the moving air.

A graphic description of two blizzards occurring in Manitoba is given below[1]:

"My first settlement was in southern Manitoba where one of the worst blizzards I ever experienced occurred in March, 1879. About 12 inches of snow covered the prairie and packed sufficiently to make good snow-shoeing. A soft wind blew out of the southwest, making the snow quite soft on top. Heavy clouds developed now with distant thunder, followed by a decided change to colder and freezing, resulting in a crust of

[1] A letter to the author from H. Hassart, Medicine Hat, Alberta; dated December, 1928.

ice forming on the snow. The wind raised to probably 50 miles an hour, the mercury falling in reverse ratio to about 10°. In two hours there was pandemonium. Great plates of ice 10 to 20 feet square would be lifted and, in falling again, would break to smaller pieces which in turn would be raised on edge and blown along the prairies like so many cart wheels of large and small sizes. The prairie looked as if it were alive—demons on a rampage. The loose snow was lifted and carried through the air as though a heavy shower of snow were falling. A blinding blizzard developed, with those icy cartwheels for good measure, travelling in every direction except in that from which the wind was blowing. Those who were in absolute safety could contemplate the fantastic aspect with great interest until the snow was too thick to see through.

"My next experience with a bad blizzard was on New Years Day, 1887. It had been snowing heavy for about 36 hours, when it cleared off with a rising cold wind from the northwest. This seemed to attain hurricane force and lasted for about 30 hours. The snow, being loose and fluffy, was piled in great waves, 10 to 20 feet high—just like ocean waves. They were miles in length, of varying distances apart, and ran somewhat west-east; bare prairie lay between. Travelling was almost impossible.

"Be the wind ever so moderate, it will move the freshly fallen snow; and as the snow is moved, it compacts. The higher the wind the more compact the snow becomes. It is driven along the surface like so much fine sand; and when the wind is high enough, the snow is lifted into the air, resulting in a 'blizzard,' although no snow is actually falling. The sky becomes entirely invisible and, to the less observant, the belief is that it is a real snowstorm. Notwithstanding all this, there is a fascination in prairie life, which blizzards can not deaden. After all winters of this sort are not so severe as one might expect."

The frequency of thunderstorms varies only slightly over this whole climatic province, Edmonton, Qu Appelle and Winnipeg each reporting an average annual total of about 20. Naturally, the colder northern portions and the more arid areas, as around Medicine Hat, report fewer, in fact only from 12 to 16. With these thunderstorms hail sometimes occurs, probably averaging once a year except at Edmonton where it appears to occur more frequently. How severe these storms may be is given in the following press dispatch from Stanraer in south central Saskatchewan, dated August 13, 1928[1]:

"This town was struck by a storm of cyclonic proportions Saturday night. Buildings were turned over and smashed, the

[1] *New York Times*, New York, Aug. 14, 1928.

stockyards were badly damaged and the driveway was blown away from a grain elevator. Communication with outside points was restored only today.

"The storm broke suddenly and destroyed several acres of wheat. No one was injured. This morning the district was swept by a hail storm. The damage which is expected to be heavy, could not be estimated.

"Saturday the hail storm drifted as far as Saskatoon district, where damage to crops is expected to reach 100 per cent.

ILLUS. 25—In portions of southern Alberta where the average annual rainfall does not exceed 16 inches, various forms of irrigation are being attempted—most of them with satisfactory results.

The Vanscoy district, fifteen miles from Saskatoon, was the hardest hit. The hail here flattened acres of grain to the ground. At Elston three horses were killed. . . . .

"At Rosetown, Sask., the storm hit a strip fifteen miles long and from six to ten miles wide, leveling the crops and blowing down small buildings."

Much has been written regarding the great advantages of the Prairie Provinces from a climatic standpoint. Usually such glowing accounts come from land-promoting organizations or from enthusiastic residents who wish to boost their communities. Certainly, the climate does possess qualities greatly to be desired; and perhaps certain combinations of these qualities render the climate unexcelled in some respects. Seasons of great drought—perhaps several of them in succession—severe blizzards in spring, destructive hail storms in mid-summer, freezing temperatures in August, or a failure of chinook, much needed to remove the snow from the open range—all these and other equally trying forms of weather do occur and work severe hardship particularly on the agriculturalist. Rodwell Jones sums up some of the undesirable effects of weather around Medicine Hat as follows[1]: "In an area of marginal rainfall

ILLUS. 26—The waters of the irrigation ditches in southern Alberta help to diminish or retard the late summer frosts so that potatoes are becoming commercially profitable crops.

the crop [wheat] shows greater correspondence with precipitation than with any other climatic element. The weather is not always favorable. A dry, late spring; the summer furnace winds of the dry belt; hail storms which reduce a wheatfield to a pitted black puddle; night frost in early August which shrivels the grain in the milk—all and each are capable of wrecking hopes in what had promised to be a good season."

Furthermore, as Jones points out, not all parts of the provinces are capable of producing crops every year. He mentions in particular southern Alberta where the average annual precipitation totals only 13 inches[2]: "In detail this semi-arid land

---

[1] Rodwell Jones, "Some Physical Controls in the Economic Development of the Prairie Provinces," *Geography*, v. 14, (spring, 1928), p. 298.

[2] Ibid., p. 293.

has small areas of white alkali soil; small areas almost barren of vegetation; and a few areas of real sand dune; while large areas are grassed so sparsely as to be easily over-stocked. In a good year some of the best wheats of Canada are produced here."

The development of irrigation projects in this region is making good crops more certain. Jones finds that over 1,100,000 acres of land here are irrigable; although up to 1925 only 214,000 acres were being irrigated.[1]

The Peace River district probably has the most desirable climate of any part of Canada lying in the same latitude. That portion of the district which lies in British Columbia has already been discussed; its climate does not differ essentially from the part of the Valley situated in Alberta except as altitude makes British Columbia slightly colder.

F. H. Kitto describes the middle Peace River Valley climate thus[2]:

"The climate of the Peace River district is excellent, and remarkably moderate considering the latitude. The air is pure and bracing: in winter, clear and crisp; and, in summer, dry and balmy. Extremes of temperature, sudden changes, and severe storms are very rare. The winters are by no means mild but are very dry, with clear skies, little snowfall, and few winds. Blizzards are unknown, but the mild Chinook winds occasionally sweep through the mountain passes from the warm Pacific, giving pleasing respites of balmy days to break the monotony of a steady cold. Spring comes early and quickly; the snow soon disappears, and the ground is dry in a few days. Ice on the lakes and rivers breaks up during the latter part of April or early in May. Seeding usually begins early in April, sometimes in March, and, at Fort Vermilion, about the first of May. Most of the rainfall occurs in June and July. The average precipitation for the full year is about twelve or thirteen inches.

"The summers are remarkable for their long days and short nights. For three months, there is almost continual light, the nights being merely a couple of hours semi-darkness, except when the sky is overcast. The days are warm.

"At Fort Dunvegan, the last light frost of spring occurs, on the average, on June 11th, and the first light frost of autumn, on August 25th. At Fort Vermilion and Peace River Crossing, the corresponding dates are June 16th, August 13th; and June 24th, August 27th.

---

[1] Ibid., p. 295.

[2] F. H. Kitto, *The Peace River District, Canada: Its Resources and Opportunities*, Dept. of the Int., Ottawa, 1922, pp. 9-10.

"Harvest commences about the middle of August. September is an especially pleasant month. The days are still warm, but the nights grow colder and the flies disappear. Life in the woods is at its best during this month. October brings heavier frosts, and the ice forms late in this month or early in November. Winter can usually be expected early in November, though mild weather until Christmas is not uncommon.

"The rigours of the climate need not be feared but houses should be substantially built to withstand the cold spells. Warmly clad, a person enjoys the out-of-door life at any time during the winter. Taken the year round, the climate is healthy and pleasant, and conducive to active and vigorous outdoor life."

A resident of Dunvegan writes that automobiles run there most of the year, and that the Peace River is frozen solid enough before Christmas to permit cars to cross safely. This writer adds that crops never fail entirely either from frost or drought. Barley, wheat, oats, corn, potatoes, tomatoes, etc. "respond to cultivation in a marvelous manner, ripening very quickly" because of the long daily period of sunshine during the growing season. Only 60 miles from Dunvegan "the world's champion wheat and oats have been grown in the last two years."[1]

Farther east in the Athabaska River Valley conditions are very similar to these, although perhaps a little more severe, as indicated by this letter[2]:

"The climate of the McMurray district is very heathful and invigorating. The winters are certainly cold, but underfoot the ground is frozen hard and dry, and the lakes and rivers are covered with a safe sheeting of ice. The snow is dry and powdery and the fall exceedingly light. The air is clear and crisp and the sky usually free from clouds. By day there is an abundance of sunshine and by night the brilliance of the stars and the Northern Lights are very noticeable. This dry clear cold is a pleasant surprise to newcomers. At 25° or so below zero children play out of doors quite unconscious of the cold. The summers are characterized by high day temperatures with abundance of sunshine. The heat is not oppressive, the air being very dry and the nights are cool. A noticeable feature is the rapidity with which winter gives way to spring, or even summer weather, the snow disappears very quickly and the ground surface dries up as fast as it thaws out. Winter commences about the beginning of November and ends about the end of March. The rivers close up about the second week in November and open up again about the middle or last week in

[1] In a letter to the author from Postmaster Lily Peters, Dunvegan, Alberta; dated Nov. 3, 1928.

[2] A letter to the author from C. Potts, McMurray, Alberta; dated December 1st, 1928.

April. Blizzards and chinook winds are unknown, or exceedingly rare. Winters and summers vary little and commence and end about the same time year after year. The effect of the climate on vegetation is very marked; raspberries, strawberries and many other kinds of berries flourish in the wild state; likewise roses, and many kinds of wild flowers. All kinds of flowers and vegetables are grown to perfection in cultivated gardens."

A summary of the climate of Alberta as a whole is given by Nichols of the University of Alberta.[1] This description applies to Saskatchewan and Manitoba to some extent. Yet it should be pointed out that the climate of Saskatchewan is more severe because it is more continental; the province is more exposed to Arctic cold invasions and less influenced by the mountains. Manitoba's climate is somewhat influenced by its location nearer water bodies; hence, it is more humid and shows smaller temperature ranges at all seasons.

"The general characteristics of the climate of this province may be said to be those typical of a continental climate of comparatively high latitude on the one hand and those peculiar to the warm dry interior valleys of the Pacific coast on the other. Whether one type or the other dominates depends largely on the paths of low pressure which come in from the Pacific and the location of high pressure areas, whether in the north or northwest, or in the south and southwest. If the low pressure systems move eastwards along very high latitudes, the climate of Alberta is balmy and dry because air is crossing the mountains from the Pacific, first being dried on the westerly slopes of the mountains and then warmed as it descends in to Alberta. These conditions give rise to the 'Chinook' type of weather which in winter cause the isotherms to curve very markedly northwards. When these low pressure areas are followed in turn by high pressures from the Pacific the weather remains dry and mild for weeks at a time. If the 'lows' move from the Pacific along more southerly parallels, say along the United States border, then precipitation occurs accompanied by stormy cold weather in winter. Also if high pressure areas come down from the Yukon or the Mackenzie Valley very cool weather, if in summer, and Arctic temperatures, if in winter, result. The major portion of the precipitation, which averages between 14 to 17 inches per annum, falls in the form of rain in the latter part of May and in June and July, the time of growth of wheat and other grains. The snowfall is usually not heavy, the winds are strong in the south and very moderate in the northern sec-

[1] A paper prepared for the author by Prof. L. H. Nichols of the University of Alberta at Edmonton; January, 1929.

tion and their most frequent direction is from the southwest. Sunshine is a notable characteristic and the humidity is low except for a few months in summer. A few very warm days are experienced every summer and some extremely cold weather during a part of each winter but the nights are always cool in summer, and sunshine and absence of wind mitigates the extreme cold of winter. The climate in general is invigorating and healthy.

"The same season in Alberta in different years varies perhaps more widely than in other parts of America because of its peculiar geographical position and its dependence on the particular trend of movement of the 'lows' and 'highs' as mentioned above. The snow is usually melted away by the third week of March and warm windy days are frequent. Heavy snow, however, may be experienced at any time up to the first week in May, and January weather prevails for a day or two occasionally. On the whole April is dry and balmy and May is warm with light rainfall and often high winds until about the third week of the month. This dry spring enables the farmer to plough and seed his land which in many parts is so heavy as not to be workable except in dry weather. The rains then come in June and July, often torrential and accompanied by considerable electrical disturbances and hail. But there are also long drawn out general rains and the hail is usually confined to small areas. There is considerable sunshine throughout the rainy season and the days are amazingly long owing to the high latitude. This accounts for the very rapid growth of vegetation. July and August have dry hot days with cool nights and there is a danger of frost in the latter part of August in certain years with the advent of high pressure from the north following rain. This is also more or less local and more confined to central and southern sections rather paradoxically. Frost is general at night in September but the days are fine and quite warm, the daily ranges in temperature being very great. October is usually a dry month with nights becoming increasingly cold with ice forming in lakes and in small streams; and yet the days, under the influence of bright sun and dry air, seem warm although the temperature is not far above freezing. Some snow usually falls about the end of the month and November may be very severe or very mild. A 'normal' November does not occur very often. The same may be said of December. These two months show the peculiarities of Alberta's climate perhaps more than any others. November and December may have heavy snows and average temperatures near or below zero Fahrenheit or they may be like a continuation of October; it all depends on the track of the 'lows' of the particular season. January and February are nearly always wintry with an occasional mild period. Not much snow falls in these two months and winds are light.

"Some interest attaches to the vagaries of Alberta climate. Some winters have been experienced when the thermometer remained below zero for months at a time and others when it barely registered freezing in midwinter. Prolonged snowstorms are not uncommon; and again there may be three or four months almost without a snowflake. Tremendous twenty-four hour variations in temperature are experienced with a change

ILLUS. 27—The long and cold, but calm, nights in early winter permit ice of remarkable clarity to form on the small lakes of central Alberta. Here, the scanty snowfall is a factor in the recreational activities of the people of Edmonton.

of wind from a southwesterly quarter to a northwesterly. People have frozen their ears in April in Edmonton and have been uncomfortably warm in February.

"The winter weather presents some unusual features. It is not at all uncommon for the lakes, which are large and numerous, to freeze early in October without a snow cover. Large crowds may be seen skating on these magnificent expanses of ice without overcoats or gloves on account of the warm sun, and yet the ice remains hard and dry because of the very clear air which allows free radiation and because of the low angle of the sun. Beside the lake others may be found playing golf or tennis in complete comfort. Albertans do not stay in because of the cold but are ardent skaters and skiiers and fond of 'hiking' in the woods to build their campfires in the snow and to enjoy the magnificent coloured displays of the aurora borealis to the full under the open sky in the evening. Snow is seldom heavy enough to interfere with motor cars and these are used throughout the winter and keep up communication with the more isolated parts.

"There is remarkably little difference between temperatures of the north and south of the province although separated by six hundred miles or more. This is especially true during cold waves. The Peace River country in northern Alberta is subject to less extremes than any other part of the province and its climate is influenced by the fact that the Rockies are at a considerably lower average elevation on its westward side. Generally speaking the climate of Alberta is warmer than in Manitoba or Saskatchewan and subject to less fluctuations which affect crops than these other two provinces. Its winter's cold may require some fortitude on the part of the inhabitants but the cold spells are likely to be brief. The balmy days of sunshine which intervene, the complete absence of sleet, winter rains or excessive snowfall, the thoroughly enjoyable summer and autumn seasons—all make Alberta's climate one that provides just sufficient rigour for a stimulant, the maximum sunshine and dryness for health, abundant precipitation for crops and yet very little excess which might interefere with outdoor enjoyment."

THE HUDSON BAY REGION

A long annual period of solid or floating ice makes Hudson Bay and the adjacent waters distinctly an arctic sea. There is no part of the year when the whole Bay is entirely free of floes. No sooner has the winter ice along the margins of the Bay and in the broad estuaries been broken up by the spring thaws than ice begins to drift in from Fox Channel. Part of this ice moves into Hudson Bay itself and part into Hudson Strait—usually the result of north winds. Consequently, the Strait is closed to navigation until late in July—occasionally as late as August. The rivers and harbors of the Bay, however, are open about the middle or latter part of May, the ice disappearing from the west coast sooner than from the east coast. By the middle of October, the ice is again solid in Hudson Strait; and by the middle of November most of the harbors of the Bay are again closed. These are average dates for the region as a whole. Obviously ice does not persist so long in James Bay as around Southampton Island; and at times, Hudson Strait is navigable as early as June and as late as November. On the other hand, there have been seasons when boats have had great difficulty in getting through the Strait at all. In 1914, the Strait was blocked until late in August.[1]

[1] W. J. Peters, "The Hudson Bay Expedition, 1914," *Researches of the Department of Terrestial Magnetism*, v. 5, The Carnegie Institution. Washington, D. C.

Not only thermal conditions but also winds have much to do with the persistence or movements of ice in these waters. Since the ice drifts into Hudson Strait from Fox Channel, it is evident that there is more open water along the north shore than elsewhere. If southerly winds set in, the ice spreads out over the whole Strait, making navigation either exceedingly difficult or entirely impossible until the winds change. In the Bay

ILLUS. 28—The difficulties of navigation in the Hudson Straits is clearly indicated by this photograph taken in July, 1923.

itself, west winds tend to drive the ice southwards, thereby breaking it up through scattering and bringing it into warmer climes; east winds tend to drive it northwards, against the drift from Fox Channel, thus hindering or blocking passage between the islands and coast at the northeast end of the Bay. The waters of the Bay itself, however, are not ice-bound at any time of year except along the shore[1], although the drifting floes do offer serious obstacles to navigation unless specially constructed, round-bottom boats are used.

The ice conditions are mentioned first because they have a profound effect, not only upon transportation through the waters but also upon the climate of the immediately surrounding lands. In fact, the chilling effects of Hudson Bay waters may be carried far inland at times—even as far as middle Manitoba. In late spring, the icy waters favor high pres-

[1] Sir P. McGrath, "The Difficulties of the Hudson Bay Route to Europe," *Dalhousie Rev.*, Halifax, v. 5, 1925, p. 76.

sure with easterly winds in northern Manitoba and north-western Ontario, and westerly winds along the east coast of the Bay. The change from winter conditions to those of spring is felt sooner at Moose Factory than at Churchill because the temperature contrasts between the land and water are more pronounced in April over James Bay than in the Churchill region. These temperature contrasts gradually recede north-wards as the ice comes in from Fox Channel and as the lands become free of snow. As a consequence, the spring months are disagreeably chilly everywhere along the coast. Except around the southern tip of James Bay, March means are below zero, and everywhere April means are well below freezing. This tendency to high pressure persists through the summer, although it becomes much weaker over James Bay in July as is evidenced by the change to southwesterly winds. By September, winds all along the west coast of Hudson Bay are pre-vailingly off-shore.

In spite of the strong marine influence of the Bay, all stations of the region have higher means in July than in August, although the difference is not considerable. The marine effect is seen, however, in the fact that October is from five to ten degrees warmer than April. Mean summer temperatures are considerably lower and mean winter temperatures considerably higher than for places of the same latitude in the Mackenzie Valley, Alberta, or Saskatchewan.

At Moose Factory, only January and February have mean temperatures below zero (–4° and –2°); while at Churchill, the months from December to March inclusive have means all lower than zero, January being –20°. The moderating effect of the waters in winter is seen along the east coast where, lati-tude for latitude, mean temperatures are fully five degrees higher than along the west coast (see Fig. 27). A one-year record at Great Whale River and a four-year record at Fort George indicate that February is appreciably colder than January, although the latter month shows the lowest temperatures on record. All the Hudson Bay coast has less extreme tem-perature conditions in winter than do the lands farther west. As near as Norway House at the north end of Lake Winnipeg, the extremes for January run from 47° down to –63°; while the highest January temperature recorded anywhere around Hudson Bay was 43° at Moose Factory, (300 miles farther south than Norway House) and the lowest, –57° at Churchill (500 miles farther north than Norway House). Winters are, therefore, cold and unrelieved by the occasional warm days which the chinook brings to the far west. At Port Nelson the highest temperature to be expected in January during half the years is only 20°; the lowest, –45°.

Spring is an uncertain season, depending largely upon wind direction. If winds prevail from the south and southwest, as they do when storm centers move far to the north, the season advances rapidly and conditions are relatively mild. Under such conditions Churchill may have temperatures of 75° in May while at Moose Factory they may reach 80° (absolute maximum for May, 95°). But if winds come from a northerly quarter, the whole month of May may pass without the thermometer registering as high as 15°. In fact, temperatures of zero or lower are to be expected during this month in at least one year out of four; the lowest May temperature on record at Moose Factory is –11°.

Although most summers have really hot days occasionally, the means are generally under 60°, and they are invariably lower on the east than on the west coasts. The highest temperature ever recorded in the region is 97° at Moose Factory; while temperatures above 90° have been recorded at that place in each of the months from May to September inclusive, and there has been no July on record in which at least 80° was not reached. On the other hand, temperatures precariously low for agricultural pursuits, have occurred in every month over all parts of the region.

Frosts are to be expected as frequently as one year out of five in either July or August at Moose Factory, and at least every third year at Port Nelson. These low temperatures presumably occur on clear nights after cold air has drifted in from the northwest. Freezing air temperatures may be independent of ice accumulations in the harbor at Port Nelson which is sometimes literally choked with ice even in July—ice so thick that people may readily walk over it. Such ice accumulations must always be attributed to northerly winds, which are not necessarily frosty but which are sometimes humid and very mild. In spite of these periods of summer cold, the frost-free period at Port Nelson is about two months. At Fort George, it is 66 days; at Moose Factory, 81 days. Thus it is evident that cultivation of the more hardy vegetables is possible in most years right up to the margins of the Bay.

Autumn, like spring, is generally delayed somewhat, September being a fairly mild month, and October well above freezing except north of Port Nelson. The waters of the Bay, in autumn, serve as a mitigator reducing the extreme monthly ranges of temperature very considerably.

At Moose Factory, Churchill, and Fort George the extreme October ranges are 87, 77, and 38 degrees as compared with those for April of 104, 89, and 83 degrees, respectively. Real winter does not set in until the middle of November. This is a time when the moving cold waves begin to come down from the Mackenzie basin, with the warm front well south of the 55th parallel, indicated by winds with a strong northerly component. This is the time, also, when the Bay begins to lose even the little heat gained during the none too effective heating of summer, for tempera-

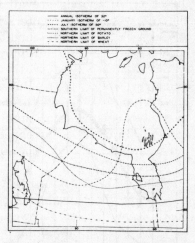

FIG. 46—Map of the Hudson Bay Region showing certain climatic features and the northern limit of specific crops. Adapted from Mecking.

tures of the waters probably never reach a point much above freezing except in the more shallow portions immediately along the shore.

Thus far only the narrow coastal stretches of land have been considered, for all the stations upon which this study is based are situated either directly on the coast or on the estuaries only a few miles removed from the Bay proper. It should be evident, however, that the same conditions do not obtain farther inland. There is a broad lowland zone, particularly to the south and west, which is a transition between the strictly continental climate of the Ontario upland and the Prairie Provinces, and the semi-marine climate of the Hudson Bay coasts. The gradual change to warmer summers is reflected in the natural vegetation of the zone: along the coast (excluding most

of James Bay) the summers are too short and cool to permit
tree development except in the most favored spots; but with
increasing distance from the coast, small spruce begin to appear
and shortly the whole landscape becomes densely forested. If
one proceeds southwest along the Nelson River, he finds the
average frost-free period increasing in length about one day
for each advance of 15 miles. To what extent other tempera-

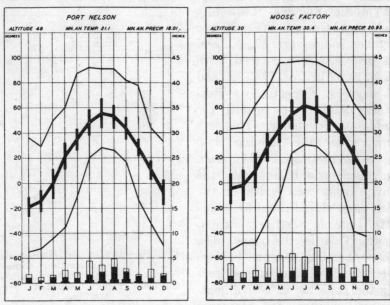

FIG. 47—Temperature and precipitation charts for Port Nelson and
Moose Factory.

ture conditions change is not definitely known, since there are
no regularly reporting meteorological stations in the zone. With
the completion of the Hudson Bay Railway, from The Pas to
Churchill, and the settlement of the region which the railway
will serve directly, doubtless the meteorological conditions will
become better understood. Nevertheless, some notion of the
climate may be gained by a comparison of the records for stations on the Bay with those of Fond du Lac (at the east end
of Lake Athabaska), The Pas and Norway House (in middle
Manitoba), and Fort Hope (on the Albany River in northern
Ontario). Kindle is inclined to the opinion that the decrease
in elevation from the Height of Land in Ontario to the James
Bay coastal plain and the proximity to that body of water more

than compensate for the higher latitude in the matter of temperature control. He also states that from September 12 to 13, 1929, nine inches of snow fell at Kapuskasing (well south of Moose Factory) and some near Lake Superior and east of Georgian Bay, but that the failure of this widespread snowfall to extend north into the James Bay coastal plain was noteworthy.[1]

The distribution of precipitation about Hudson Bay differs essentially from that of places farther south and west; that is,

ILLUS. 29—The limited forest areas (containing only small trees), alternating with muskeg, is indicative of short, cool summers, and hence frozen subsoil, throughout large sections of the Hudson Bay plains. This shows the Hudson Bay Railway and the Nelson River.

it takes on characteristics of both marine and continental types. The normal amount of precipitation is not far from 15 to 20 inches annually, more falling around James Bay than farther north. If the record at Fort George may be considered representative of conditions on the east coast, then it may be said that nearly 50 per cent of the annual total falls there in the winter half year with a distinct maximum in January and a secondary maximum in August and September, all months when westerly winds off the water predominate. With the exception of February and April, the precipitation is quite uniformly distributed with reference to months. On the south and west coasts, August and September are distinctly months of heavier precipitation, with the winter months comparatively dry. This

[1] E. M. Kindle, "The James Bay Coastal Plain," *Geogr. Rev.*, v. 15, 1925, pp. 235-6.

sort of distribution is also seen in the records for Fond du Lac, Norway House, Fort Hope, and even far into Quebec at Mistassini Port or at Fort Chimo on Ungava Bay—that is, at least two-thirds of the precipitation comes during the summer and autumn.

Dependability of rainfall is not an important economic factor in this province, because the lateness of the spring thaws and the relatively small evaporation factor assures sufficient moisture for the needs of the limited agriculture practiced. Moreover, hardly a month passes that measurable precipitation is not received. In a 33-year record at Moose Factory, the wettest year received about twice as much precipitation as the driest year. Compare with the 34-year record at Medicine Hat where the amount received in the wettest year was nearly three and one-half times that received in the driest year.

Of the total precipitation received annually around Hudson Bay, about one-third comes in the form of snow; and this, in spite of the fact that winter is a relatively dry season. The average annual snowfall amounts to approximately five feet around the margins of the Bay. As far south as Port Nelson, snow has been known to occur in every month, although it is rare in July and August. At Moose Factory none has been recorded for those months, and only a trace for September. The maximum appears to come in late fall and early winter. Excessively heavy snows do not occur in this region—at least, not as they do in middle Ontario and southern Quebec; the most ever observed around the Bay in any month is about three feet.

Concerning the character and course of the weather around Hudson Bay there is considerable conflict of opinion. Apparently, one year may differ radically from another, depending upon the amount and duration of ice in the Bay and the frequency and course of cyclones. It may be safely stated in general that late winter and early spring are often clear, calm and free from stormy days (see Table 25). The cloudiest days and the greatest frequency of rainy days come in late summer and early fall. Fogs generally occur with calm or light north winds. On the water, they are frequent in summer because, even on the finest and warmest days, the warmed air from the land mixing with the air over the cold water produces vapor. This condition persists through the summer into September; by that time the air is less heated, and the waters are not so cold. Later in the autumn, particularly near the shore, air coming off the water and in contact with the frozen ground or air over it, gives rise to "frost smoke." In winter, the same conditions will cause the air to be filled with icy spicules.[1] This phenomenon disappears as soon as ice forms to a considerable distance out from shore. Frost smoke is also common on the Bay itself and offers a serious handicap to navigation.[2]

From the climatic viewpoint there are doubtless agricultural possibilities for some parts of the wide transition zone mentioned earlier. The fact that the ground is never completely thawed is a serious obstacle—serious, because it prevents satisfactory drainage. To what depths deep frost and thaw penetrate is not definitely known; it is recognized, however, that conditions vary markedly from year to year. In a particularly favorable year, the soil may thaw down as much as four feet.[3] Waldo states that though there are trees and vegetation, the frost reaches to a depth of fifty-seven feet below the surface, and that in digging graves at Port Nelson they had to blast after reaching a depth of eighteen inches.[4] In constructing the railway to Churchill, considerable effort was expended without the aid of machinery in stripping off the thin layer of thawed muskeg. As the newly exposed surface thawed, a few more inches could be stripped away.[5] In Fig. 46 is shown the southern limit of permanently frozen ground; this chart also shows the northern limit of successful, though not necessarily commercially successful, cultivation of certain crops. One witness of conditions around Fort Albany on James Bay states that he had seen oats grow to perfection there; and that he had seen peas, turnips and cabbage growing in great plenty and perfection.[6] Another states that he saw very good potatoes and turnips growing in the gardens at Churchill.[7] Most authorities agree that along the south and west coasts certain native grasses grow sufficiently well for the support of cattle, and that cattle would do well if properly cared for. McKenna once stated that the cold at Nelson House in north central Manitoba was no more intense than that considerably farther south but

[1] *Contributions to Our Knowledge of the Meteorology of the Arctic Regions*, v. I, p. 2.
[2] McGrath, op. cit., p. 81.
[3] *Contributions to Our Knowledge of the Meteorology of the Arctic Regions*, v. I, p. 1.
[4] Fullerton Waldo, op. cit., p. 19.
[5] Lewis R. Freeman, "Farthest North by Railway," *World's Work*, v. 56, 1928, p. 314.
[6] E. J. Chambers, op. cit. pp. 33-4.
[7] Ibid, pp. 37-8.

that "frost sets in rather sooner, and tarries rather longer than it does at the north end of Lake Winnipeg. Roots and vegetables planted about May 24 do well and are gathered about September 15. The presence of so much water so regulates the temperature that there are few frosts either early or late

ILLUS. 30—Traveling over long distances in the Hudson Bay region of Northwest Territories necessitates temporary shelters. Mean temperatures above 50° for July permit forests of considerable size where drainage is good.

to make growth uncertain; yet, in my experience, wheat is not a sure crop. All depends on the season. Oats and barley will do well any time."[1]

Concerning the Lake St. Joseph district in northern Ontario, it was once reported[2]:

"The climate, in the immediate vicinity of the lake at all events, appears to be sufficiently good to admit of the growth of a variety of crops. At Osnaburgh House, near the east end, where the soil is of sandy nature, the principal crop cultivated at present is potatoes, but early Indian corn, peas, beans, and a variety of roots and other vegetables, to say nothing of a profusion of flowers, were in a flourishing condition at the end of July. In former years, when cattle were kept at the post, barley was said to have been a regular crop. Hay grows very

[1] Ibid., p. 37.
[2] Ibid., p. 38.

luxuriantly.   I was creditably informed that pumpkins and muskmelons had frequently ripened at this establishment.

"Doctor Bell, before the Senate committee of 1887, testified: 'Potatoes and all such vegetables would grow in Hudson bay district, but the immediate influence of the sea is unfavorable for gardens.   Gardens close to the sea do not flourish as well as gardens inland.   The frequent change from heat to cold and the fogs from the sea prejudicially affect them, and cause a sort of blight on vegetation close to the sea shore.   But a few miles inland vegetation is more rank, and you can grow potatoes and ordinary root crops.   There are plenty of grasses there to keep cattle and sheep.   There are many kinds of grasses there, also sedges, wild peas or vetches and lentils. They would make splendid feed for cattle.' "

The climatic conditions about James Bay are thus summarized by Kindle[1]:

"Mr. Ward, agent of Revillon Freres at Moose Factory, states that he has observed a temperature of 99° inside his office, which has a southern exposure.   The transient visitor, however, finds a good index of the coastal-plain climate in the luxuriant gardens kept by the post managers and the Mission at Moose Factory.   These show that all of the vegetables, including tomatoes, except corn and certain other heat-loving plants commonly grown in the Ottawa valley, do well in the Moose River valley except in the occasional seasons when summer frosts occur.

"A number of late-blooming plants were seen in blossom throughout the latter half of September on the coastal plain. Five plants in full bloom collected at Tom King rapid, Missinaibi River, on October 1 indicate that winter does not follow summer so precipitately in the James Bay region as is often supposed by dwellers in the south.   More delightful weather than that encountered during the latter half of September, on the coastal plain would be hard to find.   The mosquito and the black fly both disappear early in September, enabling one in early autumn to enjoy fully the mellow yellow tints of the poplars which deepen day by day.   The forests never attain the brilliance, however, of those of southern Ontario owing to the absence of the maple.

"The first frost seen by the writer this season (1923) came on September 3, but it was too light materially to check the growth of the potatoes at New Post.   In 1900 Niven and Burrows report the first frosts observed by them on the James Bay slope to have occurred September 6 and 9.   Ice usually closes the rivers early in November.   The lower Abitibi is reported to have been open for canoes till November 19 in 1922.   James

[1] Kindle, op. cit. p. 236.

Bay freezes over for a distance of many miles from shore in midwinter. It is reported that snow melts and the rivers open during the latter half of April."

Some notion of a year's weather in Hudson Bay itself may be gained from the following summary of conditions on the Belcher Islands as reported by Flaherty[1]:

"The climate of the islands differs widely from that of the opposite mainland. Compared with weather reports from Great Whale River for the same period, our observations gave

ILLUS. 31—The Pas is a thriving town of west central Manitoba and has developed in a clime too severe for commercial agriculture. Business in connection with the Hudson Bay Railway and the mineral wealth of the Flin Flon region has caused permanent homes to be established in this region of rigorous climate.

a far greater proportion of overcast skies and fogs, stronger and more constant winds, but higher and more equable temperatures. From October till early December winds of a velocity up to 50 miles were almost constant, and the sky was continuously overcast.

"No snow covered the ground permanently until November 15, and no ice was formed in the small lakes near the wintering base until December 4, when the long period of winds ceased and a fortnight of calm, clear weather set in. The mercury did not fall below zero until January 2—a weather condition without precedent in my experience of the North. Great Whale River early in December had a minimum temperature of –30° and recorded a constant average for the period well below zero.

[1] R. J. Flaherty, "The Belcher Islands of Hudson Bay," *Geogr. Rev.*, v. 5, 1918, pp. 543-4. Used by permission.

"On January 2 winter commenced in earnest. The month was characterized by constant drifting winds of a maximum force of 70 miles; calm days were unknown; and the average temperature was −16°. In February the winds abated; there were many days of sunshine, a few of them almost calm. The average temperature for the month was −19°. Throughout March strong winds again prevailed; by the end of the month the snowfall for the winter had reached its maximum, 4 feet; the average temperature for the month rose to −9°. In April and May there was the usual prevalence of wind, and several blizzards occurred, each covering a period of from one to two days. In the latter part of May the weather broke and became warm and summery; in fact there were heavy thunderstorms at this time. On May 28 sledging over the ice fields was at an end, and by June 10 the field ice surrounding the islands had blown off to southward. Then commenced the most trying time of the year; for hardly two days together did fair weather obtain. From mid-June onward to the time of our departure on September 13 exceedingly heavy gales of wind of from one to three days duration occurred in every week. The prevailing direction of the winds was south-southwest for not only that period but for the entire year. Days of sunshine were rare; the sky was generally overcast; and rains, accompanied usually by heavy southeast winds, were frequent. According to the natives the weather we experienced during that year was not at all typical; usually, they said, the winds were fewer and less violent, and the temperature during the winter was lower. The remarkable lateness of the freeze-up (December 23) was, they said, without precedent. The minimum temperature for the winter was −48° as compared with the lowest reported temperature on the mainland of −55°. The maximum thickness of fresh-water ice was 5½ feet, and of sea ice 5 feet. The maximum temperature for the summer, occurring on July 25 at noon, was 70°."

THE WESTERN LAURENTIAN UPLAND

Of all the subregions of interior Canada, the western Laurentian upland has the most diverse climatic characteristics. For the most part, the climate is more continental than its geographic position would indicate; it is, perhaps, more severe in winter than its latitude alone would suggest. Where water bodies are large, both summer and winter conditions are somewhat ameliorated, particularly around the shores of Lake Superior and James Bay. Where high altitude is aided by exposure to prevailing winds, winter conditions are exceptionally severe. Everywhere, the variable relief gives rise to conditions which may be strictly local, though not the less extreme.

In a broad sense, the climate may be said to be cold and moderately quiet, though snowy, in winter, and cool and quiet in summer (Table 25). Spring and autumn are seasons of extremely rapid change in point of temperature; both are seasons of considerable storminess, late autumn in particular. The climate is marked by a relatively large percentage of possible sunshine in summer, which suggests also the fact that summer is the least cloudy season, the average cloudiness being less than 50%. February and March are likewise quite clear, with averages under 50%. Autumn is the cloudy time of year, when the percentage may reach as high as 75%.

No month is colder than January, although February may at times show equally extreme conditions. Mean temperatures for the former month have a range of nearly 20 degrees over the province, Fort Hope in northern Ontario having the lowest mean temperature, −8.7°. This station is doubtless typical of the whole northwest highland portion of Ontario. Only slightly milder conditions, typified by Mistassini Post, obtain on the upland of south-central Quebec. The moderating effect of Lake Superior is seen at Port Arthur where the January mean is some 15 degrees higher than that at Fort Hope. For places located in the upper Ottawa Valley, January mean temperatures do not depart widely from 0°.

The diurnal ranges in winter temperatures are large over most of the area, from 20 to more than 30 degrees. The greater ranges occur about as frequently as the passage of well-developed highs and lows across the region. The fact that winds from the southeast, south or southwest blow at least 20% of the time in winter would indicate frequent periods of mild weather. This is reflected in the maximum temperature. Indeed, most stations may expect at least one day in every other January with temperatures above freezing; and occasionally 45° or more may be experienced. On the other hand, the frequent visitations of cold air from the northwest send mean minimum temperatures well below zero; and there is no winter when −20° is not experienced. The lowest on record fall below −40° for all parts of the region; −54° has been recorded at Fort Hope and Mistassini Post, and −60° at White River, Ontario, and Doucet, Quebec. White River likewise comes very near the Canadian record for mean daily ranges of temperature, with 30.7 degrees for March; this record is exceeded only by Fort

Vermilion, Alta., with a mean daily range of 30.8 degrees. Such extremely low temperatures as come to this station, located about 50 miles northeast of Lake Superior, must be attributed to its altitude and location almost on the Height of Land, giving exposure to the cold waves of the northwest. Since average wind velocities here rarely exceed four miles per hour, the low temperatures may be due, not entirely to cold winds, but also

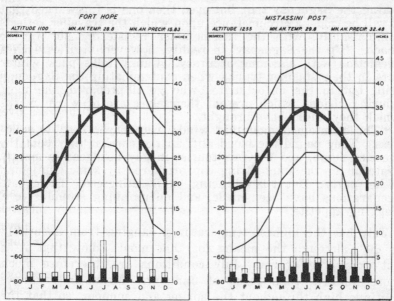

FIG. 48—Temperature and precipitation charts for Fort Hope and Mistassini Post.

to the snow cover and radiation during clear nights when the air is relatively dry. Lack of air drainage is doubtless an additional factor. The extremes experienced by White River are probably not unusual for this Laurentian land. Fort Hope, 250 miles to the northwest, Kapuskasing, and Doucet, are close rivals. Most of these places have had zero temperatures in every month from October to May inclusive. Zero temperatures, however, are rarely experienced in any part of the region between April and October inclusive.

The breakup of winter toward the end of March, and the arrival of summer by the first of June leave but a short spring —shorter in the northern portion of the region than in the southern. Consequently the change from winter to summer

conditions is very rapid. June, however, is not always free
from frost; in fact, at White River, frost is to be expected in
more than half of the years. Many miles directly eastward in
the Lake St. John district, one traveller describes the apparently not unusual conditions experienced on a trip up the
Saguenay River during summer[1]:

"For obvious reasons midsummer is the accepted season for
taking the Saguenay trip, but even then one is forewarned that
it will be cold—a circumstance upon which the traveller reflects
complaisantly, with the thermometer registering 90° in the
shade. 'Up the Saguenay' in reality, however, verifies such a
prediction with alarming accuracy. Canny folks pack winter
furs in their steamer trunks when contemplating the Saguenay
trip; but to the unfortunates who go ill-prepared, the most
alluring visions which present themselves are of warm wraps
which they might have brought.

"Those untamed mountain winds were never bred to mildness. They pound the blood stiff in the cheeks; they beat the
muscles numb, and the fair tourist in gay headgear is meekly
grateful for the snug-fitting cap proffered by some gentleman
of her party. But it is a bracing, exhilarating cold, if adequate
preparations have been made, and an unfailing stimulus to a
flagging appetite."

July has the highest temperatures, ranging from about 61°
to 66°, although the means for that month show that it is
not excessively warm. July conditions are, therefore much
more uniform than those of January. Mean daily ranges
continue high throughout the spring and summer, so that the
tendency toward late spring, and even mid-summer, frosts is
always present, unless a water body is present to moderate a
cold snap. On the other hand, extremely high temperatures
are not uncommon, not only in summer, but in spring and early
autumn as well, temperatures of 80° or more having been
recorded at most stations from April to September inclusive.
All stations have recorded 90° in at least one month—even 99°
at Fort Hope; and temperatures above 80° are to be expected
every year throughout the region. In spite of these exceedingly
high and low temperatures of summer, the extreme ranges are
much greater in winter. Thus at Fort Hope, these ranges
approach 100 degrees in winter but only about 70 degrees in
summer. These ranges are fairly typical of the whole region.

[1] Mary S. Williams, "Up the Far-Famed Saguenay," *The Canadian Magazine*, v. 29, 1907, p. 329.

As would be expected, the greatest range, 113 degrees in December, occurs at White River.

Though spring is a short season, autumn is even shorter. Summer is everywhere definitely passed by the middle of September; and winter arrives early in November. For most of the region, only October of the autumn months has a mean temperature as high as between 32° and 50°; but even in this month, freezing temperatures occur every year. Of all the year, however, the so-called autumn months have the smallest mean daily ranges of temperature, dropping to as low as 13 degrees, which is barely two-thirds of the spring ranges. Yet, these small ranges are not so significant with respect to the frost hazard as are those in the spring. Except in the Ottawa-James Bay depression, the first frost comes, on the average, early in September. Consequently, a sharp drop in temperature after that date means little economic loss to crops. The average frost-free period over the entire district varies greatly: as low as 81 days in the north around Fort Hope; as high as 111 days at Lake Superior and in the upper Ottawa Valley.

Summer is the rainiest season over most of this Laurentian Upland, and autumn receives more precipitation than either winter or spring. July is the month of maximum precipitation in the Ontario section. Farther to the east, the maximum is delayed until August, September or even October. Of the less than 20 inches annual total of precipitation in the northwest, nearly 50% comes in the months of May to August inclusive. Farther east and south where the amounts increase to 25 and 30 inches, these months receive less than 40% of the year's supply. The actual amounts, however, in these months increase both east and south. Thus, the whole region receives sufficient rainfall during the growing season for all forms of agriculture practised, the decreased temperatures to the north making the decreased amounts of rain quite effective. The climate becomes increasingly humid with progress eastward into Quebec.

North of the 50th parallel, more than a third of the total precipitation comes in the form of snow; and the amount will hardly run less than one-fourth for the rest of the region. The snowiest month may be November, December or January; rarely is it later, and never earlier. Snow in measurable quantities is to be expected from October to May inclusive—even

ILLUS. 32—These large spruce trees near Lake St. John, Quebec, are indicative of the abundantly moist, though cool, summers of the Laurentian upland. The heavy snows of the long winters aid in the exploitation of these timber resources.

over a longer period in the extreme northwestern and northeastern limits of the region. The average annual amounts of snowfall vary with relief and exposure from 60 to 120 inches in the northern portions and from as little as 36 inches at Port Arthur to more than 150 inches at the east end of Lake Superior. Brooks has shown diagramatically the detailed effects of the Great Lakes and winds on the distribution of snowfall near their borders. He has found that early in winter the snowfall of the immediate shores is generally less than that at a short distance inland; although later in winter the snowfall near the shore tends to more nearly equal that of the higher land.[1] Heavy snows are frequent in south-central Quebec, as much as five feet falling in a single month. At the eastern end of Lake Superior nearly seven feet has been recorded in a single month. The difficulties of rail transportation under such conditions are real, as the Canadian National and Canadian Pacific Railways have discovered.

In certain years, rainfall may be so greatly reduced during the growing season as to affect crops seriously; this is particularly true in middle Ontario. The practice of agriculture has been quite local in character and quite largely confined to garden stuff or forage crops so that the dependability of precipitation has not become an important question agriculturally. Certain forms of agriculture are becoming quite important in the clay belt with the settlement of the region through the development of the mining industry. The failure of rain, especially during summer and early autumn, which does sometimes occur, is, therefore, of considerable economic significance. This failure of rain also permits the development and spread of forest fires over vast areas. Every traveler in this dominantly forest land reports the devastating results of these fires. The fact that the forests were virtually intact before the white man came is an indication that the fires were not started by lightning, though over most of the region thunderstorms average two to four a month from June to September. Fortunately for the forest rangers, strong winds and gales are infrequent. It is of interest to know that the amount of precipitation in the wettest year rarely exceeds twice that of the driest. Months with excessively heavy rainfall are unknown, the greatest amount on record being 9.21 inches during one July at Port Arthur. On account of the small evaporation, however, some years have been so wet that crops in the clay belt were ruined or left in the fields on account of the difficulty of harvesting.

The number of days on which measurable precipitation falls is quite variable. In the far northwestern portion, as typified by Fort Hope, the number averages 110; at Abitibi, in the Ottawa-James Bay depression, only about 85; in the Quebec portion and middle Ontario, 140 to 145. At Port Arthur where the prevailing winds are offshore, the number is only 100. In every case the greatest frequency comes in fall. Throughout

[1] C. F. Brooks, "The Snowfall of the Eastern United States," *Monthly Weather Review*. v. 43, 1915, pp. 8-9.

the region, the number of rainy days exceeds the number of snowy days by from 10 to 40.

In certain portions of the northern sector of the Ontario upland, the short, cool summer and the low water temperatures do not permit decay of the sphagnum moss which is said to accumulate to depths of from two to ten feet in muskegs, consequently such areas are unsuitable for any kind of crop.[1]

ILLUS. 33—The excessively cold winters and occasional summer frosts have not prevented prosperity from coming to this farm in the Lake Temiskaming district of the Laurentian upland in eastern Ontario.

McInnes states that where soil conditions permit, only small gardens are maintained with any success, although timothy and clover grow almost luxuriantly. He adds further[2]:

"The climate, as would be expected in these latitudes, and in a wilderness country approximately a thousand feet above sea-level, is somewhat severe. The summer temperature, though on occasional days rising as high as 85° Fahr., averages very much lower, and the nights are practically always cool. Frosty nights often continue into the early summer, and recur again in the autumn before most grain crops would be ready for harvesting."

Where the altitude is under 1000 feet and where exposure is not adverse, the growing of the more hardy vegetables and even certain cereals becomes increasingly profitable with progress eastward as well as southward, particularly where water bodies

[1] Chambers, op. cit., p. 48.
[2] Ibid., p. 48-9.

are of sufficient size to permit a certain, though limited, degree of amelioration. Thus, Bell found the climate around Lake St. Joseph to be mild enough to admit of a variety of crops, among them potatoes, early Indian corn, peas, beans, and other vegetables.[1]

The greatest handicap to settlement and exploitation of this western Laurentian upland is the same which applies to the other humid muskeg and forest portions of middle and eastern Canada, namely the mosquito. During the months of June, July, and August, the weary traveller is seldom free from its vexing and troublesome presence. Every visitor from the region returns with the same disturbing tale. This writer is perhaps more cogent than the average, yet none the less truthful.[2]

"The least said about the first night in camp at Pakitanika the better. We said more than enough at the time. The answer is mosquitos. When the door was opened they met us in myriad swarms with loud buzzes of welcome. We lighted smudges, we slung bed nets, we smeared hands and faces with dope, perhaps we swore a little, but the one thing we did not do that night was sleep."

Fortunately, protection from this annoying insect, and the still more annoying black fly, is not impossible; and the traveller who goes properly prepared experiences a minimum of inconvenience.

THE LOWER LAKE REGION AND ST. LAWRENCE VALLEY

Latitude, water and the storm control are the chief determinants in the climate of this narrow region, an appreciable portion of which extends farther south than any other part of Canada—the southernmost extremity even to the latitude of northern California, Chicago or Providence. Two subdivisions of the region are distinguishable: the Ontario Peninsula extending northward to about the 46th parallel; and the Ottawa and St. Lawrence valleys.

The climate of the Ontario Peninsula resembles very markedly that of lower Michigan or western New York. The waters of Lakes Huron, Erie, and Ontario serve as decided amelioraters of climate and render the seasons of the Peninsula

[1] Ibid., p. 38.
[2] Albert Britt, "Hunting for the Movies," *Outing*, v. 74, p. 11.

even less extreme than any portion of the interior of the United States in the same latitude but not similarly situated with respect to water bodies. Farther north, the influence of the lake waters is much reduced; altitude becomes of much significance; and the climate gradually merges into that of the Laurentian upland. With progress down the St. Lawrence Valley, there is increase in latitude and a consequent decrease in the general temperature level. Since the region lies in the most frequented storm path on the continent, the cyclonic control is everywhere dominant, and variableness of the daily weather, especially in winter is the rule. There may be sharp changes of temperature but the periods of extreme conditions are not prolonged—that is, there are no long periods of severely cold nor of excessively warm weather.

Stupart characterizes the climate of the Peninsula as follows[1]:

"The climate of the peninsula of Ontario is much warmer than that of the northern parts of the province. It is true that the first part of March is usually rather cold, but bright sunshiny days and swelling buds, together with the rapid disappearance of the snow which now lies only in sheltered places, give omen of spring, which soon comes on apace. Light snowfalls occasionally occur in April but this month with a mean temperature of about 43°, 3 inches of rain, and 190 hours of bright sunshine, is truly spring, and before the close of the month wild flowers are in bloom and trees are leafing out.

"With a high percentage of bright sunshine and ample rain, vegetation makes rapid progress during May. Frosts are quite infrequent, and by about the 24th of the month most of the trees are in full leaf.

"The summers, while warm, are not oppressively so, the mean temperature of July, at the more southern stations, being but a shade above 70°, and a few degrees lower in June and August. Wholly overcast and rainy days are of rare occurrence, the rain falling in showers and thunderstorms of short duration; indeed from the middle of June until the end of August we may expect no day without a few sunny hours. The autumn sets in very gradually, and while frost may sometimes occur as early as September 20, it is usually well on in October before there is anything severe, and toward the end of November before the mean daily temperature falls to the freezing point.

"Northward and eastward from Lake Ontario to the Ottawa valley the spring opens somewhat later than in the south, but from mid-April until the end of August, the temperature and rainfall are much the same as in the southern part of the prov-

[1] R. F. Stupart, "The Climate of Canada," *The Handbook of Canada*, University of Toronto Press, Toronto, 1924, pp. 111-112.

ince, modified in certain districts by the effect of higher altitude, and in others by lying to the eastward of and in proximity to the Great Lakes. September, however, shows a more rapid downward trend of temperature. Killing frosts occur at an earlier date and the whole northern country is usually covered with snow before the close of November, while all the southern counties are still bare."

Along Lake Erie, winter (mean temperatures below freezing) is barely three months long; at Toronto, this season increases to four months; and in the northern portion of the region it is still further extended to five months. The mean January temperatures for the northern and southern margins of the division show the greatest extremes: e. g., Port Dover, 22°; and Algonquin Park, 8°. For the southern half of the region, hardly a winter passes in which temperatures above freezing are not recorded; indeed temperatures of 50° are frequent. In the northern half, increasing latitude and increasing distance from the Lakes limit maximum temperatures in most years to perhaps 35° or 40°. Minimum temperatures reach the extreme limit most frequently in February, and in most years they fall well below zero. Every year Toronto experiences temperatures of lower than 10°, the extreme minimum in 87 years being –26°. Parry Sound, in spite of its situation on the east side of Georgian Bay, has had an extreme minimum of –38°; although in half the years not lower than –20° is to be expected.

As in the northern upland of Ontario, spring comes quickly and is of short duration. For most of this region, only April has a mean between freezing and 50°. May is distinctly a mild month, and temperatures of 90° or higher in that month are not unknown. On the other hand, freezing temperatures are frequent. South of the 44th parallel frost does not occur on the average after the first week in May; at Parry Sound, frosts continue about 10 days longer.

Summer temperatures are much more uniform over this district than are those of winter, the means for July over the entire area varying only three degrees. Mean daily ranges in summer, however, are equal to or exceed those of winter. All parts of the region, except those portions where water bodies exert a pronounced moderating influence, have recorded temperatures of more than 100°; although, on the average, the extreme maxima do not go much above 90°. Except for the far northern portion, June, July, and August are free from frost; and, in normal years, frost does not come until after the middle of September.

September, like May, is a mild month; October is characteristically autumn, the mean for the month averaging not far from 47° over the entire Peninsula. November with a mean of 12 to 15 degrees lower and occasional minima of zero becomes

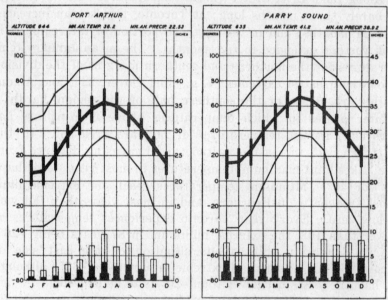

FIG. 49—Temperature and precipitation charts for Port Arthur and Parry Sound.

a winter month for all parts except along the margins of Lake Erie and southern Lake Huron. Although Lake Ontario, like the other Great Lakes, never freezes over, the harbors are usually ice-bound for a part of the winter at least. At Toronto, the harbor is frozen 90 days, closing, on the average, December 26 and being free from ice again March 25.

The mean annual precipitation for the whole Peninsula does not depart widely from 30 inches; and its distribution by months is remarkably uniform, particularly near the Lakes, as is seen in the records for Toronto. Moreover, the precipitation shows a high degree of dependability from year to year, illustrated again by Toronto; in fact, this section has the most reliable rainfall in all Canada. On account of the varied location of stations with respect to exposure and water bodies, the month of maximum precipitation, on the average, differs considerably; at Port Dover, it is January; at Pelee Island, May; at Madawaska, July; at Toronto, September; at Parry Sound, December. The month of minimum precipitation shows nearly as much variability. These features are not so significant as they might seem because of the pronounced uniformity of the monthly distribution; any month of the year may be unusually wet or dry. Along the east shores of Lake Huron, from which the westerly winds can pick up large quantities of vapor from the relatively warm water, fully two-fifths of the annual precipitation comes in the form of snow; along the lower margins of the Peninsula, only one-fifth; in the highland lake section, about one-fourth. Five feet of snow in one month is not unknown along Lake Huron, and even as far south and east as Toronto.

The monthly distribution of the number of days with measurable precipitation does not show such a close relation to the amount of rain and snow as might be expected; that is, December tends to be the most inclement month with rain or snow on half the days. June, July, and August on the average have about one day in three rainy. Winter is likewise the cloudiest season with an average percentage of 70 to 75. Summer is characterized by a preponderance of fair days, the percentage of cloudiness being 45 to 50, and the percentage of possible sunshine ranging from 55 to 65. There is a greater frequency and intensity of cyclonic storms in the winter half-year with higher wind velocities for that season. This is borne out by the record at Toronto where the average wind movement from December to February is 13.5 miles per hour (only 8.2 from June to August) and the average number of days with gales is six (only one in summer). Farther north, winds are much lighter, the average at Parry Sound being 10.5 miles per hour in October and 6.5 in July. Table 25 shows the percentage frequencies of the different weather types.

The climate of the lower Ottawa and St. Lawrence valleys differs from that of the lower Ontario Lake Region chiefly in its greater degree of winter cold. Montreal has a January mean nine degrees lower than Toronto, and Quebec 12 degrees lower. The extremes to which temperatures drop are also appreciably lower for Montreal and decidedly lower for Quebec, the record at the latter being –34°. On the other hand, the St. Lawrence Valley experiences mild periods in winter quite as frequently and to almost the same degree as the lower Peninsula.

A noteworthy characteristic of the region of the lower Ottawa and St. Lawrence valleys is the remarkable uniformity of the monthly or seasonal climate from one year to another, the greatest difference in the means of either January or July being

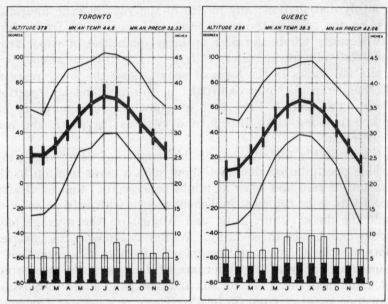

FIG. 50—Temperature and precipitation charts for Toronto and Quebec.

only three degrees. The mean daily ranges are likewise very nearly the same, although Quebec has a mean annual temperature four degrees lower than that of Ottawa or Montreal. This may be attributable to the heavier snowcover of Quebec which would delay the advance of spring there.

The effect of the higher latitude of Quebec compared with Montreal is seen in the length of the frost free period, 135 days at the former, and 168 days at the latter. At Montreal, on the average, both May and September are free from frost; at Quebec, spring frosts are to be expected until the middle of May and autumn frosts after the 11th of September. The St. Lawrence at Montreal is closed to navigation in normal years about December 16, and is not open again until April 21.

The amount of precipitation is another characteristic differentiating the Lower Lake Region from the lower St. Lawrence Valley, Quebec receiving about ten inches more annually than Toronto. April is the driest month, although the average is well above two inches. There is no well-defined month of max-

ILLUS. 34—Climatic conditions are almost ideal for general farming in the portion of Quebec lying just north of New York and Vermont.

imum precipitation, and the summer half-year receives almost precisely the same amount as the winter half-year. At Montreal, December, January, and July are months of maximum precipitation; at Quebec, July and September; and at Ottawa, June and July. Snowfall increases with progress down the Ottawa and St. Lawrence valleys; the average amount ranges from about 70 to nearly 150 inches. The snowfall of the lower St. Lawrence is heavy near Quebec and in parts of the highlands (see Fig. 6). Exceptionally heavy snowfalls are no more common here than in the Peninsula; but because of fewer winter thaws, the St. Lawrence district has a fairly persistent snowcover which tends to increase in depth until March.

The annual number of days on which measurable precipitation falls varies directly with the annual amount of rain or snow, the average number for Montreal and Quebec being 156 and 162, respectively. More than half the days of January and only a third or less of the days of August have snow or rain; and the number of snowy days in a year is about twice the

ILLUS. 35—The ameliorating influence of the Great Lakes permits peach and apple orcharding on a large scale in the southern part of the Ontario Peninsula.

number of rainy days. The lower St. Lawrence is cloudier than the upper valleys or the Lake Region, the average cloudiness ranging from 62% in August to 76% in November; this is reflected in the average per cent of possible sunshine (Quebec annual, 38%; Ottawa annual, 44%). Storminess likewise increases toward the northeast; the average wind velocities at Montreal and Quebec are almost twice those at Ottawa and a third greater than those at Toronto.

The advance of spring in the St. Lawrence Valley, although characterized in some years by a slowly melting snowcover, is none the less rapid. Likewise, summer gives way to winter with equally surprising rapidity. The course of the seasons at Montreal is described by Stupart as follows[1]:

"March is essentially a winter month, but April is on the mean nearly as warm as in Toronto, the May normal is higher and the summer months are all slightly warmer than in Toronto. The September and October normals are both quite similar to the corresponding figures for southwestern Ontario, but

ILLUS. 36—A long growing season is necessary for a tobacco crop like this one grown in the southwestern end of the peninsula of Ontario.

in November the thermometer shows a more rapid downward trend, and then follows a winter with a normal temperature 10° lower than in Toronto. For four months the ground is usually covered with a depth of between one and three feet of snow. Eastward in the St. Lawrence valley the summers are cooler and the winters decidedly colder, and with the retardation of the opening of spring, consequent upon a higher latitude and the more gradual melting of a snow covering, it is not until May that the leafing of the trees is at all rapid; mid-September, too, usually sees the brilliant autumnal colouration of the foliage."

Some features of the climate of the Lower St. Lawrence are vividly, though perhaps somewhat extravagantly, portrayed in the following excerpt[2]:

"The control of the weather is decidedly cyclonic. The most persistent wind is the southwestern. We do not need a wind-

[1] Ibid., p. 113.
[2] Roderick Peattie, "Climate in the Lower St. Lawrence Valley," *Bull. Geogr. Soc.,* Philadelphia, v. 21, 1923, pp. 33-4.

rose to point this out to us when all travellers in the region must observe that wooden windmills are set fixedly toward the southwest. The habit of the wind is acquired not only from the prevailing continental tendency, but also the river channel must aid in directing it to this persistent direction. Especially on the upper estuary, the winds may change with the tides. In

ILLUS. 37—Numerous cyclonic storms bring heavy snowfalls to southern Ontario and make transportation difficult.

Quebec-Labrador there is a northeast wind that is very severe and that may hold for a week at a time.

"Spring in the Lower St. Lawrence blooms suddenly and gloriously. As soon as the snows are off the ground (in Quebec this is in the beginning of April), the fields take on their first green, and develop quickly. The suddenness of the season is accompanied by a delightful lack of rain. Winter comes all the way to meet the summer, and summer is not shy. The foliage develops in a fortnight. The summer heat is not oppressive before August, and in the north never is so. The heavy covering of winter snow prevents the ground from freezing deeply. The capuchin of winter is hardly cast aside before the farmer is bare-armed and bare-chested in the fields. At Betsiamis and beyond, the season is seriously retarded and the trees do not begin to bud until early June, nor is the ground warm enough for early planting.

"The rapidity of the approach of summer may be seen in the celerity with which the ice breaks up. About Quebec and the Ile d' Orleans the ice is thick enough to make a common roadway for man and beast. One may awake to find the firm ice of the day before now restless and dangerous. A few -hours and the ice begins to disappear. Suddenly, with little warning, it is gone. To quote a typical example: on the 16th of April of a certain year it was safe for driving, on the 19th it could be used for walking only, by the 21st open spaces had appeared, and on the 24th canoes were being freely used on the water.

"The summer is blessed with a sufficiency of rain. With so short a summer the farmer must work with intense and

ILLUS. 38.—A normal winter scene in Quebec.

unremitting energy. There is little social life other than that which the laborers enjoy in the fields. Winter comes all too soon. A single maple on the hill flies a scarlet signal and the country-side breaks forth in color. The harvest must be hastened, for shortly the snow advances and the world capitulates to winter.

"The winter is severe. Throughout the western portions, however, the cold is dry and invigorating. In the woods the lumbermen wear two and three flannel shirts at a time and as many pairs of trousers. Without a wind a temperature of plus 10 degrees to minus 10 degrees is not uncomfortable. Most of the cabins are actually in the woods or at the edge of the forest and fuel may be found in the door-yard.

"The most disagreeable part of the year is November, a cold and gloomy month. The temperature is low and the relative humidity high, causing sleet storms. I have wondered whether or not it were possible that many of the larger islands of the St. Lawrence were uninhabited because of the high sensible temperatures of the damp winter's winds directly from off the river, rather than because of the difficulties of communication. Sleighing in Lower Canada is said to be of five months' duration as against two in Upper Canada."

CHAPTER VII

EASTERN CANADA AND NEWFOUNDLAND

The transition from the strictly continental climate of interior Canada to the modified marine type of the eastern shores is a broad and fluctuating zone. At times, and especially in winter, the extreme cold and dryness of the interior is brought by west and northwest winds to the very edge of the continent. At other times, the moderating influence of the Atlantic and the Gulf Stream are carried many miles inland on a persistent south or southwest wind. The average of these two extremes gives much of this region what may be termed a littoral climate.

If the Labrador is excepted, all parts of the region experience winters that are mild, at least for their latitude, mean January temperatures ranging from about 8° to 24°. Winter lingers long and gives way only gradually to spring which, in turn, may last well into June. Summers are not hot; they are even disagreeably cool in the northern portions. As far as temperatures are concerned, the summers are short, and become increasingly shorter with increase in latitude, so that they are barely present as far north as Labrador. Thus, autumn conditions follow rather closely those of spring; they continue through October and, in certain favored places, into December. The slowness with which the marine ice disappears and the sea warms favors high pressure in spring over the waters to the east of this region, so that chilling winds with a strong easterly component are frequent from March to June. By fall, however, the waters have become appreciably warmer than in spring, their warmth in contrast to the rapidly cooling land favoring low pressure and consequent southwesterly winds. Thus, autumn, with October at least 10 degrees warmer than April, compensates in a measure for the unfavorableness of spring.

In spite of the fact that much of this region is in or near the paths of cyclonic storms, there are probably more quiet days than windy ones, as is indicated by Table 26. Eastport, Maine, is fairly representative of the southern portion of the region, and St. Johns of the extreme eastern littoral. It will

170

be noted from this table that in winter most of the days are classed as cold, half of the days are classed as fair, and only a quarter of them as windy; and that, in combination, more than half are either cold, fair and quiet, or cold, snowy and quiet, while only about one-sixth are cold, snowy and windy. In summer, few of the days may be considered as hot, more than half of them as fair, and five per cent or less as windy; from a third to a half of all the days are moderately cool, fair and quiet.

TABLE 26. PERCENTAGE FREQUENCIES OF WEATHER TYPES REPRESENTATIVE OF EASTERN CANADA AND NEWFOUNDLAND

	Winter		Summer	
	Eastport	St. Johns	Eastport	St. Johns
Cold	83	79		
Cool	17	21	4	23
Moderate			87	67
Hot			1	10
Fair	56	49	66	58
Windy	31	26	3	5
Cold; Snowy; Quiet	16	18		
Cold; Fair; Windy	13	9		
Cold; Fair; Quiet	37	36		
Cold; Snowy; Windy	18	15		
Cool; Rainy	10	17	3	13
Cool; Fair; Windy	1	2		
Cool; Fair; Quiet	5	2	1	10
Moderate; Rainy			30	27
Moderate; Fair; Windy			3	4
Moderate; Fair; Quiet			54	35
Hot; Rainy				1
Hot; Fair; Quiet			1	8

In spite of the strong marine influence, latitude is a determining control of considerable importance in the climate of this region. New Brunswick, Prince Edward Island, and Nova Scotia, comprise an area which has very similar climatic characteristics throughout, due in large measure to its small range of latitude, from 43.5 to 48.0 degrees. The maritime portions of Quebec including Anticosti Island, the Gaspe Peninsula, and the south shore of the Labrador Peninsula, with a latitudinal range of only four degrees, likewise have a climate which varies only slightly from one section to another. Newfoundland, surrounded on all sides by water, is a distinct entity and has characteristics peculiar to its marine location. The coast of Labrador, in spite of its large range of eight degrees of latitude, has strikingly similar climatic characteristics throughout its extent, a fact attributable to the Labrador Current along its shores. The essential features of the climate of each of these four sub-regions will be taken up in turn.

THE ATLANTIC PROVINCES

New Brunswick, Nova Scotia and Prince Edward Island comprise the so-called Atlantic Provinces. Their combined area of 51,000 square miles is approximately equivalent to that of England or New York State. The configuration of the coast-lines of Prince Edward Island and Nova Scotia is such that there is no point in either of these provinces which is more than 35 miles from the sea. Two-thirds of the total periphery of New Brunswick is washed by ocean waters. It is the warming effect of the sea which keeps the mean January temperatures of Nova Scotia everywhere between 20° and 24°—about the same as those of Central New York, from two to five degrees of latitude farther south. The January means all along the southern coast, from Sydney to Yarmouth, do not differ by as much as one degree. Prince Edward Island, located in the lee of New Brunswick and Nova Scotia, experiences winter conditions slightly more severe and roughly equivalent to those of the upper St. Lawrence. The New Brunswick shores begin to resume continental characteristics, with mean temperatures for January ten degrees below those of Nova Scotia; while the northwestern interior, not only because of its greater distance from the sea but also because of its greater altitude, has winters as severe as those of Quebec. Where the marine influence is strongest, February is fully as cold as January, and March and April only slightly warmer than December and November, respectively.

A significant feature of the winters of these three provinces is their relatively small daily ranges of temperature, the average varying from 13 in November and December to 23 degrees in February. It is evident, therefore, that the extremes of temperature are correspondingly moderate—certainly, very moderate compared with those for the same latitudes on the Great Plains of the United States. Except in the interior of New Brunswick, there is never a winter during which the temperature does not reach at least as high as 32°; even 60° has been recorded at Annapolis Royal in January, and most parts of the region have experienced winter temperatures of at least 50° at some time during their periods of record. In most winters, below zero temperatures are to be expected, perhaps as often as four years out of five. The lowest on record at Halifax is –28°; at Sydney, –25°; and at Chatham, –39°. At Halifax six

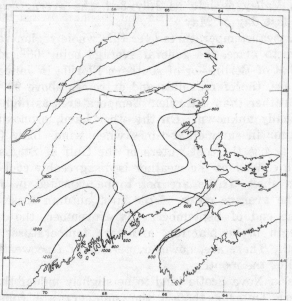

FIG. 51—Annual Hygrothermal units for New Brunswick and Gaspe.

months out of twelve (November-April) have had below zero temperatures. Occasionally, a month may be unusually mild or unusually severe, as at Sydney for example, where the January means have varied from 12 to 30 degrees, and where the February variation has amounted to more than 20 degrees. These departures from normal are as great as those which occur in Ontario or even in more continental locations.

For the most part, spring is three months long, only July and August having mean temperatures above 60°. Where the sea influence is strongest, June is not so warm as September. Over most of New Brunswick, however, the influence of the land to the west permits solar heating to be more effective in June, so that month has more of the characteristics of summer than of spring. In spite of the slowness with which spring gives way to summer, the sea influence is not continually the dominant control; for there are days in May and June and even in April when temperatures do go to 80° or beyond. Such conditions are more frequent along the southern margins of the region than on Prince Edward Island or along the east coast of New Brunswick. Freezing temperatures, on the average, have occurred at Halifax as late as June 13th, and in the fertile Annapolis Valley as late as July 3rd, the average date here being the last day of May.

In July, mean temperatures over this whole region vary little from place to place, the general average being 65°, about the same as that of Berlin—or of southern Florida in January. The summers are, therefore, mild; and extremes above 90° are the exception rather than the rule. Temperatures as high as 100° are practically unknown. On the other hand, pronounced cool periods occur in summer at times when winds blow from the northeast across the cool waters of the Gulf of St. Lawrence; under such conditions the weather is disagreeably cool. So far as records show, frosts are not to be expected in July and August, the average dates of the first autumn frosts coming toward the end of September. By November, the rigors of winter begin to be manifest and zero temperatures are not exceptional. There are, however, periods of fine weather even to the end of the month.

Winters in Nova Scotia tend to be slightly milder than those of southern Ontario, though the summers are considerably cooler. Over most of New Brunswick, however, winters are much colder than those of Toronto, while the summers are slightly cooler. These are conditions to be expected from the more northerly location, the influence of the sea being insufficient to overcome the effects of the higher latitude. Unusually severe winters do visit places even so favorably situated as Halifax, where in 1904-05, frost is reported to have penetrated as much as six feet. The normal depth of frost in Halifax is only two feet, the fairly permanent snowcover preventing deeper penetration.

The precipitation over the Atlantic Provinces is abundant at all seasons. It is greatest in the vicinity of Halifax, where the average annual total exceeds 55 inches. Farther east along the southern or outer coast of Nova Scotia where the cool "bank" waters come close to the shore, the average is reduced by as much as 15 inches; but along the deeply indented coast of Cape Breton Island, 45 to 50 inches is the usual precipitation. The low-lying island of Prince Edward, the protected Annapolis Valley, and the low, northern and eastern portions of New Brunswick, are, in spite of their locations and exposures, well-watered with about 40 inches.

The marine influence is dominant in the monthly distribution of precipitation. Northern New Brunswick is the exception; here the summer half-year receives slightly more precipitation than the winter half-year and late summer is the season of the maximum. Over the rest of the region, September, October, November or December may be the month of maximum, and winter is always wetter than summer. There is, however, no dry season, for no month anywhere receives less than two inches. Droughts are unknown, although there may be seasons when the rainfall is too light for a maximum agricultural yield. Such a condition obtained at Charlottetown in 1924 when the total precipitation for the year was only 18.5 inches, or 46% of the normal. But this was a most unusual year and is an extreme instance. Floods are, likewise, rarities, not because the rainfall may not at times be excessive, but because streams are short and there is no great accumulation of water to swell the lower courses. The precipitation is, on the whole, well-distributed throughout the year, and entirely ample for the type of farming practiced.

Connor has worked out, by a very ingenious method, some hygrothermal units for New Brunswick.[1] The total for a year are shown on the map in Fig. 51. Certain optimum temperatures are arbitrarily selected for each month as follows:

	Apr.	May	Jun.	Jul.	Aug.	Sep.
Day—lower limit	60	60	70	70	70	60
Night—lower limit	43	43	50	50	50	43

No attention is paid to an excess of temperature. The number of days and the number of nights in which the temperatures are as high as those shown are counted. The day numbers for each month are multiplied by the night numbers, and this product is multiplied by a rainfall factor, the weight given this factor varying with the amount of rainfall. Thus, rainfall in

[1] A. J. Connor, *Climatology, The Province of New Brunswick*, Dept. of the Int., Ottawa, 1921, pp. 14-21.

excess of four inches per month is not particularly significant and it is, therefore, given less consideration. To the agriculturalist, this map is of considerable interest. It reveals the fact that the southern coast portion of the province is not so well suited to crops as the western, southern-interior, and eastern portions. Along the extreme northern limits, the total

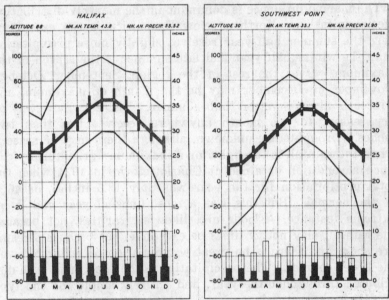

FIG. 52—Temperature and precipitation charts for Halifax and Southwest Point.

units for the year are barely equivalent to those of July and August around Fredericton.

The amount of snowfall in a year over the Atlantic Provinces varies with distance from the sea as well as with latitude. The normal amount at Halifax is 77 inches; at Charlottetown, 96 inches; at Fredericton, 100 inches; and in the highlands of northwestern New Brunswick, well over 100 inches. The snowfall, however, is quite variable from year to year; and it is not unusual for one month to have half of what is received normally in a whole year.

An extreme year is described by F. W. W. Doane[1]:

"The winter of 1904-5 will long be remembered for its excessive snowfall. The first sleighs appeared on the streets of Hali-

[1] F. W. W. Doane, "Meteorological Notes," *Proc. and Trans. of the Nova Scotia Inst. of Sci.*, Halifax, 1908, pp. 362 5.

fax during the evening of December 13th and runners were in
continuous service until March 27th.

"Snowstorm followed snowstorm in rapid succession until
streets, roads and railways were piled high, blockading traffic
and paralyzing business. Each heavy storm was pronounced
the worst by far for the past twenty to fifty years, yet each
succeeding storm seemed worse than its predecessor.

"In the city the street railway company managed to get their
lines open after each storm, except in the western suburbs, the

ILLUS. 39—Cyclonic storms moving down the St. Lawrence Valley or along
the Atlantic coast bring heavy easterly gales to the coast towns of
maritime Canada.

track from Coburg Road to Willow Park being snowed under
on February 11th by a heavy gale and storm and remaining
closed until April 5th. On portions of the main line the snow
piled so high that the sweepers could not throw it clear and on
some streets the track became walled in by four feet of packed
snow. Streets became impassable and teamsters were obliged
to utilize the cleared sidewalks in order to reach their des-
tination.

"In the country, blizzard after blizzard blocked the railways
until not a wheel turned for days on any line in Nova Scotia
except on the Yarmouth to Barrington line. Slight thaws following the great falls of snow caused the water to lodge along
the rails, the snow preventing it from running off. Then frost
came suddenly, the thermometer falling below zero and miles
of rails became incased in a solid mass of ice, which could be
removed only by the thaws of spring or the pickaxes of hundreds of men. The smaller roads succumbed during the first
week in February, the heavy storm of January 31st having
stolen a march on the 'weather man' whose prediction was 'fair

and cold' and tied them up as completely as if they had never been completed.

"Then on top of a month of snowstorms which had partially paralyzed railway communication in Nova Scotia and practically put an end to all trade between the capital and provincial points, came another storm, the severest of them all (Feb. 15-17). The Intercolonial Railway flyers were buried on Folleigh Mountain and the line to Sydney completely closed,

ILLUS. 40.—The waters of the Bay of Fundy retard the advance of spring in the Annapolis Valley, thereby checking the blooming of the apple trees until danger from spring frosts is past. The advance of autumn is correspondingly delayed so that the apple crop is almost a surety.

through traffic not being in good working order again until the 27th. The Dominion Atlantic Railway was unable to get a train through from Halifax to Yarmouth until March 9th.

"In Halifax, business of all kinds suffered. The raging, howling blizzards sent blinding drifts sweeping in every direction. The milk train was cancelled for the first time since it became known as such and the condensed article sold at a premium. In order to relieve the tightness in the meat market two cattle dealers were obliged to bring their droves through on foot from Annapolis County. Funerals had to be postponed until the roads could be made passable. Buildings suffered from the depth and weight of snow on roofs which strained them and caused them to leak and in some cases to collapse. Men, women and children moved about the streets on snow shoes.

"Outside the city the conditions became even more serious, and places depending on the railway obtained relief none too soon. Hundreds of cars of freight were stalled along the Intercolonial Railway, numbers of locomotives were isolated, coal hoppers innumerable were imbedded in deep snow drifts, water gave out in stalled engines and trains were without heat, causing passengers to suffer much inconvenience and discomfort. . . .

"One incident reported in connection with the snow blockade on the Folleigh·Mountain is worthy of note: A farmer who was working his weary way along a country road with a pair of horses and load of hay was stopped at a railroad crossing by a 12 to 14 feet cut in the snow which had been opened by

ILLUS. 41—Lumbering will doubtless always remain the dominant industry of interior New Brunswick, because the relatively short frost-free period permits only a limited agriculture.

an Intercolonial Railway train leaving the sides perpendicular. The crossing problem was solved by backing the snow plow into the cut and driving the team over the bridge thus temporarily provided."

The number of days with precipitation and the average annual number of inches of precipitation are almost directly proportional, the ratio being about three to one (except at Chatham where it is nearly four to one and at Annapolis where it is slightly less than three to one). Thus the greatest number of rainy or snowy days, 167, is found near Halifax. The Annapolis Valley with 119, has the fewest. The latter, however, is cloudier than the interior of New Brunswick.

The Atlantic coasts of both New Brunswick and Nova Scotia are both more foggy than other portions of the Atlantic Provinces. The number of foggy days in a year at Halifax averages 54, most of them occurring from May to September. These fogs result when southeasterly winds blow from the warm Gulf Stream waters across the cold bank waters which are found from Newfoundland southward to the Gulf of Maine. The northern portions of these provinces are surprisingly free from fogs, the yearly total at Charlottetown being only five and at Chatham only four.

Nova Scotia is stormy, particularly during the winter half-year when cyclonic storms are frequent. Its exposed location permits winds to blow from the ocean on three sides—and the lack of friction over the water allows storm winds to blow with undiminished fury. Although the average wind velocities are only 12 or 13 miles an hour at this season, the number of days with gales is large: 37 at Halifax and 29 at Sydney, January being the month of greatest frequency at the latter and March at the former. When high pressure dominates, the weather tends to be much calmer—attributable in part to the fact that the winds are then offshore. The protected location of Prince Edward Island renders that land remarkably free from high winds; in summer, gales are unknown.

MARITIME QUEBEC

The subregion, Maritime Quebec, embraces the Gaspe Peninsula and the island of Anticosti as well as all of the north shore of the Gulf of St. Lawrence. In spite of the name given to the province, its climate is not strictly marine; in fact, most of the area has conditions more like those of western Quebec than of Newfoundland between which two regions it is a transition. The winters which are long, continuing from November through April, are not really so severe as the latitude might indicate, but summer, as Toronto knows that season, (that is, with mean temperatures above 60°) does not exist. Instead, spring, in its full glory in July, gives way to autumn which begins in August. The influence of the sea crowds out the real summer conditions altogether; on the other hand, it prevents mean winter temperatures from dropping much below 10°.

This does not mean that maritime Quebec is a bleak and inhospitable land. The season from June through September is refreshingly cool—never hot and muggy; infrequently cold as freezing. Temperatures may occasionally mount to 80°, although there are some years when one of these months may pass without a temperature higher than 65°. Frost in July is unknown, and is rare from June 10 to September 1st. In an average year, the growing season is from three and one-half to four months long, except along the north shore. Consequently, the cultivation of crops requiring a long and cool, but frost-free, period is entirely successful. On the whole, extremes of temperature from day to day, during the warmest part of the year, are small, the mean daily ranges varying from 10 to 12 degrees.

In winter, conditions are somewhat more variable, though the ranges, which in places mount to 18 or more degrees, are still five or more degrees less than the winter ranges of the Prairie Provinces. January in this region is about equivalent to January in southern Alberta, although the extremes are slightly greater in Alberta. On Anticosti Island, a normal winter has extremes ranging from about 38° to –20°. The lowest temperature ever recorded in the region is –40°.

Precipitation is rarely either inadequate or excessive. The average fall is about 30 inches per year, well distributed by months. The marine influence is seen in the slight tendency toward fall and winter maxima, although the summer half-year, May to October, receives more than the winter half. Even though the precipitation may be adequate for crops grown, there is considerable variability from one year to another. At Harrington Harbour the total precipitation in 1913 was three and one-half times that in 1924; at Southwest Point on Anticosti Island, 1920 received more than four times as much as 1905. The wettest years, however, are seldom flood years because the precipitation is fairly evenly distributed over the year. These wide variations over a period of years presumably result from a change in the intensity of cyclones or possibly in the paths they take. The weather maps show that the cyclonic storms over this region were much more intense in 1920 than in 1905. The frequent occurrence, during the winter months, of temperatures above freezing, on the front of a low pressure area, accounts for the fact that only one quarter of the annual total precipitation comes in the form of snow, the number of rainy days during the year being approximately twice the number of snowy days.

Unlike protected Prince Edward Island, most of this region is subject to fogs, which probably average 25 to 35 a year on

Anticosti and along the north shore of the Gulf; on the exposed portions of Gaspe, they are even more frequent. The months of greatest frequency are from April through September. At Madeline in northern Gaspe heavy sea fogs probably occur, on the average, one day out of three during spring, summer, and fall; these are sufficiently heavy on the windward flanks of the mountains to yield considerable precipitation. A recent report concerning this region follows[1]:

"Mr. J. E. Daw, engineer for the Brown Company, describes an interesting case of fog in the Gaspe Peninsula on the south shore of the Gulf of St. Lawrence. These fogs, he writes, form frequently in the spring, summer, and fall when warm, westerly winds, blowing over the cold water, are chilled and the moisture condensed to fog. During the past summer when hardly any rain fell in the region, and creeks and wells dried up, the fog kept the foliage green and fresh. 'The common basket fern,' he says, 'which requires a lot of moisture, grew to abnormal size. Some time ago I walked through a *dry* swamp, where these ferns were above my shoulder. On the mountain sides tree growth was very luxuriant, with every tree to be found that grows in Canada, even to the basswood and butternut, which require a soft and humid climate.' "

One of the most noteworthy facts regarding the climate of this region is the high frequency of gales, especially during the winter months when cyclonic storms are dominant. At Harrington Harbour, they average 71 a year; at Anticosti, where winds from the west and south have a clear sweep, the average is 119. The normal wind velocities are likewise high in winter, ranging from 15 to 23 miles per hour in January. Even in summer, the winds are strong enough to be irritating—probably never averaging less than 10 miles per hour. Fortunately, the heaviest gales come at a season when, chiefly because of ice, there is little or no shipping.

NEWFOUNDLAND

Because of its great length of coastline, Newfoundland, like Nova Scotia, has a climate dominated by the marine control. Its relatively small area (it is no larger than the state of Pennsylvania) is deeply indented, so that no point in the country is more than 70 miles from salt water. Unlike Nova Scotia, however, each of its three sides is exposed to oceanic influences,

---

[1] N. H. Bangs, "Sea Fog in the Gaspe Peninsula," *Bulletin of the American Meteorological Society*, v. 10, 1929, pp. 143-44.

although the west coast is sufficiently near Quebec to feel the continental influences when west and northwest winds prevail. Altitude is also of some significance as evidenced by the tundra type of vegetation which replaces the forested land at all elevations above 1000 or 1200 feet: ridges devoid of trees alternating with forested valleys are features of the interior landscape.

Although the climate of Newfoundland may be characterized as marine, it is, however, less so than Vancouver Island lying

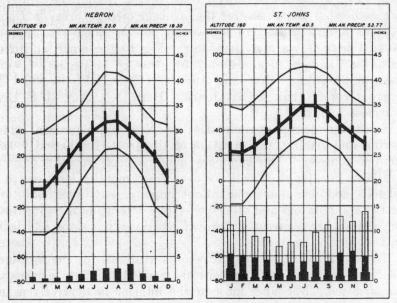

FIG. 53—Temperature and precipitation charts for Hebron and S⁴. Johns.

in the same latitude. Winters are mild and the summers are cool almost to the point of extinction since there are few places on the island where even July mean temperatures reach 60°. The waters, cold or warm, which surround the island are above the freezing point of salt water and serve to keep winter temperatures well above the normal for the latitude. In summer, the cold, ice-laden waters of the Labrador Current along the east coast, and the tendency toward cold bank waters between the Gulf Stream and the south shore as well as along the west coast, keep the island almost constantly cool.

The oceanic influence is most pronounced on the Avalon Peninsula which projects far into the sea; here February is slightly

colder than January. Yet, Victoria, British Columbia, in about
the same latitude as St. Johns, is 15 degrees warmer in January,
the mean at the latter being 23°. In July Victoria is hardly a
degree warmer. Extremes are also much greater at St. Johns
where temperatures of zero or lower are experienced in more
than half the years, and where 40° or higher at least once for
almost every January and February is the rule. In summer,
on the other hand, a temperature of 90° is a rarity; in fact,
anything as high as 90° is looked upon as most unusual. Farther west, as on the southwest coast of the island, the winters
are somewhat more severe, the average being three or four
degrees lower. Summers are cooler to the same extent, but
August here is warmer than July. Far to the north at Belle
Isle, the January mean is only 9°; this is 11 degrees lower
than at St. Johns. July and August at Belle Isle are about 7
degrees cooler than at St. Johns. Here, too, August is the
warmest month.

Since the dominant industries of Newfoundland are lumbering and fishing, the duration of the frost-free period is of
limited concern. The summers may be cool, yet the period
available for plant growth is over four months long on the
island's southern lowlands. Consequently, hay and oats for
cattle, and potatoes and other vegetables tolerating a cool growing season are successfully grown wherever the slope and soil
in this section permit.

There are no meteorological records available for the interior
of Newfoundland; the temperature conditions there can only
be surmised. But since most of the interior is relatively near
the sea, it is evident that extremes of temperature should be
only slightly greater than those along the coast. The absence
of tree growth on the higher situations must be attributed in
part to lower summer temperatures, presumably under 50°.
Insufficient drainage, however, may be a more important factor
than temperature, in which case it is quite possible that the
mean of 50° may be exceeded during at least one month. There
is no question, however, that settlement of the interior has
been retarded because of the inability to carry on successful
agriculture, though the continual and annoying presence of
the mosquito during the two or three warmest months of the
year has been another contributing factor. Either cause would
be sufficient to deter permanent human occupation of the land;

although political and economic conditions have played an important part in keeping the interior undeveloped.

The precipitation of Newfoundland is almost everywhere abundant, only a small strip on the west coast having under 30 inches. The southeast half of the island experiences the heaviest amounts—as much as 54 inches at St. Johns. The monthly distribution, though fairly uniform, is, however, somewhat unusual. At Port aux Basques, where the temperature curve shows strong marine characteristics, the precipitation is almost equally divided between the summer and winter half-years. At Belle Isle, where August is appreciably warmer than July, the summer half-year is decidedly the wetter. And at St. Johns, where the marine influence on the temperature curve is less pronounced, the winter half-year receives 12% more precipitation than the summer half. In each of these three cases, the oceanic effect is seen in the fact that the monthly maxima occur in January, October or November; while the minima occur in May and June. So far as records can show it, droughts are unknown; for it is exceptional when less than the equivalent of one inch of rain is recorded in any month.

In the northwest portion of the island, snow makes up about one-quarter of the annual precipitation. The amount of snow decreases from north to south and from west to east; so that at St. Johns, the average yearly fall of 96 inches makes up less than one-fifth the total precipitation. Occasional years have unusually heavy snows. Thus, one February at St. Johns, the fall exceeded nine feet; and falls of four feet or more in one month are not infrequent. In southern Newfoundland, snow rarely if ever occurs from June to September. Toward the northern margins, and presumably in the interior also, only July and August fail to receive measurable amounts.

Even though its precipitation is not excessive, the weather of Newfoundland should, perhaps, be classed as rainy. At St. Johns rain or snow falls on the average between three and four days a week; while at Port aux Basques more than four days out of seven receive measurable precipitation. At either station, autumn and winter have the greatest frequency of rainy or snowy days. This is reflected in the cloudiness which is greatest at those seasons. At Port aux Basques, both December and January have an average cloudiness of 88%; September, although the least cloudy month, has an average of 66%. At

St. Johns the weather is somewhat more fair, so that December and April, the cloudiest months, have only 74%; August, with 56%, is the clearest month. See Table 26 for the frequencies of summer and winter weather types at St. Johns.

There is a common impression abroad that Newfoundland is wrapped in eternal fog. As a matter of fact, the island is less foggy than the southeast coast of Nova Scotia; records show that 40 to 45 foggy days a year is the average for the most susceptible places in Newfoundland, while at Halifax the average is 54. At St. Johns, April and July are the most foggy; at Port aux Basques, June and July hold the record. The fact that the Grand Banks are rarely free from fog has probably given rise to this misconception of the island's fogginess. On the Banks, according to fishermen, fogs occur in all kinds of weather and with all kinds of winds—even with west, northwest and north. Wet fogs, sometimes known as "temps bouche," are not nearly so frequent as dry fogs; the latter, however, are just as dense. Perret states that the relative humidity in dry fog is often as low as 85%; once in 1907 it was only 71%; and in a fog of four days duration in 1904 near St. Johns, the humidity was never higher than 73%.[1] These dry fogs occur mainly in calm weather; winds tend to dissipate them so that sailors refer to winds as fog-eaters. At times, fogs are so shallow that mast heads may be seen above them. The sun shining on them gives rise to the term "white fogs." These are frequently dazzling, and the refraction of light in them causes mirages so that a beach may be mistaken for a steep cliff.[2]

The southeastern tip of Avalon Peninsula is more subject to fogs than other portions of the island; in fact, the sea fogs are so close to the shore, that any point of land jutting into the ocean experiences the same conditions as the water surface itself. This is seen in the fact that Cape Race one year reported 120 hours of foggy weather in May, 400 in June and 404 in July. It is said that the interior tends to have clear skies in summer, so that local fogs occur on lakes with steep banks not only at night with minimum temperatures but also during the day after a sudden change of temperature.[3]

A significant feature of the Newfoundland climate is its great variability from day to day or from week to week espe-

[1] Robert Perret, La geographic de Terre-Neuve, E. Guilmoto, Paris, 1913, p. 135.
[2] Ibid., p. 136.
[3] Ibid., p. 138.

cially in the colder part of the year when cyclonic storms are better developed and more frequent. There is also a wide variation in mean temperatures for any month from year to year. At St. Johns in 1920, the January mean was only 15.3°; in 1892, it was 31.2° for the same month. The extremes for February means have been even greater; 31.9° in 1898 and 12.5° in 1923. Conditions are less variable in summer, and are least so in October.

The winds are an important factor in causing sudden changes in temperature over a period of a few days, or even during one day. In a single morning, winds have been known to blow successively from each of the eight points of the compass. Winds from the southwest tend to be warm and dry as they descend the east slopes of the island. Northwest winds are dry and cold. Those from the northeast are chill and damp; from the southeast moist and foggy. The degree of warmth or cold is entirely relative, depending on the season; the velocity of the wind appears to be a factor also. Perret states that a temperature of 76° was observed at St. Johns when icebergs were readily visible; and that, because of the dryness of the wind as it descended from the interior, water had to be poured on the house roofs in order to prevent fire.[1] He states further that when a wind continues from the west for three or four days, there is a wide difference between wet and dry bulb readings, and the relative humidity may drop to 10%, which seems almost incredible. At Bishops Falls a temperature of 98° is reported by Perret as being observed once when a west wind was blowing.[2] When these dry winds persist for several days, their low humidity causes the soil moisture to be evaporated rapidly, resulting in local droughts of considerable significance. The Avalon Peninsula is too small and low to experience with west winds the same degree of warmth and dryness as the main portion of the island; so that fogs frequently result along its east shores as the west winds meet the cold air over the icy waters of the Labrador Current. Such conditions obtain most often in the spring half-year (January-July).

Obviously, the changes in wind direction result from the movements of low pressure areas. The number of these storms occurring in a single winter month is really surprising. Thus,

[1] Ibid., p. 115.
[2] Ibid., p. 127.

26 passed over Belle Isle in January, 1900. When the storms
are intense, wind velocities are high. Houses, therefore, are
generally constructed with double walls and with double doors
and windows to keep out the wind and finely divided snow
which penetrates through even the smallest apertures.[1] Poudrin
is the term used to denote a wind blowing fine snow. Persons
exposed to it have difficulty in breathing comfortably; and,
according to Perrett, there are instances of people having been
killed by it.[2] Such occurrences are probably more frequent and
severe where cold winds blow over water, the spray being frozen
in the process. Houses situated near shores have their roofs
white through the accumulation of salt from the ocean spray
driven there by the wind. Because of the variableness in the
force and direction of the wind, nights are often warmer than
the days, particularly in winter; and it is not unusual to find
the lowest temperatures for a 24-hour period occurring with
bright sunshine. This is due to the fact that the northwest
winds which bring the cold and clear weather no sooner become
established than they are forced to give way to easterly winds
with the advance of another low pressure area. During the
month of February, 1904, the daily maximum occurred thirteen
times before noon or after 6 o'clock in the evening; in July of
the same year, the maximum occurred twelve times outside the
usual afternoon quarter.

Another phenomenon, perhaps more common in Newfoundland than in any other part of North America, is the glaze or
ice storm, referred to locally as silver thaw. Such storms usually
occur when a south wind sets in. The ground and the air near
it are still below freezing, so that the rain resulting from warm
moist air over-riding the surface layer freezes as soon as it
comes in contact with the object below freezing. Some of the
streets of St. Johns are protected by iron railings as aids to
walking during these ice storms.

On the whole, it must be admitted that the climate of Newfoundland has desirable qualities equal to or greater than those
of most places in eastern North America. For the latitude,
its climate is certainly superior. The rapid weather changes
are not extreme enough to be more than stimulating. Plenty of
moisture at all seasons, mild but certain winters, cool and

---

[1] Ibid., p. 116.
[2] Ibid., p. 139.

delightful summers, and freedom from many of the epidemics
so common on the continent to the west—all add to the health-
ful and invigorating influences of the Newfoundland climate.

THE LABRADOR

The term, The Labrador, as used here comprises only a relatively narrow strip along the Atlantic coast of the Labrador
Peninsula, extending from about 52 to 60 degrees north latitude. Physically it is characterized by deeply indented fiord-
like bays backed by land, high or even mountainous since it
ranges in altitude from about 1500 feet in the south to as much
as 6000 feet in the north. The climate along this entire stretch
of coast, approximately 600 miles in length, is strikingly the
same, the difference in latitude making a difference in degree
rather than in kind.

The cold Labrador Current with its load of floes and icebergs
causes the immediate coast to be bleak and barren. Toward the
northern margin of this region, the land is entirely bare of
woody growth, even shrubs, and for firing people must depend
on what drift wood is washed up, or on seal-fat lamps.[1] Near
the heads of the larger bays and fiords and along the lower
stream courses, the aspect is in marked contrast, the barren or
treeless landscape being replaced by forest vegetation of considerable size. That is, altitude remaining the same, the greater
the distance from the open sea the more luxuriant the plant
growth. The reason is clear when the surface water temperatures for summer are considered: on the open sea, 40° to 45°;
in the bays, 50° and higher. Thus, along the coast, the growth
of garden vegetables is almost impossible; while a little distance
inland, cabbage, carrots, potatoes and other vegetables may be
grown with a fair degree of success if properly protected against
summer frost.

On the whole, the climate of The Labrador is subarctic to
arctic. That is, mean temperatures for the warmest month
range from slightly over 50° to a little below that figure.
Hebron, located near the 58th parallel, is quite typical of the
north shore. South of Hebron, the climate may be considered
as a gradual transition to that experienced on Belle Isle or the
north tip of Newfoundland. The summer weather of the whole
coast, however, tends to be uniform. In winter, there is a

[1] W. T. Grenfell, *Labrador*, The Macmillan Co., New York, 1922, p. 227.

pronounced decrease in temperature with increase in latitude. At Hebron, August is the warmest month with a mean of 48°; January is the coldest with a mean of –6°. For the latitude, its summers are exceedingly cool, its winters relatively mild. The oceanic influence keeps the mean annual range of temperature down to 54 degrees, very appreciably lower than the 76 degree range at Churchill or the 72 degree range at Fort Chipewyan, both in the same latitude.

As far as temperature is concerned, winter begins in October and continues into May; summer does not exist. There are, however, occasional days when real and delightful summer weather occurs, the maximum temperature mounting to 80° or higher. On the other hand, it is rare that a month passes without frost. Winter cold as known in the Prairie Provinces is likewise rare, the lowest temperature on record at Hebron being only –42°. March to August show the largest diurnal ranges of temperature, October and November the least, the average for the two latter months being only 10 degrees.

Precipitation along the coast ranges from 20 to 25 inches, most of which comes in autumn. January and February have the least rain or snow. These months are also the least cloudy. The increasing hours of sunshine at this season, make these months and March the finest of the year. As early as 1776, Capt. Cartwright was favorably impressed with the Labrador weather when he wrote[1]: "Notwithstanding the weather is so extremely severe, yet the cold feels healthy and pleasant; much more so than the winters of Europe; nor does it ever cause a person to shake." Not all winters are so free of storminess as these facts might indicate. The highest wind velocities occur from November to January, and about one day in twelve has winds of gale force. A heavy snowfall followed by high wind may occasionally give rise to a condition similar to this described by Capt. Cartwright[2]: "This morning, two-thirds of my house was so entirely drifted over, as to appear like a hill; and nobody would suppose it to be any other, were it not for the top of the chimney." The shifting of the prevailing wind to a northeasterly quadrant during the period from May to August means increased cloudiness and chilly damp weather.

[1] C. W. Townsend, *Capt. Cartwright and His Labrador Journal*, Williams & Norgate, London, 1911, p. 189.
[2] Ibid., p. 221.

It is also at this time that most of the few dense fogs are experienced: one day each in May and June, three in July, and two in August on the average. That fogs are so infrequent along this coast is a point to be stressed; Belle Isle is really the northern limit. Grenfell states that "many times as we have steamed out of the strait [of Belle Isle] in thick fog, and passed the

ILLUS. 42—The fiorded coast of northern Labrador affords some protection from Atlantic gales. The absence of trees and of cultivated lands bear certain testimony of the chill and bleak summers.

southern corner of Labrador, we emerged from what, on looking back, resembled a dark wall, to bask suddenly in the clearest of sunshine."[1]

The character of the weather by months and the effects of that weather upon the people have been so graphically described by Grenfell that his account is here presented verbatim[2]:

"*January.* The second coldest of the winter months; only occasional temperatures above freezing, and then only for a short spell. The whole country everywhere is under ice and snow. The first winter mail arrives from Quebec by dog train. Natural bridges make it possible to cross all the rivers, bays, and arms of the sea. Thus, traveling is usually begun in this month, though in the green woods snow is not yet hard packed, and consequently one has to go round the 'drogues,' as we call them. The dogs are able to go fifty to sixty miles in a day. The shortness of the days is the chief drawback. The settlers

[1] Grenfell, op. cit., p. 70.

[2] From W. T. Grenfell, *Labrador*, pp. 74-80. By permission of The Macmillan Co., publishers.

are all in their homes in the woods at the heads of the bays. They are trapping fur, hunting deer, and lumbering. The great herds of deer are in the low marshes and woods near the landwash, and are often obtainable in great plenty. Willow grouse and rabbits are plentiful at times in the woods. Harp seals are being netted as they pass south along the Labrador coast. The sea is impossible to navigation during this month.

"*February*. The coldest month with seldom any 'let up'— temperatures in the north even falling on rare occasions to 45-50° below zero F. Traveling is improved by the heavier falls of snow, which fill the dangerous hollows and smooth off the rough, rocky points. The Arctic ice blocks the coast and keeps the swell from breaking up the ice in the bays. The Strait of Belle Isle is choked. The hood and harp seals are working southwards in the sea off Newfoundland and in the Gulf, to whelp on the loose floes around which they find fish. Fox-trapping with hunting for marten or sables, minks, musquash, and other species is in full swing on the land.

"*March*. A splendid, bright, bracing, cold month. The reflection of the sun from the snow makes it imperative to protect the eyes with coloured spectacles, since a single day's exposure will blind a man. The skin gets so tanned that whites begin to resemble Indians in colour. White settlers never lose the tawny colour. This constant sun bath, in spite of low temperatures, has an excellent tonic effect on weakly people. The snow is now hard, and it is as easy to travel through thick woods as in the open. Much longer distances can be covered by the dogs in a day; they can be given their heads to choose their own paths. Furs are in their prime. The annual seal hunt from Newfoundland takes place, and all along the southern seaboard the settlers are on the watch for baby seals on the ice. Some of the birds are breeding, e. g., the Canada jay. Settlers are cutting logs and hauling them out for summer firewood. Some traps are now taken up, as certain furs cease to be in prime condition.

"*April*. The bright, hot sun in the middle of the day begins to thaw the snow, which freezes hard again at night. Traveling is done mostly in the early morning. The ice at times clears off enough to leave a narrow strip of open water along the exposed coast. Ducks and geese, with other smaller birds, such as the snow-bunting and the northern shrike, begin to arrive from the south. Some men are now netting seals if the season is early; others are still working at twine for summer use. Shooting sea-birds from the headlands offers good sport. Fur shows clear loss in value. Many settlers return to summer fishing stations, using dogs and komatiks to transport all their summer necessities out to the islands. Others who take care of and repair the stations of our summer visitors are hard at work on houses and stagings. On fine days these men, while at their outside work, venture off on the running ice. Most years, however, the ice is too hard near the shore, and to go off far from shore, hauling small boats on runners, is restricted to the hardier and more venturesome. Through the ice of the ponds in southern Labrador, good trout fishing can be obtained.

"*May*. Navigation as far as the south part of the east coast is practicable, though onshore winds will bring the floe-ice in at any time and block all the harbours and bays. Still, one or two venturesome vessels come down with safety to southern Labrador, seldom taking any harm from the ice beyond what they are liable to at any time of year. American bankers are baiting in the straits, and French fishermen from Newfoundland arrive on the Treaty Shore opposite. The first steamer to carry mails leaves St. John's for Labrador. The rivers and bays break up. The last of the people move out to their summer homes for the fishery. Good trout fishing is to be had in the rivers or in the lakes through the ice. Foxes have their young and sea-birds are nesting all along the coast on the islands and rocks. Many people gather the eggs and store them for eating. Traps are all taken in by the first day, as the fur is now losing colour and the long 'king' hairs fall. Seals are beating north; swatching or shooting them from the ice pans as they come up to take breath forms a very favorite pastime. Old harps and bedlamer seals are caught on southern Labrador in great frame nets. Farther north the Eskimo are hunting the walrus. The deer are all going north and taking to the hills. The native bears leave their caves; any white bears that have gone south on the floes begin to work north again.

"*June*. Most of the snow has gone, though in places it remains to the water-level. Ground is still hard frozen, with occasional frosts at night. Arctic ice still besets the coast. Fishing vessels work down along the straits and the southern part of the east coast. Some years the mail boat gets as far as Hamilton Inlet; other years ice inside the islands is as hard as at any time in the winter. In the straits the cod-fishery is in full swing, while on the east coast the southerners in the schooners are up the bays getting wood for firing, for stages, etc. Americans, Canadians, and West Coast Newfoundlanders are trawling in the straits and Gulf. The sea is very calm, owing to the ice outside. The brilliancy of the sun, the innumerable icebergs, the return of the whales, and the fleets of fishing vessels make the scenic effects some of the best in the year. In the inlets the salmon and trout fisheries are being prosecuted. Deer seek the hills to avoid the mosquitoes. The does are with their fawns in the woods. Black bear seek the fish along the land-wash. Most of the small bird visitors from the south have arrived. Lean dogs wander about everywhere, searching for meat, for they are no longer fed, and as yet there are no fish heads and offal for them.

"*July.* Most of the ice and snow are gone from the land. The ground at the heads of the bays thaws out enough to sow seed. The main steamer now usually reaches her northern limit at Nain, visiting all along as she goes. The caplin are working into the land farther north and attracting the codfish. Salmon in the river begin to take the fly. The young ducks and other sea-birds are hatched out. Pleasure schooners can get down among the Eskimo who are now out at their summer fishing stations in skin tents. The salmon fishing with nets in the inlets is going on, and the cod-fishery begins with the caplin school. Mosquitoes hatch out and are troublesome.

"*August.* Southern cod-fishers reach their extreme northern limit, and fish are taken as far as Cape Chidley. Caplin begin to die or leave the shore, cod following them out of the bays. The salmon-fishery in the sea is at an end. The salmon and trout in the rivers rise to the fly well. The best fiords and the least-known northern bays are accessible to pleasure yachts. Icebergs in greatest abundance are now to be seen. They are continually driving south with the Arctic current. The flappers of water-fowl are big enough to shoot. Old ducks and divers are moulting, and, being unable to fly, escape pursuit only by diving. The first foreign vessels with dried fish leave the coast. Cloudberries and other berries, e. g. bilberries, currants, raspberries, begin to ripen. Formerly large flocks of curlew came down to feed on these. The young geese in the bays are beginning to fly.

"*September.* Hooks and lines replace the large trap nets, as the cod are now only to be taken in deep water. Northern schooners begin to come south with cargoes of green fish. The first snow falls about Cape Chidley, and frosts begin to set in at nights. Deer are to be had in the country. Geese and black duck are seeking the salt water in the daytime, and may be shot flighting. The mosquitoes are no longer troublesome. Grouse are to be shot on the hills, and afford excellent sport. Small migratory birds begin to leave. Berries are plentiful and add materially to a camper's menu. Caribou leave the hills for the marshes. All together, this is the best month for sportsmen to visit Labrador, except for salmon fishing.

"*October.* The southern fishermen mostly leave. Pleasure schooners must do the same. Fish are still to be taken in deep water with long lines. Frosts at night are often severe, and many harbours begin to 'catch over' with ice.

"Ducks and geese leave the coast. Deer are rutting, but are now nearer the seaboard in the leads and marshes. The winds are high and cold, but they are nearly all westerly and off the land; thus the sea is often smooth alongshore. The most disastrous storms, however, have occurred in this month. All the trappers are busy taking supplies into the country and preparing their traps. Otters, foxes, mink, beaver, etc., come in season. They are, however, not really 'prime.' Large Labrador herring are taken in gill nets. Lesser auks, puffins, murrelets, and other diving birds are very plentiful, passing south. The lakes all freeze over, and the hilltops are all capped with snow.

"*November*. The last of the southerners leave. The mail steamer makes her last visit. Winter has really arrived. Not a craft left afloat on the coast by the end of the month. Trapping is especially now for foxes and mink on the seaboard. Many settlers on the 'outside' are engaged with seal nets. The rest have gone to their homes among the trees at the bottom of the long bays.

"The last of the ducks and geese leave. Hares, rabbits, grouse, etc., assume their winter colouring. Dogs are now fed up for their winter work. Lumbermen are in the wood cutting logs.

"*December*. The short days tend to make this the most dismal month, but the dog driving begins and the assumption of snowshoes, or 'ski,' also helps to enliven matters. Any game killed now will remain good till June, being hard frozen as soon as killed. All along northern Labrador many seals are being netted. Even the large rivers are now safe to cross on the ice, but in some of the arms of the sea there is still no ice that will bear, owing to the tide. Some of the best furs are now taken in the country. The first dog mail leaves for Quebec at Christmas."

THE LABRADOR PENINSULA INTERIOR

There is probably no other large single area on the North American continent about the climate of which so little is known. Its east-west extent, from 500 to 1000 miles, and its north-south extent through about ten degrees of latitude give this region an area considerably larger than British Columbia. So far as it is known, most of the Peninsula is a moderately high, rolling plateau averaging about 2000 feet in elevation. The fact that winds blowing over it from west, north or east have come from ice-cold waters means that the climate cannot be other than cool in summer and raw in winter, especially near the shores.

This general inhospitability of the climate has prevented, to a considerable degree, thorough exploration of the interior and the development of any of its natural resources. Another factor has been the inability to raise vegetable food. Even as far south as Mistassini Post, which lies on the extreme southern margin of the region, summer frosts are so prevalent that potatoes, about the only crop attempted, rarely mature. Obviously, farther north in the interior, conditions would be even less favorable for vegetable growing. At Fort Chimo, near Ungava Bay, mean temperatures for July and August are slightly above 50°; so that by using considerable care, lettuce, radishes, and turnips sometimes mature.

A third, and probably the most significant factor, which has militated against the development of the country, has been the mosquito and his potent ally, the sand-fly. There is no escape from the ravages of these insects. Prichard who followed up the Fraser River from Nain, over the divide and down into the George River Valley, refers to mosquitoes as follows[1]: "As to their numbers, I am hopeless of giving any idea of them. Suffice it to say that when Hardy put his military blanket out to air, phalanxes three or four deep settled upon it, until its colour changed from brown to grey—a seething and loathesome mass of insects; and presently as we moved about, above each of us rolled a pillar of mosquitoes, revolving and buzzing, and thousands strong." At another time the same author relates[2]: "I covered my face with a veil, but could get no clear air through it, so thickly did the mosquitoes settle." Leonidas Hubbard, who lost his life in October, 1903, in attempting a traverse from Grand Lake to the George River, wrote in his diary as follows[3]: "Sand-flies awful—nasty, vindictive; bite out chunks and streak our hands and faces with blood. Mosquitoes positively friendly by contrast. Tried net—could not see; then tried dope—some help." At other places in his diary are found such phrases as: "flies awful"; "flies hellish"; "mosquitoes—millions."

Since there are no permanent habitations of the white man in this vast wilderness of forest, muskeg, tundra and swamp, the only knowledge of the meteorology must come through study of the reports of casual visitors and by adopting an extrapolative method in the use of the available records of the margins. Fort Chimo in the north, Fort George on the west, Mistassini Post on the south, and the Labrador coast stations on the east furnish data upon which an estimate of the climate of the interior may be based. From the records of these stations, it

---

[1] H. H. Prichard, *Through Trackless Labrador*, Sturgis and Walton Co., New York, 1911, p. 68.

[2] Ibid., p. 76.

[3] Casper Whitney, "The Leonidas Hubbard. Jun., Expedition into Labrador," *Outing*. v. 45, 1905, pp. 643-689.

would appear that the interior possesses a continental climate in modified form. That is, mean temperatures for July are presumably a little above 50° wherever the altitude does not interfere; and mean January temperatures probably range from –10° to –20°. These are essentially the conditions at Fort Chimo; there is no reason to believe that the climate of the interior is any less rigorous. Extreme minima of –30° to –50° are probably not unusual. Since there are no known winds of chinook character in any part of this region and since probably half the area is 200 miles from salt water, the winters must be continuously severe and unrelieved by frequent days above freezing as in the same latitudes west of Hudson Bay. In summer, temperatures of 80° or higher are probably not uncommon. Eighty-eight degrees has been recorded as far north as Fort Chimo, and 94° has been reported from Northwest River.[1] In the southeastern portion of the region around Lake Melville, the summers must have mean temperatures well above 50° in order to account for the native tall, straight spruce, one of which was measured and found to be nine feet in circumference.[2] Prichard, however, in his trip across the Height of Land at 58 degrees north latitude, mentions the dwarfed character of the vegetation, most of it too small even for firewood.[3] The protected and better drained river valleys appear to abound in good-sized spruce and juniper. It is said that the walls of buildings at Fort Chimo are constructed of logs, although trees there rarely exceed ten inches in diameter.[4]

The precipitation is probably everywhere between 20 and 30 inches. What percentage of this comes in the form of snow is difficult to say. Snow usually begins in September and lasts through May and most reports indicate that it rains a little at least every other day from June to August. The alternation of sunshine and showers evidently prompted Mrs. Hubbard to call the upper George Valley a "land of rainbows."[5]

A summary of the climate of the Labrador Peninsula as reported by A. P. Low is given below[6]:

[1] Kindle, *Canada North of Fifty-Six Degrees*, p. 61.
[2] (Mrs.) Leonidas Hubbard, Jr., "Labrador from Lake Melville to Ungava Bay," *Bull. Am. Geogr. Soc.*, v. 38, 1906, p. 533.
[3] Prichard, op. cit., pp. 97 and 101.
[4] Kindle, op. cit., p. 61.
[5] (Mrs.) Hubbard, op. cit., p. 538.
[6] A. P. Low, *Extracts from Report on Explorations in the Labrador Peninsula*, Dept. of Colonization, Mines and Fisheries, Province of Quebec, Quebec, 1915, pp. 11-12.

"The summer season begins almost simultaneously through-out the interior, and the jump from winter into summer, occurs as a rule during the first two weeks of June, when the snow disappears, and the ice leaves the rivers and lakes, except the largest, where it often remains until July. With the disappear-ance of the snow and ice, the temperature during the day rap-idly increases, and the leaves are almost immediately put forth by trees and bushes. During 1894, frosts were of almost nightly occurrence until June 28th, when a thin sheet of ice was formed in the vessels about camp, and slight flurries of snow fell in the morning. After this date no frost was noted, but, ther-mometers having unfortunately been broken, the exact tempera-ture could not be taken. To the north of latitude 52°, snow falls and ice begins to form in the small lakes about the middle of September. From early in October the snow remains perma-nently, and all the smaller lakes are solidly frozen, so that, for the greater part of the interior plateau, there is at most only three months of summer. The temperature during the winter season is often very low on the interior high lands, away from the influence of the sea. The coldest months·are December, January, and February.

"According to reports of the Indians, the ice in Lake Michi-kamau is 7 feet 6 inches thick on the average, and the amount of continuous frost to form such a thickness must be very great. The ice in Lake Winokapau, in the deep valley of the Hamilton River, was from actual measurement found to be 4 feet 9 inches. From the journal kept at the post on this lake, between 1866 and 1874, the first snow generally fell about September 20th and continued until June, the latest record being June 10th. The lowest temperature recorded was 55° below zero. Geese and summer birds arrived on or about May 10th. From the jour-nals at Northwest River port, the lowest temperature recorded from 1867 to 1893 was 53° below zero. There are several observations of 45° below zero, which appears to be the mini-mum winter temperature of most years. At Rigolet where the temperature is moderated by the open sea, the thermometer rarely registers 40° below zero. At Fort Chimo, where the open sea is not far distant, 45° below zero is said to be the lowest temperature registered. The summer temperature of the Atlantic coast region is considerably lower than inland or along the western coast. As a rule the thermometer in the interior—north of Mistassini—rarely rises above 80° during the middle of the day on more than a few days during the summer season.

"The temperature depends greatly on the direction of the winds. During the summer, south and south-west winds pre-vail in the interior, and are accompanied by higher temperature and often overcast sky, with drizzling rain. The west and northwest winds bring clear weather with lowering temperature, especially during the winter season. North and north-east winds are usually accompanied by heavy storms of rain and snow, with cold moist atmosphere. East and south-east winds, as a rule, blow with clear, pleasant weather.

"The precipitation of moisture over .the interior area is not great. During the winter the snowfall varies from three to six feet, and the greater part of it descends during the periods of north and north-east wind, which are not common; the north-west wind, blowing at least three-quarters of the time

ILLUS. 43—Even in mid-August parts of Ungava Bay are choked with ice which drifts in from the Hudson Straits.

during the winter season, is accompanied by a bright clear atmosphere. During the summer season, the precipitation, if not great, is constant, as a day rarely passes without drizzle, or thunder showers, which lower the temperature.

"At Northwest River, the head of Hamilton Inlet freezes completely over between the 1st and 15th of December, and opens again between May 15th and June 15th. Snow falls early in October, and from that date to about the first week in May, the latest record being July 2nd. At Rigolet, the outer part of Hamilton Inlet rarely or never freezes solid before the middle of January, and in some winters does not close at all. This is due to the strong currents in this part of the inlet. Sandwich Bay, nearly one hundred miles farther south, generally freezes over in the end of December, and the same time may be taken as that of the closing of most of the larger fiords of the Atlantic coast. About Fort Chimo, the lower grounds are permanently covered with snow by the 1st of December, this covering remaining until the 10th of June. The higher hills retain snow until the last of August, and by the middle of September snow again covers the tops of the distant high hills."

CHAPTER VIII

THE ARCTIC PRAIRIES AND ARCHIPELAGO

The region under consideration in this chapter embraces all the islands of the so-called Arctic Archipelago; it also includes a large triangular area of the mainland of Canada situated north of the 60th parallel west of Hudson Bay and north of the 50-degree isotherm for July (Fig. 29). This whole Arctic region comprises probably 20% of the total area of the Dominion. In general, it is marked by the absence of tree growth; yet there are numerous outliers of spruce, poplar, birch, and other trees lying well within the region. O'Neill states that birches, six inches in diameter, are found in the upper Mackenzie Delta; and that willows eight to ten feet in height are found within a few miles of the coast, although at the coast they are only two feet high.[1] A fur-trader from Victoria Island stated that willows and alders there grew large enough for use in building the sides and roofs to cabins.[2]

The climate of the Arctic, as this region may well be called, is characterized as a whole by long, though not exceedingly cold, winters, short summers, and relatively long transition seasons. The term season should not be considered to mean the same as in southern Canada. Winter as understood in the south is really ten months long in the Far North; the remaining two months are like spring or autumn. If, however, changes are based on length of daylight and darkness as well as on cold and warmth, then the four seasons mentioned may be distinguished. Around Coronation Gulf,

"The Eskimos divide the year into five parts and conduct their movements accordingly. A decided break from the grip of winter occurs about the middle of April, and by the end of May all the snow has disappeared from the land except where large drifts remain along the cliffs. The sun is quite hot in April, the seals come out on the ice and the caribou begin their migration to the northern islands. In May, the wild-fowl arrive and after them the small birds; the sun shines for twenty-

[1] J. J. O'Neill, "Geology and Geography," *Report of the Canadian Arctic Expedition, 1913-18*, F. A. Acland, Ottawa, 1924, pp. 15A-16A.
[2] Alexander MacInnis, *New York Times*, March 3, 1925, p. 22.

four hours and the vegetation responds rapidly so that by the middle of June many wild flowers are in bloom, the slopes and valleys are green and small mammals are seen everywhere. At this time the flies begin to make their presence felt, and soon the mosquitoes are so numerous that one is reminded of summer in northern Ontario. Black flies are rare on the coast, but are too abundant for comfort along some of the rivers.

"The rivers are usually free of ice early in June, and by July, most of the small lakes are open. Great Bear Lake breaks up about June 20th and the ice in Coronation gulf at about the same time. The ice is then rapidly crushed into small pieces and disappears before August. Of all the ice on the Arctic coast, that which offers most obstruction to navigation is in Beaufort sea. This ice drifts around all summer and responds to all variations of wind and tide.

"By September, the days are shortening and light snowstorms occur and, by October, all the small lakes are frozen. The swift rivers freeze before the middle of the month, the migratory birds depart for the south and, by the end of the month, the shore ice is thick enough to permit travelling by sled. The sun disappears altogether in November; but, even in the middle of December, on clear days there is sufficient light for traveling for about five hours."[1]

With few exceptions, altitude plays a small part in the climate because the lands are relatively low. The relief, however, is varied; it is, therefore, significant especially in the localities where observations have been taken, most of these points being located in protected bays and fiords. In most cases these situations favor higher rather than lower temperatures, because of the adiabatic warming of the air as it descends into the fiords. Mean and minimum temperatures in winter apparently are not so low as farther south in the interior of the continent.

Where the land mass is large and where the water bodies are ice-covered, winters may be somewhat more severe, taking on the characteristic features of a continental climate. In the summer, however, the cold and generally ice-choked waters prevent mean temperatures from exceeding 50°; for, in the course of the summer, the old ice no sooner shows signs of disappearing than the new ice of the waning summer begins to form. Moreover, even though the insolation in summer is almost continuous, it is relatively weak; and so much is reflected or applied directly to melting snow and ice, thawing out the frozen surface and evaporating water from the thoroughly soaked ground

---

[1] O'Neill, op. cit., p. 72A.

that the surface and the air in contact with it do not become very warm.

Precipitation is uniformly light, being under 10 inches except along the southeastern margins of the region. A three-year record at Fort Conger shows less than 4 inches a year. Snowfall, likewise, is light, the annual total, particularly in the middle and western portions, not exceeding two feet. Snow, except in the warmer seasons, comes in the form of minute spicules which form so compact a mass that a cubic foot of this snow will weigh 30 pounds; that is, two inches of this snow may be equivalent to about one inch of rain.[1] Near open waters onshore winds sometimes bring in frost fog which yields some precipitation, but which offers a serious handicap to navigation. Ordinary fogs are probably no more frequent than farther south, certainly not so frequent as in the region of contact between the Labrador Current and the Gulf Stream.

All seasons tend to be stormy. Unlike middle latitudes, however, the north is not so stormy in winter as one might expect. At this season the paths of cyclones are well to the south, although there are times when storm centers cross Hudson Bay and Labrador, usually on their way toward southern Greenland. Then they bring heavy snows to the southeastern section of the Arctic. Also, well developed cyclones occasionally cross the region farther north when "the winter winds of the Far North are almost unimaginable by anyone who has never experienced them."[2] On the other hand, a December or January may pass with only calm and clear weather being experienced. Spring is stormy, as the belt of storms moves northward. Summer is, on the whole, relatively quiet. At this season cyclonic storms are not so frequent nor so well developed. Autumn, when water bodies are still open and markedly in contrast with the rapidly cooling lands, is unquestionably the stormy season, the worst months being October and November.

Chipman and Cox characterize the climate and the human responses to it in the region around Coronation Gulf as follows[3]:

"The Arctic coast region is subject to fewer extremes of temperature than is northern Ontario or the prairie provinces. During three years on the Arctic coast we had no temperature

[1] Contributions to Our Knowledge of the Arctic Regions, p. 312.

[2] R. E. Peary, The North Pole, F. A. Stokes, New York, 1910, p. 178.

[3] Kenneth G. Chipman and John R. Cox, "Geographical Notes on the Arctic Coast of Canada," Report of the Canadian Arctic Expedition, 1913-18, F. A. Acland, Ottawa, 1924, p. 32B.

lower than –50° F. in the winter, nor can the writers recall any above 76° F. in summer.

"The cold is by no means extreme in Coronation gulf, but a penetrating wind blows almost continuously. We have seen dogs from the interior, accustomed to a dry windless temperature of 60 to 70 degrees below zero, that were miserably cold in zero weather on the coast. The gulf is completely frozen over during the winter and the cold is accompanied by less humidity than in other parts of the Arctic, where there is open water during this season. Blizzards are common, but are neither as frequent nor as severe as in a more mountainous country, or one with more open water; and, generally, air conditions are much more stable.

"In Coronation gulf there is continuous daylight for more than two and a half months in the summer, from May 10 to August 1. For about one and three-quarter months of this time the sun is continuously above the horizon. On the other hand, during December and January the sun does not appear above the horizon for over a month. This period is not entirely dark for there are from four to five hours a day of very fair light.

"Precipitation is very light. The snowfall in winter does not exceed two feet, and in summer there is seldom heavy rain. The ground is usually free from snow, except in an occasional gully, for three or four months during the year.

"There is little doubt that fur clothing is best suited to the country. It is light, more comfortable, and warmer than any white man's clothing that could be taken in. That worn by the Eskimos of Coronation gulf, however, is not very satisfactory for the use of white men. Anyone with experience could have suitable clothing made in the district but the maximum comfort can be secured from the clothing made by the Alaskan or Mackenzie Delta Eskimos. They select and dress the skins more carefully; the clothing is better made; and the design and fit are, in every way, more satisfactory for the use of the white man. The skin used for clothing is almost invariably that of the caribou killed in the early fall before the hair has grown too long.

"A sleeping bag made from long-haired winter caribou skin is lighter, warmer, and more comfortable than either woolen blankets or eiderdown. A sleeping bag, weighing nine pounds, with a light canvas cover (weighing three pounds) to keep out the snow, is comfortable at any temperature.

"For use in the summer, the clothing of the white man is better than that of the Eskimos; but for the greater part of the year, native clothing is to be preferred."

North of the arctic circle the phenomenon which is particularly significant in the climate of the region and which has a most profound effect upon the lives and activities of its few inhabitants is the seasonal changes in the length of daylight and darkness. Indeed, even south of the arctic circle, these changes are of considerable importance if not so extreme.

A reference again to Table 4 shows the approximate number of hours the sun is above the horizon on the 21st day of each month at the various latitudes. This table reveals the fact that the southern limit of the Arctic may have a maximum duration of sunshine of less than 20 hours; although over most of the region, because it lies well north of the arctic circle, the sun may remain continuously above the horizon for more than one day—even as long as five months at the northern extremity of Ellesmere Island, 83 degrees north latitude.

Ekblaw who spent four years with the Crockerland Expedition to northern Greenland and Ellesmere Island, vividly describes the annual succession of daylight and darkness at Etah situated on the northwest coast of Greenland on Smith Sound, about 77 degrees north latitude. The description applies equally well to all of the region north of the arctic circle except as altitude of the sun or the total time the sun is above the horizon might alter it.[1]

"At Etah the period of so-called Arctic night begins on October 21 when even at noon-day the sun does not rise above the horizon in the due south, unless by refraction it should still appear to do so. After the sun has first disappeared it lights the southern sky quite brightly and for several noonday hours each day, but this daily period of twilight rapidly shortens and grows fainter until by mid-November only a noonday flush indicates south, and even this soon after fades away, and for almost two months, Thule is a land of darkness.

"This Arctic night is not so dark nor so disheartening as the imagination of temperate and tropical peoples is wont to picture it. Even when most intense at the winter solstice, the Arctic 'midnight,' the darkness, except in times of heavy cloudiness and storm, does not approach the utter blackness of tropical midnight. For ten to twelve days of every month the moon circles the sky, often when in its fullest phase; the brilliant stars Vega, Capella, Arcturus and others in the magnificent Arctic constellations that revolve about Polaris almost at the zenith, give noticeable light; most of the light that falls from moon and stars is reflected from the glittering snow-and-ice fields; and the eyes of the Eskimo, like those of the animals and birds that winter there, become adjusted to the diminished light, and

[1] W. E. Ekblaw, *The Polar Eskimo; Their Land and Life*, Doctor's Dissertation, Clark University, Worcester, 1926. Used by permission of the author.

all activities go on but slightly retarded or restricted by the absence of sunlight.

"Then about mid-January the soft rose and gold of the noon-day flush reappears on the southern horizon and waxes longer and brighter each day until at noon on February 21, the upper limb of the sun, large and red, gleams soft and bright above the southern horizon for a few moments. The sun has come back. The long night is over. The next day the whole sun appears, and seems to roll along the horizon a few degrees for a few minutes; the next day it has risen quite above the horizon and covers an arc of several degrees; the next few days the time and the arc lengthen fast.

"In a month, when the vernal equinox has come, the sun is above the horizon for twelve hours, and set for twelve hours; but because of the brilliant twilight the day is really almost or quite eighteen hours in length, and night is reduced to a scant six hours of darkness—a pale gray darkness that is not darkly black even at midnight.

"The time of sunshine lengthens each day, and night grows lighter, until on April 21 there is no sunset. The sun merely dips down to the horizon due north at midnight, and begins at once to rise to another circle a little higher than the day before. Day by day it rises in the sky until the summer solstice, when the full glory of Arctic day with the sun at maximum meridian height floods the whole top of the world within the Arctic Circle.

"For two months more the twenty-four hour sunlight continues but through these two months the daily circle sweeps nearer and nearer the horizon, finally to dip down below it due north at midnight on August 21. As the midnight sun sinks down behind the high cliffs, the long east-west fiords are veiled in shadow and grow so cold that ice begins to form, and the inland lakes set among the high hills fast freeze solid. Winter begins to come as soon as the sun begins to set.

"After August 21, the midnight twilight is bright for yet two weeks, and though the sun sets for a longer time each night there is but little darkness until the autumnal equinox, and then it is only a heavy gray dusk at midnight. But after September 21, night, such as it is, comes on apace and the winter begins in real earnest. All the streams freeze solid, there is no melting even at noon, and the ice-foot appears along the strand.

"As mid-October approaches, the arc the sun describes across the southern sky grows daily shorter, the hours of night grow longer and darker, and sunrise and sunset fast merge into one continuous flush over the southern sky; on October 21 the last thin wafer of the sun's red disk slips along the horizon due south, and winter and night again become one and the same. The ice-foot forms firm and fast along the shore, and rapidly the fiords and bays freeze over.

"When first the sun appears in February, it gives merely a red light, with no appreciable heat; it lies so low in the sky that most of its heat rays are filtered out. At the vernal equinox the sun is a scant twelve degrees above the horizon at noonday, less than one-eighth the way to the zenith, about as far as it has risen at half past seven that same day in New York. Even at midsummer height at the time of the summer solstice, the noonday sun at Etah is not quite thirty-six degrees above the horizon, less than ten degrees higher than the midwinter noonday sun at New York.

"These low-angled rays of the sun reflected from the snow-and-ice-clad surface, can have but little heat effect, though they serve to light the land brilliantly. The advantages of the steep southward facing cliffs upon which the sun's rays fall most perpendicularly during the period of early spring sunshine, is thus emphasized. As the sun rises higher and higher in the sky, the cliffs and steep slopes are heated even more rapidly, and as the arc of the sun's route across the sky is extended northward farther each day until sunset and sunrise merge due north, even the northward facing cliffs share in the direct heat, though noon on the northward facing cliffs and midnight on the southward facing cliffs are cold and chill in shadow.

"On horizontal surfaces the snow and ice do not begin to melt until after mid-April, when the midnight sun begins and the noon sun is eighteen degrees high—and then only in sheltered situations. Mid-May comes before general noontime melting begins; and until the first of June the noon temperature rarely rises above freezing on gray or overcast days. The chill winds sweeping down from the great reservoirs of cold off the ice-cap and the polar seas to the northward counteract the increasing effect of the sun's more vertical rays until about mid-June.

"It is only from mid-June to mid-August that the sun is generally effective throughout the twenty-four hours, melting snow and ice from the flat lands and inland pools. The inland streams and pools and lakes begin to open about midsummer— a few in sheltered recesses among hills or at the foot of southward facing slopes open as early as June first—and begin to freeze at night about mid-August, when the sun's rays at noon again form an angle of eighteen degrees with the earth's surface as they did in mid-April.

"From mid-August to mid-October the time of freezing each day lengthens fast. By mid-September most of the streams are frozen dry, and scums of salt water ice form along the shore to spread far out over the sea whenever the wind is in the north or clouds darken the daytime skies. The sinking sun gives little heat for a month before it disappears.

"After the sun has disappeared and the cold shadowless twilight of noonday and the gray dusk of night have set in, freezing goes on apace. All land water is frozen and only high winds and surging waves or racing tides, prevent the laying of a solid sheet of ice over the whole sea.

"While yet the sun is high enough in summer to yield appreciable heat, cloudy and overcast skies tend to lower the temperature and retard melting. After the sun has gone, low lying

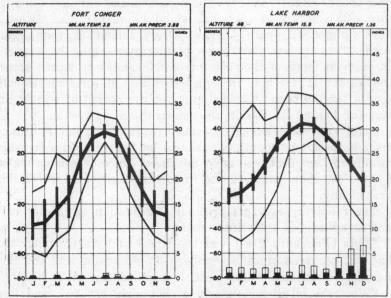

Fig. 54.—Temperature and precipitation charts for Fort Conger and Lake Harbour.

clouds particularly tend to blanket the heat given off by the open water. Summer clouds lend chill; winter clouds hold heat."

One of the most trying effects of the long hours of sunshine comes in the form of snowblindness, especially in early spring when the ground is still covered with snow, and clouds are few. Persons foreign to the region are particularly susceptible to this affliction and need to protect their eyes against the intense reflected insolation.

Of all the seasons winter has the most profound effect upon the people of the Arctic. Most activities during the other seasons are preparations for this long period of cold. The long period of darkness each day or over a series of days permits only a minimum of hunting and trapping especially in the far north.

As pointed out earlier, minimum winter temperatures in the northern islands are not extremely low, although mean temperatures are lower than most of those experienced in the interior of Canada. The lowest average mean temperature, –29°, comes in January; some places in the Mackenzie region have means slightly lower. The highest mean January temperature, –22°, occurs at Herschel Island (7 years); the lowest at Fort Conger (2 years) and at Dealy Island (1 year), each with –37°. Below zero mean temperatures may be expected throughout much of the region from November to April. Hence, though the lowest may in some years and at some places come soon after the time of lowest sun, yet the period of winter cold lags far behind it. Minimum temperatures as low as –60° are probably not uncommon, especially in January and February; though these two months appear to be the only ones in which minimum temperatures have not been above freezing. Figs. 54 and 55 show some of the important temperature relations graphically.

The following excerpts give some indication of the intensity and steadiness of the winter cold:

"This [February 21st] was the finest and warmest day that had yet occurred since November. It was calm, and the thermometer continued rising until it reached zero at midnight."[1]

"We froze oil of almonds in a shot mold at –40°, and fired it against a target, which it split, rebounding unbroken."[2]

"It was little more than a school boy's experiment to fire a ball of frozen mercury through an inch plank."[3]

"After Christmas the weather turned very cold; the coldest spell we had was from January 9th to January 14th, when the minimum readings were as follows: –57°, –51°, –56°, –59°, –51°."[4]

Anderson found, however, that "winter temperatures on the coast average considerably warmer than at most points in the interior" around Bathurst Inlet.[5]

All explorers of the northland are agreed that the winter precipitation is light, and that the number of days during which it occurs is few. At Wellington Channel, snow fell on only 11

[1] *Contributions to Our Knowledge of the Meteorology of the Arctic Regions*, p. 49.
[2] Ibid., p. 49.
[3] Ibid., p. 49.
[4] Ibid., p. 162.
[5] R. M. Anderson, "Recent Explorations on the Canadian Arctic Coast," *Geogr. Rev.*, v. 4, 1917, p. 261.

days between one November and the next April, the total number of days for the year being 39, with 9 days additional when rain occurred. At Port Leopold snow occurred on only 4 days during the four-month period November to February; for the year there were 70 precipitation days.[1] Snow spicules, however, may be frequent even on the clearest days.[2] These spicules often yield a good proportion of the winter snowfall.

ILLUS. 44—In the arctic winter tiny spicules make up the snow which, though quite porous, is nevertheless very compact. Temporary, but comfortable, shelters are quickly made from blocks of this snow. The scene is from Bernard Harbour on the mainland near Coronation Gulf.

Sverdrup states that in the latter part of March the weather was misty and the still damp air so laden with rime that fine needles of ice fell continuously. He found travel was somewhat heavy on the dust-like, newly fallen snow.[3] It is only this very compact snow that the Eskimos use for their igloos. Hann states that on Melville Island, the snow cover amounts to less than two inches, and that by the middle of April it will measure only five inches.[4] He explains the small amount of snow by stating that snow flakes do not form with a temperature lower than $-9°$.[5]

Stefansson states that 75 to 90 per cent of the surface of Arctic lands is nearly free from snow at all seasons, since the

[1] *Contributions to Our Knowledge of the Meteorology of the Arctic Regions*, p. 322.
[2] Ibid., 128.
[3] Otto Sverdrup, *New Land*, Vol. I, Longman's Green & Co., New York, 1904, p. 352.
[4] Julius Hann, *Handbuch der Klimatologie*, Bund III, J. Engelhorn, Stuttgart, 1911, p. 594.
[5] Ibid., p. 595.

little that falls is swept into the lee of the hills[1]; and Peary observed that musk-oxen are permitted to graze in winter on Ellesmere Island because the wind sweeps the snow off the grasses and tiny willows.[2] One of the Canadian police patrols found considerable difficulty in sledging across the Arctic Prairies north of Chesterfield Inlet because of the lack of snow.[3] At Winter Harbour it was reported that "there was at this period [April] more snow upon the ground than at any other time of the year, the average depths on the lower parts of the land being four or five inches, but much less upon the hills; while in the ravines a very large quantity had been collected."[4] On the other hand snowfall may be considerable at times as Sverdrup experienced at Rice Strait: "When the mate tried to go out of the hut he found that we were entirely snowed up, and he had to break through the roof of the porch and shovel a way from there. Over the whole of the large hollow in which the tent stood lay an even sheet of snow, several yards deep. Of the great stack of meat, about nine feet high, we saw not a trace."[5]

There is considerable conflict of opinion regarding the storminess of the Arctic winter. Calm and clear weather seems to characterize the season some years; and during other years several blizzards follow one another in rather rapid succession. On the whole, the western portion of the archipelago, far from open water, has calmer weather and less snow than the eastern portion near the stormy open sea. Peary vividly describes conditions as experienced at his base off northern Ellesmere Island[6]:

"The north and northwest winds sweeping down along the coast are the coldest; but for absolutely insane fury, the winds from the south and the southwest, falling off the highland of the coast with almost the impact of a wall of water, are unsurpassed anywhere else in the arctic regions. Sometimes these storms come on gradually, the wind from the northwest steadily increasing in force and swinging through the west to the southwest, gathering fury with every hour, until the snow is picked up bodily from the land and the ice-foot and carried in blinding, horizontal sheets across the ship."

[1] Kindle, op. cit., p. 79.
[2] Peary, op. cit., p. 183.
[3] Kindle, op. cit., p. 79.
[4] *Contributions to Our Knowledge of the Meteorology of the Arctic Regions*, p. 262.
[5] Sverdrup, op. cit., p. 95.
[6] Peary, op. cit., p. 178.

A year spent at Port Leopold revealed that December was the calmest month and that February was exceptionally stormy.[1] One year the Gulf of Boothia showed calms to be frequent from December to March, and the clearest weather to occur in February and March.[2] Jenness states that in the district around Coronation Gulf January was generally the coldest, darkest and stormiest month in the year, the only month

ILLUS. 45—June 25, 1928, at Wakeham Bay on the northern coast of the Labrador Peninsula, is much much like March along the upper St. Lawrence.

that the Eskimos really dreaded. Blizzards often confine them to their houses five days out of seven, and even if a hunter should brave the storms he could find no seal holes through the driving snow.[3] An expedition to Northumberland Sound in 1852-53 reported: "As yet we scarcely admit the existence of a gale, we certainly have not experienced fierce ravages of tempests or hurricanes."[4] Not many degrees from the same locality, Sverdrup later reported a wind in December reaching 59 feet per second with the thermometer at –57°![5] A report from Wellington Channel states that calms are most frequent by night, that below –40° it does not blow hard, and that at –60° wind is not experienced.[6]

[1] *Contributions to Our Knowledge of the Meteorology of the Arctic Regions*, p. 322.
[2] Ibid., p. 46.
[3] Diamond Jenness, *The People of the Twilight*, The Macmillan Co., New York, 1928, p. 59.
[4] *Contributions to Our Knowledge of the Meteorology of the Arctic Regions*, p. 169.
[5] Sverdrup, op. cit., p. 121.
[6] *Contributions to Our Knowledge of the Meteorology of the Arctic Regions*, p. 182.

It is not to be supposed that all of the vast Arctic region under consideration is climatically a unit. Undoubtedly conditions vary in this region over a given distance quite as much as they do in southern Canada. The factors of land and water (and ice), latitude, relief, prevailing winds and storms apply in some degree to all parts of the Arctic. The diversities in winter appear to be greater than those in summer.

The climate of the eastern and southern coasts of southern Baffin Island is essentially different from that of the Arctic

ILLUS. 46—The snow cover on the ice of Wakeham Bay in February makes transportation relatively easy and certain.

in general because here the dominating control in winter is not so much latitude as water—the Labrador Current through Davis Strait and the waters of Hudson Strait. Even though these waters are cold, by comparison with the frozen lands they are relatively warm and tend to ameliorate the winter conditions immediately along the coasts, temperatures for that season ranging from 10 to 20 or more degrees higher than in the Mackenzie Valley in the same latitude. As in a marine climate, February is the coldest month, although both February and March show the lowest recorded temperatures, –50° at Lake Harbour in February, –55° at Kingua Fjord in March (one year record). Winter conditions lag on into March and early April in spite of the higher sun and longer daily period of sunshine. In fact, this lag is pronounced far north in Rice Strait where the swift current keeps the waters open throughout the year. This condition is probably emphasized more on the Greenland than on the Ellesmereland side. During the eleven years of record at Lake Harbour, January is the only month which has not shown temperatures above freezing. On the other hand, there was one February when the temperature failed to go as high as 0°. Temperatures below zero have occurred in all months except June to September, inclusive.

Comparatively heavy snowfall is a characteristic of this coastal stretch, the average annual being about nine feet. One December there was six and one-half feet. November and December are the the months of heaviest precipitation; February and March are the months with fewest stormy days. As pointed out in Chapter II, it is this southern end of Baffinland which lies in the path of vigorous late autumn cyclones which cross from Hudson Bay to join the St. Lawrence procession over the North Atlantic. Prevailing winds are north and east throughout the long winter.

The transition, from the coldest of winter to the time when snow leaves the exposed places and plant life is renewed, is generally a long period in the Arctic. The difference between this transition period and winter is not a difference in temperature conditions, for temperatures as low as –13° have occurred in May and as low as 13° even in June; it is rather a difference in the length of day. In March the days begin to be longer, and by May they may be 20 or even 24 hours long over most of the Arctic. It is during this spring or "cold-daylight" season that the native is most active. Hard snow and ice permit easy sledging; long daylight hours permit a maximum of hunting. Sverdrup, however, observed that in spite of the low temperatures in March, with minima of –50° and below, the sun near noon could work miracles in clear calm weather.[1] And Jenness states[2]: "We lingered a fortnight on the sea-ice [Victoria Island], reveling in the mild weather of the Arctic spring. Day and night were hardly distinguishable, for the end of April saw the midnight sun. . . . . The nights were preferable for travelling, because at 7 P. M. the melting slush of noon began to freeze again and the heavily laden sled glided along more easily." "The mild weather of the Arctic spring" means average temperatures from March to May of –25° up to 15°

[1] Sverdrup, op. cit., p. 138.
[2] Jenness, op. city., p. 99.

or 20°. Yet, the apparent or comparative mildness of this season is certified by most of those who have visited the region. Sverdrup says of the 17th of May: "Today, splendid, beautiful weather; mild and calm, with sparkling sunshine."[1] According to Douglas in writing of the Arctic Prairie[2]: "It turned mild very suddenly that afternoon [April 30]; we had a strong south wind and the temperature rose to 40° . . . . it kept mild and the warm south wind blew all through the night."

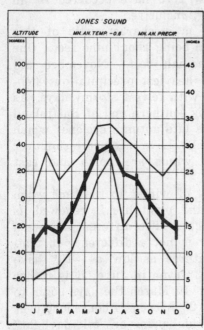

FIG. 55—Temperature chart for Jones Sound Region.

That low temperatures are the rule, however, is indicated when Ekblaw reported that in May, Lake Hazen and its outlet, the Ruggles River, in north Grant Land, were frozen solid.[3] Douglas found river ice over six feet thick in April.[4] In the Gulf of Boothia one year ice continued to increase in thickness into May, reaching 10 feet on the sea at the end of May.[5] A recent statement by a feature writer concerning the experiences of an inspector of the Royal Canadian Mounted Police gives the following[6]: "Traveling across the interior of the northwest part of Baffin Land, he crossed many lakes, frozen solid in that northern climate. So solid does the water freeze that he was able to climb a waterfall. Then the weather became bad. A five-day blizzard set in. The mercury dropped till even the coal oil used as fuel froze solid and had to be thawed out by means of native lamps before it could be used." Anderson found along the Arctic coast that the coldest weather of his winter occurred on March 31, the record

[1] Sverdrup, op. cit., p. 284.
[2] George M. Douglas, *Lands Forlorn*, G. P. Putnam's Sons, New York, 1912, p. 181.
[3] Statement to the author.
[4] Douglas, op. cit.
[5] *Contributions to Our Knowledge of the Meteorology of the Arctic Regions*, p. 49.
[6] James Montagnes, *The New York Times*, November 25, 1928, p. 9.

being −46°, and "the thermometer rose to 9° below zero at 4:30 p. m. the same day."[1]

One of the greatest handicaps to traveling on the ice of salt water bodies at this season is the presence of monster pressure ridges which develop as the result of tidal movements, ice expansion, and wind pressure. Ekblaw experienced these in crossing the Channel between Grant Land and Greenland[2]: "South of the ridge [40 feet high] the ice was thrown up in great mountain-like ridges and cordilleras of ice-piles, the most chaotic expanse of rough ice I have ever seen. . . . . As far as we could see with our glasses, the ice was as rough as that we had just passed through. . . . . In seven hours of utmost exertion we made only three miles." Peary found pressure ridges varying from a few feet to a few rods in height, and from a few rods to a quarter of a mile in width.[3]

Towards the end of April and during the first part of May, the higher sun and the almost 24 hours of continuous sunshine begin to make themselves felt in raising temperatures, in clearing the lands of snow, and in reducing the ice of the streams and lakes. From Winter Harbour, Melville Island, came this report[4]:

"The changes of temperature during April were rapid, 'the thermometer having ranged from −32° to 32° in the course of 20 days. There was at this period more snow upon the ground than at any other time of the year, the average depth on the lower parts of the land being four or five inches, but much less upon the hills; while in the ravines a very large quantity had been collected. The snow at this time became so soft from the influence of the sun upon it, as to make walking very laborious and unpleasant.' "

On May 21, at the same place, brown soil began to appear; on May 24, showers of rain. It is during May that small creeks begin to run, the water flowing deep over the ice before the latter has time to melt or be broken up.[5]

Concerning the storminess of this transition season, like that of winter, there are some conflicting statements. Doubtless, some years are relatively calm, others relatively stormy; and,

[1] Anderson, op. cit., p. 258.
[2] W. E. Ekblaw, Appendix, *Four Years in the White North* (by D. B. Macmillan), Harper & Bros., New York, 1918.
[3] Peary, op. cit., pp. 194-5.
[4] *Contributions to Our Knowledge of the Meteorology of the Arctic Regions*, p. 262.
[5] Douglas, op. cit., p. 189.

as mentioned earlier, location with respect to latitude, water bodies and relief must likewise be important factors. Such considerations are suggested by Sverdrup's statement regarding conditions about April 20 in Bay Fjord on the west side of Ellesmere Island[1]: "The snowfall apparently is inconsiderable so far up the fjords, and as the evaporation is great, and this is a country where there is always blowing what we call a 'cow-storm' (a gale so strong that it blows the horns off the cows), all the snow had disappeared." In the latter part of May, also, he found the wind so strong as to sweep dogs, sledges and men sideways across the ice far out of their course and to an alarming degree. Small snow drifts on the ice were their only salvation.[2] It is probably true that winds at times in any season are strongest at the mouths of fiords where the descending air in the fiord may be joined by the normal air movement over the unobstructed bays. This condition may be more pronounced when pressure is high over the Arctic, for north and northwest winds appear to be the strongest. On the other hand, the few east winds which are experienced are generally referred to as gales, evidently the result of a strong cyclone invading the region from the west and southwest.

The transformation of the landscape with the coming of summer (part of June, all of July, and part of August, though not as summer is known in southern Ontario) is evidently quite amazing to one who is not accustomed to witnessing it. The magical disappearance of snow and the rapid plant growth, particularly the herbaceous flowering plants, and the arrival of both land and sea birds in countless numbers—often before the snow disappears—are occurrences of constant remark. Sverdrup observed sandpipers as early as May 30, and a large flock of Brant geese a few days later "where there was not yet so much as a thawed patch, or a puddle big enough for a goose to put its beak into."[3] In July he observed abundance of bird life[4]: "And what life and movement was there! On the top of it [a rocky island in Jones Sound] the gulls were nesting; in the clefts and fissures lived thousands of black guillemots, and well sheltered under the sides of the mountain

[1] Sverdrup, op. cit., p. 132.
[2] Ibid., p. 384.
[3] Ibid., pp. 290-1
[4] Ibid., p. 311.

were long rows of eider-ducks' nests." His description of
weather in June is most inviting[1]:

"The fine weather of the last few days had awakened nature
out of her sleep, as it were, at a single stroke. The sun now
shone warm and clear. Plains and slopes smiled their greeting
to us under their many-hued covering of flowers. Ice-water
streamed in the brooks, and rushed in torrents over the preci-
pices. Near the tent a covey of ptarmigan were walking about,
and from the hillside we heard the cry of a cock; while out
on the ice the seals stretched themselves in enjoyment of the
warmth, and the long-tailed ducks splashed about in the leads.
Nowhere does one notice the magic power of the sun as in the
polar regions; it creates summer in the space of a few days. . . . .
The heat inside the tent was almost unendurable. We tried
lying outside the bags, but it was too warm. Then we stripped,
garment by garment, till we were almost naked, but even then
we could hardly bear it. It [June 13] was the hottest day I
ever spent under canvas."

Parry at Repulse Bay in August found that "nothing could
exceed the fineness of the weather about this time; the climate
was, indeed, altogether so different from that to which we had
been accustomed in the icy seas as to be a matter of constant
remark. The days were temperate and clear, and the nights
not cold, though a very thin plate of ice was usually formed
upon the surface of the sea in sheltered places and in pools of
water among the floes."[2]

Land birds in great variety migrate to the Arctic for these
few warm months: humming-birds, warblers of various kinds,
chickadees, and so-called camp robbers. One writer speaks of
wild, golden shouldered "bees which make honey from the flowers and make their hives in willows and alders to hide from
polar bears which like honey the same as other bears."[3] Other
insect life is likewise abundant, caterpillars being observed as
early as May 27 in Assistance Bay, and about the middle of
May on Melville Island. Jenness, while on Victoria Island,
found that the early summer warmth

"was not an unmixed blessing, for it hatched out myriads of
mosquitoes, that rose and fell in the atmosphere like the motes
in a sunbeam. How so many could exist was a mystery.
Wherever we travelled they hovered around us like bees swarm-
ing, and no smudge could keep them at bay. My tent became

[1] Ibid., p. 166.
[2] M. W. C. Hepworth, "Climatological Observations at an Arctic Station in Repulse
Bay," *Quarterly Journal of the Royal Meteorological Society*, v. 31, 1905, p. 326.
[3] *New York Times*, March 25, 1928, p. 22.

the common refuge, for its doorway of fine netting resisted all their assaults, though they pattered on the roof like rain. Outside everyone wore mittens as in winter, and my companions beat their faces with loon skins as automatically as a band-conductor wields his baton. Only on the ice could we escape the insects, their flight being limited to about a quarter of a mile, unless the wind carried them farther. The animals suffered almost as much as ourselves. Our dogs tried to burrow in the ground to protect their feet and noses."[1]

Throughout the southern part of the Arctic, and particularly over the Arctic Prairies or the miscalled Barren Grounds, the mosquitoes and black flies are the bane of mammalian existence of all sorts; there is little escape from their constantly pestering presence.

Mean July temperatures range from about 35° in the northern portion of the Archipelago to 50° on the extreme southern limit. These approximate the January means experienced from Washington, D. C., south to Charleston, S. C. Freezing temperatures are to be expected practically every July even as far south as Chesterfield Inlet; while maximum temperatures of 50° to 70° are frequent. At Chesterfield Inlet, 84° has been observed, and at Pond's Inlet, about 9 degrees farther north, 77° has been recorded. Mean daily ranges of temperature in July are not large because the sun is above the horizon continuously. Cloudiness, which averages from 50% to 70% during this month, would tend to increase the range. The extreme ranges in July are likewise smaller than those at other seasons, the greatest occurring usually in March and April. The average change from the coldest to the warmest month is strikingly similar for all parts of the Arctic, being everywhere 70 to 80 degrees. These ranges are 20 to 30 degrees lower than in the Mackenzie Valley and parts of the Prairie Provinces.

July is also the rainiest month, though the season of maximum precipitation (rain and snow) comes later, from August to October. Rain, however, is probably more noticeable because of its wetting effects; hence, the reference to "a downpour which lasted for two days in Jones Sound."[2] Yet a wetting from a rain of this sort caused little hardship to the Sverdrup party exposed to it, for "as soon as we were back at the tent and laid our things on the sand they were dried directly. When

---

[1] Jenness, op. cit., p. 146.
[2] Sverdrup, op. cit., p. 312.

the air is dry, and a strong wind blows without ceasing the thermometer showing 46° to 48° F. in the shade, water soon evaporates, and snow and ice vanish like dew before the sun."[1]

Summer days are not all "lovely days" with "a weather wonderful as only the land of the midnight sun can offer."[2] At Cape Sheridan "on the summer solstice, June 22, midnoon of the Arctic summer and the longest day of the year, it snowed

ILLUS. 47—Caches of food, even though untinned, may be preserved indefinitely in a polar climate such as this on the Arctic coast near the mouth of the Mackenzie.

all night; but a week later the weather seemed almost tropical, and we suffered from the heat, strange though as it seems to say."[3] Even 15 degrees farther south on Victoria Island toward the end of July "a snow-storm, not an unusual occurrence even in the height of summer, delayed our departure a few days."[4] All records and reports from the Arctic indicate that fogs are infrequent in summer and in the milder months of the transition seasons. When the moist winds blow across the ice-cold waters of channels, bays, and lakes, fogs may be expected on the windward shores.

Warm as summer days are, they make up a season too short to make much impression on the ice of Arctic seas. Winds and tides are quite as effective in opening channels as are high tem-

[1] Ibid., p. 303.
[2] Ibid., p. 303.
[3] Peary, op. cit., p. 330.
[4] Jenness, op. cit., p. 173.

peratures; but, on the contrary, winds and tides are equally effective in closing the leads and channels which the melting causes. The "Fram" was ice-locked in Jones Sound for two summers; and although the heat of the sun on clear days was sufficient to melt as much as two inches of ice off the top, it was on July 2nd that "this was the end of the fine-weather period. Northerly winds set in, and the mist, grey and clammy, came sailing down upon us. This, unhappily, was to be the prevailing weather that summer."[1]   Late July and early August are usually the periods of greatest open water, particularly salt water. Yet, in Jones Sound on August 12th there was clear weather and frost with new ice strong enough to hold up dogs, and in some places men, while "day after day the thermometer stood at the freezing point."[2] Opposite conditions obtained the next year when the ice cleared early out of Jones Sound permitting the release of the "Fram," that summer being as extremely warm as the preceding had been cold. Anderson reports that in July, 1913, for the first time in 25 years, ships were unable to reach Herschel Island from Alaska. He also states that in August, 1913,

"east of Point Barrow we found the Arctic Ocean practically filled with heavy ice. In that part of the world there are no true ice-bergs; but enormous pressure ridges often form along tide-cracks or are heaped up by gales along the edge of the floe fields, where they are cemented by spray and spring thaws and augmented by snow drifts. These masses are sometimes of immense size, rising thirty or forty feet out of water—too large to melt during the short summer. The ice conditions east of Point Barrow seem to depend largely upon the prevailing winds during early summer. If the winds are easterly the ice masses move out to the northwestward of Point Barrow and Wrangel Island, leaving an open ocean for navigation. If the winds are westerly the great ice-pack is jammed against the northern coast of Alaska and the region about the mouth of the Mackenzie where there is no easterly exit."[3]

Between the Arctic Prairies and Victoria Island ice is generally solid during the greater part of June in ocean harbors, beginning to break up the last of that month and in early July. Farther inland, the fresh water streams break up three or four weeks earlier; in fact, the summer season begins

---

[1] Sverdrup, op. cit., p. 304.
[2] Ibid., p. 319.
[3] Anderson, op. cit., p. 244.

earlier and earlier as the distance from the cold Arctic waters increases. Yet summer temperatures far back in the Arctic Prairies are lower than those of the Mackenzie Valley in the same latitude.

Everywhere in the Arctic where the marine control is strong (i. e., on the islands and coastal stretches), autumn is much warmer than spring, October being from 5 to 15 or more degrees warmer than April. In spite of this greater warmth,

ILLUS. 48.—Even as far north as Aklavik (less than 50 miles from the Arctic Ocean), spruce attains sufficient size as to be useful to the people of the region. The month is December.

the autumn months are really winter months, as far as temperatures are concerned. That is, October is as cold at Chesterfield Inlet as January is at Halifax, and Pond's Inlet has an October mean as low as the January mean at Montreal. Early autumn, August to October, is the season of preparation for the long northern twilight.

All explorers and other visitors recount the storminess of this season. There may be prolonged periods of relative quietude as Peary observed at Cape Sheridan; yet even after that, ice pressure, largely the result of winds, caused serious damage to the ship, "Roosevelt."[1] In the Coronation Gulf district on Victoria Island snow which fell incessantly for three days during the second week in September "did not melt again,

[1] Peary, op. cit., p. 176.

and every lake was solidly bound with ice."[1] In September, 1851, between Banks Island and Victoria Island ice piled upwards of 100 feet along or near the shore with west and northwest gales.[2] The fated Hall Expedition in November, 1871, in Smith Sound experienced a storm so severe that the ship, "Polaris," which had been frozen in was loosened, the ice being broken up and carried away. And it was in October of

ILLUS. 49—This snowy view near Chesterfield Inlet would hardly indicate the fact that maximum summer temperatures here have been known to reach 80° and more.

the next year that pressure of the ice became so great in a heavy storm as to crush the Polaris, necessitating its complete abandonment.[3]

In the district around Coppermine River, Douglas found autumn weather to be very changeable from day to day, September 1 being cited as an example: "The weather went through some sudden and violent changes today: from a lovely placid morning it turned to a stormy afternoon with a strong northwest wind, ... but fortunately it lasted only a couple of hours, then turned to a quiet, sullen evening."[4] Sverdrup experienced some hard storms in the region about Jones Sound

[1] Jenness, op. cit., p. 173.

[2] Contributions to Our Knowledge of the Meteorology of the Arctic Regions, p. 415.

[3] C. H. Davis, North Polar Expedition. Government Printing Office, Washington. 1876, pp. 236 and 429.

[4] Douglas, op. cit., p. 128.

in both October and November; his reference to one under which he had been laboring follows[1]:

"I think it blew even more, if that were possible, when the mate and I turned out to see after the dogs. . . . . The snow had drifted so much that my team were only just able to keep on the top of it. . . . . They had mounted and mounted, now had literally got to the end of their tether. . . . . The night that followed I shall never forget. I have experienced many a stormy night in the polar regions, but not many like this."

Concerning November 9th of the same year he makes this statement[2]:

"The wind came on apace. Again the north wind swept swift and strong down the valley, and out through the fjord; and the more it blew the colder it became. To begin with, we had $-33°$ to $-35°$ F., but later the mean temperature was $-40°$ to $-57°$ F. Day after day the wind blew with merciless strength; sometimes as a stiff breeze, sometimes as a gale. The air was clear, but the fjord and valley smoked with snow that was whirled up and about."

The following excerpts concern the district around Coppermine River:

"We had fine weather [October], the thermometer as yet going only to zero at night time. . . . . The shallow head waters were frozen right to the bottom; Sandy Creek was solid ice clear through."[3]

"All November and most of December the weather was very uniform; the minimum temperature was about $-20°$. For a few hours in the course of the day it would rise to some 10 or 15 degrees above the minimum. On November 11th, the thermometer went down to $-36°$, a minimum that was not reached again until December 22nd when temperatures fell rapidly and the *grand froid* of winter began. In November and December the weather was mostly dull and cloudy, with an incessant light snowfall which amounted to very little in the aggregate. At the end of December the weather turned clear and bright and was commonly so until the following July."[4]

Humidity has only casually been mentioned, for there are few authentic records of either absolute or relative humidity. It is true, however, that the absolute humidity is always low

[1] Sverdrup, op. cit., v. II, pp. 94-5.
[2] Ibid., pp. 104-5.
[3] Douglas, op. cit., p. 145.
[4] Ibid., p. 160.

particularly in winter, a fact evidenced by the almost continuously low temperatures, the large percentage of clear days, and the greatly reduced precipitation. On the other hand relative humidity must be comparatively high, evidenced more by its effects than by actual measurement. The small, so-called capacity of the cold air for water vapor is shown by this account from Sverdrup[1]:

"In very severe cold—say, about –58° F.—I often noticed, that when the 'Primus' was lighted, a thick layer of rime formed on the canvas of the tent. When this layer grew still thicker, long wooly tassels would hang down from the roof, and with the slightest puff of wind or touch of the tent, came down like snow. . . . . This phenomenon may be described as a kind of hoar-frost. . . . . Peary who was ten or fifteen miles farther north at the same time, says that on the same day they had –67°. It was then that seven of his toes were frost-bitten, and had to be amputated. . . . . Early next morning we turned out and made haste to Fort Juliana, where we set to work as soon as possible to dry our fur clothes and the sleeping bags, which had become wet through and through in the space of only twenty-four hours."

Peary describes something of the same sort which occurred on board the "Roosevelt" at Cape Sheridan[2]:

"Every week or ten days throughout the winter we had to remove from our cabins the ice caused by the condensation from the moist air where it came in contact with the cold outer walls. Behind every article of furniture near the outer walls the ice would form, and we used to chop it out from under our bunks by the pailful.

"The books were always placed far forward on the shelves, because if a book were pushed back it would freeze solid to the wall. Then, if a warmer day came, or a fire was built in the cabin, the ice would melt, the water would run down and the leaves of the book would mold."

There are many other phenomena of Arctic meteorology which have not been and cannot be taken up in a treatise of this kind, among them being the aurora, refraction of sunlight, halos, parhelia, inversions of temperature, and so on. Furthermore, the region is so vast, the conditions from place to place so diversified, and the weather data so few, scattered and fragmentary, that it has not seemed feasible to attempt more than

[1] Sverdrup, op. cit., V. I, p. 98.
[2] Peary, op. cit., p. 180.

an occasional interpretation of the weather and climate as described.

As indicated earlier in this chapter, the men who have lived through several years of Arctic weather, almost without exception, bring back glowing reports. Even Stefansson's "old friend Jim Fiji," a native of Samoa, after being taken to Herschel Island through his own error, was so enthralled with conditions after three years of life there that he never would consent to live elsewhere.[1] With proper clothing man can be as comfortable in the polar regions as anywhere; and the Arctic darkness of winter is "about as depressing on the northern coast of Canada as the darkness of midnight on Broadway."[2] Perhaps the greatest advantage of living in the far north is the almost complete absence of pulmonary diseases. Eskimo men, as a rule, succumb during middle life, not through disease so much as through accident, generally drowning in the struggle for meat and skins.

Agriculture as practiced in southern Canada is obviously impossible in the Arctic. Trapping, hunting and fishing have always been the activities of the few people. The possibilities of organized musk-ox (ovibos) and caribou grazing over the vast stretches of Arctic grasslands may be remote; yet they have been seriously considered by the Dominion Government.[3] The presence of petroleum, coal, gold, and other minerals known to exist, and the possible discovery of many others will, as demands for these minerals increase, cause the white man to penetrate farther and farther into the great northland, even as he is doing today in the upper Mackenzie. O'Neill's conclusion is as follows[4]: "It may be seen, then, that as far as the climate is concerned, there is nothing to prohibit settlement. Game and fish abound and there should be little difficulty in establishing a mining industry if the mineral deposits prove to be valuable. Underground mining could be carried on throughout the whole year without much inconvenience."

[1] Stefansson, *The Northward Course of Empire*, pp. 106-9.
[2] Kindle, op. cit., p. 54.
[3] Reindeer and Musk-Ox," *Report of the Royal Commission upon the Possibility of the Reindeer and Musk-Ox Industries in the Arctic and Sub-Arctic Regions*, Dept. of the Int., Ottawa, 1922.
[4] O'Neill, op. cit., p. 72A.

BIBLIOGRAPHY

BIBLIOGRAPHY*

ALLBRIGHT, W. D.: Some Climatic Characteristics of Central Alberta; B. A. M. S., v. 3, 1922, p. 171

AMUNDSEN, ROALD: The Northwest Passage, 2 vols.; Archibald Constable & Co. Ltd., London, 1908

ANDERSON, R. M.: Recent Explorations on the Canadian Arctic Coast; G. R., v. 4, 1917, pp. 241-266

BEGG, ALEXANDER: Early Exploration in North-West Canada; S. G. M., 15, 1899, pp. 351-356

BELL, ROBERT: A Survey in Baffinland, with a Short Description of the Country; G. J., v. 18, 1901, pp. 25-43

BLANCHETT, GUY H.: Narrative of a Journey to the Source of Coppermine River; B. G. S. P., v. 24, 1926, pp. 163-177

BROOKS, C. E. P.: The Meteorology of Hebron, Labrador, 1883-1912; Q. J. R. M. S., v. 45, 1919, pp. 163-167

BUCKINGHAM, H., SR.: The "Southwest" or "Wet Chinook"; M. W. R., v. 35, 1907, pp. 175-176

CHAMBERLAIN, T. C.: Significant Ameliorations of Present Arctic Climates; Jour. of Geology, v. 31, 1923, pp. 376-406

CLAYTON, H. H.: World Weather Records; Smithsonian Inst., Washington, 1927

CONNOR, A. J.: Modal Atmospheric Streaming in Wet and Dry Seasons in the Canadian Wheat Belt; B. A. M. S., v. 3, 1922, pp. 35-36

CONNOR, A. J.: Precipitation in Canada (in The Canada Yearbook, 1926); Dominion Bureau of Statistics, Ottawa, 1926, pp. 42-46

CONNOR, A. J.: Relation of the Weather to the Yield of Wheat in Manitoba; Monthly Bulletin of Agricultural Statistics (Dominion Bureau of Statistics), Ottawa, April, 1918

*B. A. M. S.: Bulletin of the American Meteorological Society, Worcester, Mass.
B. G. S. P.: Bulletin of the Geographical Society of Philadelphia, Philadelphia
G. J.: Geographical Journal, London
G. R.: Geographical Review, New York
M. W. R.: Monthly Weather Review, Washington
N. G. M.: National Geographic Magazine, Washington
Q. J. R. M. S.: Quarterly Journal of the Royal Meteorological Society, London
S. G. M.: Scottish Geographical Magazine, Edinburgh

CONNOR, A. J.: The Temperature and Precipitation of Alberta, Saskatchewan and Manitoba; Meteorological Service, Toronto, 1920

CONNOR, A. J.: The Temperature and Precipitation of British Columbia; Meteorological Service, Toronto, 1915

CORNISH, VAUGHAN: On Snow-Waves and Snow-Drifts in Canada; G. J., v. 20, 1902, pp. 137-172

CURRAN, W. T. and CALKINS, H. A.: In Canada's Wonderful Northland; G. P. Putnam's Sons, New York, 1917

DAVIS, C. H.: North Polar Expedition—U. S. S. Polaris; Government Printing Office, Washington, 1876

DAY. P. C.: Monthly Normals of Sea-Level Pressure for the United States, Canada, Alaska, and the West Indies; M. W. R., v. 52, 1924, pp. 30-35

DAY, P. C.: Precipitation in the Drainage Area of the Great Lakes, 1875-1924; M. W. R., v. 54, 1926, pp. 85-106

DECARIE, J. L.: Climatology; Statistical Yearbook (Provincial Government), Quebec, 1915, pp. 118-128

DENISON, F. NAPIER: The Climate of British Columbia; M. W. R., v. 53, 1925, p. 354

DICKIE, FRANCIS: The "Booming" Arctic; Contemporary Review, New York, v. 132, 1927, pp. 232-236

DOANE, F. W. W.: The Frost and Drought of 1905; Proc. and Trans. Nova Scotia Inst. of Science, Halifax, v. 11, 1905-1906, pp. 623-632

DOANE, F. W. W.: Meteorological Notes; Proc. and Trans. Nova Scotia Inst. of Science, Halifax, v. 11, 1904-1905. pp. 361-372

DOUGLAS, GEO. M.: Lands Forlorn; G. P. Putnam's Sons, New York, 1914

EKBLAW, W. E.: Appendices (I-V) in "Four Years in the White North" by D. B. MacMillan; Harper & Bros., New York, 1918

EKBLAW, W. E.: The Polar Eskimo; Their Land and Life; Doctor's Dissertation, Clark University, Worcester, 1926

FLAHERTY, R. J.: The Belcher Islands of Hudson Bay; G. R., v. 5, 1918, pp. 453-454

FREEMAN, LEWIS R.: Farthest North by Railway; Worlds Work, New York, v. 56, 1928, p. 307

GANS, MARGARETE: Das Hudsonmeer; Aus dem Archiv der Deutschen Seewarte 44, Hamburg, Jahrgang 1926, No. 1

GRASSHAM, R. T.: The "Dry" Chinook in British Columbia; M. W. R., v. 35, 1907; p. 176

GREELEY, ADOLPHUS W.: Report on the Proceedings of the U. S. Expedition to Lady Franklin Bay, Grinnell Land, v. 11; Government Printing Office, Washington, 1888

GRENFELL, WILFRED T.: Labrador (Revised and Enlarged); The Macmillan Co., New York, 1922

HANBURY, DAVID T.: Through the Barren Ground of Northeastern Canada to the Arctic Coast, G. J., v. 22, 1903, pp. 178-190

HANN, JULIUS: Handbuch der Klimatologie, v. 3; J. Engelhorn, Stuttgart, 1911

HANN, JULIUS: Zum Klima von Labrador; Meteorologische Zeitschrift, v. 31, 1896, pp. 117-118, 359-360, 420-423

HEPWORTH, M. W. C.: Climatological Observations at an Arctic Station in Repulse Bay; Q. J. R. M. S., v. 31, 1905, pp. 317-326

HUBBARD, MRS. LEONIDAS, JR.: Labrador, from Lake Melville to Ungava Bay; B. G. S. P., v. 38, 1906, pp. 529-539

HUNTSMAN, A. G.: Oceanography (in Handbook of Canada); University of Toronto, Toronto, 1924, pp. 274-290.

JENNESS, DIAMOND: The People of the Twilight; The Macmillan Co., New York, 1928

JONES, RODWELL: Physical Controls in the Development of the Prairie Provinces; Geography, London, v. 14, (spring) 1928

KINDLE, E. M.: Arrival and Departure of Winter Conditions in the Mackenzie River Basin; G. R., v. 10, 1920, pp. 388-399

KINDLE, E. M.: Canada North of Fifty-six Degrees (The Land of Long Summer Days); The Canada Field Naturalist, v. 42, 1928. (Also published by Dept. of Interior, Ottawa)

KINDLE, E. M.: The James Bay Coastal Plain; G. R., v. 15, 1925, pp. 235-236

KITTO, F. H.: The Peace River District; Dept. of the Interior, Ottawa, 1922

LAMBERT, H. F.: The Conquest of Mt. Logan; G. J., v. 68, 1926, pp. 1-26

LEE, S. C.: Some phases of the Climate of Manitoba in Relation to Agriculture; B. A. M. S., v. 3, 1922, p. 36

LEFFROY, SIR J. H.: Proc. Royal Geogr. Soc., v. 8, 1886

LINSSEN, RUDOLPH: Beitrage zur Kenntnis du physischen Verhaltnisse in Gebiete der Neufundlandbank; Robert Norske, Borna-Leipzig, 1914

Low, A. P.: Report on a Traverse of the Northern Part of the Labrador Peninsula from Richmond Gulf to Ungava Bay, No. 657; Geological Survey of Canada, Ottawa, 1898

MacMillan, D. B.: Etah and Beyond; Houghton Mifflin & Co., Boston, 1927

MacMillan, D. B.: Four years in the White North; Harper & Bros., New York, 1918

Mohn, H.: Meteorology: Report of the Second Norwegian Arctic Expedition in the "Fram" 1898-1902. No. 4; A. W. Brogger, Christiana, 1907

McCurdy, A. W.: Factors which Modify the Climate of Victoria; N. G. M., v. 18, 1907, pp. 345-348

McDiarmid, F. A.: The Climate of the Canadian Yukon; M. W. R., v. 36, 1908, p. 178

McGrath, Sir P.: The Difficulties of the Hudson Bay Route to Europe; Dalhousie Review, Halifax, v. 5, 1925, pp. 76-85

Newhorn, Rt. Rev. Bishop: From Churchill to York on Snowshoes; Climate, London, v. 2, 1901, pp. 112-120

Nordenskjold, O. and Mecking, L.: The Geography of the Polar Regions; American Geographical Society, New York, 1928

Patterson, J.: A Meteorological Trip to the Arctic Circle; Jour. Royal Astron. Soc. Canada, Toronto, v. 9, (March) 1915, pp. 101-120

Peary, R. E.: The North Pole; F. A. Stokes, New York, 1910

Peattie, Roderick: Climate in the Lower St. Lawrence Valley; B. G. S. P., v. 21, 1923, pp. 31-36

Perret, Robert: La Geographie de Terre-Neuve; E. Guilmoto, 6 Rue de Megieres, Paris, 1913

Peters, W. J.: The Hudson Bay Expedition, 1914; The Carnegie Inst., Dept. of Terrestial Magnetism, Washington, Researches, v. 5, 1926, pp. 289-313

Prichard, H. V. H.: Through Trackless Labrador; Sturgis and Walton, New York, 1911

Shelford, Victor E.: Naturalists' Guide to the Americas; Williams & Wilkins Co., Baltimore, 1926

Steffanson, V.: Some Erroneous Ideas of Arctic Geography; G. R., v. 12, 1922, pp. 264-277

Steffanson, V.: The Northward Course of Empire; Harcourt, Brace & Co., New York, 1922

STEFANSSON, V.: Refraction and Daylight in the Arctic; G. R., v. 17, 1927, p. 157

STUPART, R. F.: Barometric Pressure in Northwest America and Temperature of the Pacific Currents; B. A. M. S., v. 8, 1927, pp. 168-169

STUPART, R. F.: Canadian Climate; Report Eighth International Geogr. Congress, Washington, 1904 (1905), pp. 294-307

STUPART, R. F.: The Canadian Climate; Symons's Meteorological Magazine, London, v. 38, 1903, pp. 1-4, 31-33, 66-70

STUPART, R. F.: The Chinook in Southern Alberta and Temperature Inversions at Sulphur Mountain, Banff; Proc. & Trans. Royal Soc. Canada, Sect. III, Montreal, v. 4, 1910, pp. 51-52

STUPART, R. F.: The Climate of Canada (in The Canada Yearbook, 1927-28); The Dominion Bureau of Statistics, Ottawa, 1928, pp. 41-63

STUPART, R. F.: The Climate of Canada; Handbook of Canada, University of Toronto, Toronto, 1924, pp. 106-115

STUPART, R. F.: The Climate of Canada; S. G. M., v. 14, 1898, pp. 73-81

STUPART, R. F.: The Climate of Canada Since Confederation (in The Canada Yearbook, 1924); Dominion Bureau of Statistics, Ottawa, 1924, pp. 31-34

STUPART, R. F.: The Climate of Northern Ontario; Trans. Canadian Inst., Toronto, v. 9, 1912, pp. 149-152

STUPART, R. F.: The Climate of Southwestern Alberta; Trans. American Climatological Assc., Philadelphia, v. 30, 1914, pp. 9-15

STUPART, R. F.: Climate of Yukon Territory; M. W. R., v. 35, 1907, pp. 16-17

STUPART, R. F.: The Factors which control Canadian Weather (in The Canada Yearbook, 1924); Dominion Bureau of Statistics, Ottawa, 1924, pp. 26-31

STUPART, R. F.: The Influence of Arctic Meteorology on the Climate of Canada Especially (in Problems of Polar Research); American Geographical Society, New York, 1928, p. 39-50

STUPART, R. F.: Meteorological Stations in High Latitudes; M. W. R., v. 51, 1923, pp. 10-11

STUPART, R. F.: The Variableness of Canadian Winters (Author's Abstract); M. W. R., v. 52, 1924, p. 351

STUPART, R. F.: Climate, (in "The Oxford Survey of the British Empire: America," v. 4, chapter II; A. J. Herbertson, Ed.); Oxford University Press, London, 1914, pp. 56-77

SVERDRUP, OTTO: New Land, Vols. I and II; Longmans, Green & Co., New York, 1904

SYKES, CECILY F.: A Bad Winter in Alberta; Chambers Journal, 7th Series, London, v. 17, 1927, pp. 158-159

TOWNSEND, C. W.: Capt. Cartwright and His Labrador Journal; Williams & Norgate, London, 1911

WALDO, FULLERTON: Down the Mackenzie through the Great Lone Land; The Macmillan Co., New York, 1923

WARD, R. DEC.: Climate, Considered Especially in Relation to Man; G. P. Putnam's Sons, New York, 1918

WEBBER, B. C.: March Winds [re Ontario]; M. W. R., v. 31, 1903, pp. 136-137

WHITE, ARTHUR V., assisted by CHARLES J. VICK: Water Power of British Columbia; Commission of Conservation, Ottawa, 1919

WHITNEY, CASPER: The Leonidas Hubbard, Jun., Expedition into Labrador; Outing, Albany, v. 45, 1905, pp. 643-689

———

Atlas of Canada; Dept. of the Interior, Ottawa, 1915

Contributions to Our Knowledge of the Arctic Regions (Pts. I-V); Meteorological Council, London, 1885

Cloud Observations at Toronto; Q. J. R. M. S., v. 27, 1901, pp. 195-196

Deutsche Uberseeische Meteorologische Beobachtungen; Deutsche Seewarte (1890-98), Hamburg

Extracts from Reports on the District of Ungava; Dept. of Colonization, Mines, and Fisheries, Quebec, 1915

The Gaspe Peninsula; Natural Resources Intelligence Service, Ottawa

A Labrador Expedition; N. G. M., v. 15, 1904, p. 185

Monthly Record of Meteorological Observations; Meteorological Service, Toronto

Natural Resources of the Prairie Provinces; Dept. of the Interior, Ottawa, 1923

New Brunswick: Its Natural Resources; Dept. of the Interior, Ottawa, 1921

Oil and Gas in Western Canada; Dept. of the Interior, Ottawa, 1920

Report of the Canadian Arctic Expedition 1913-18; F. A. Acland, Ottawa, 1924

Report on a Traverse of the Northern Part of the Labrador Peninsula from Richmond Gulf to Ungava Bay, No. 657; Geological Survey of Canada, Ottawa, 1898

Resources and Possibilities of Northern Manitoba (Issued by Commissioner of Northern Manitoba); The Pas Herald, The Pas, Manitoba, p. 12.

CLIMATIC DATA

Because of lack of space, certain abbreviations are used in the tables of temperature and precipitation data which follow in the succeeding pages: High Mn., *highest monthly mean*; Low Mn., *lowest monthly mean*; Mn. Max., *mean maximum;* Mn. Min., *mean minimum*; H. Max., *highest maximum;* L. Max., *lowest maximum;* H. Min., *highest minimum;* L. Min., *lowest minimum*; M. D. R., *mean daily range*; Ex. R., *extreme range*; Wet Yr., *wettest year on record*; Dry Yr., *driest year on record*; Mn. Sn., *mean snowfall*; Max. Sn., *maximum snowfall*; Pr. Das., *average number of days with 0.01 inch or more of precipitation*; T., *trace of rain or snow.*

In the second vertical column headed Y. R., meaning the number of years of record, B indicates a broken or incomplete record.

TEMPERATURE DATA

ABITIBI, QUEBEC

48° 43′ North Latitude   79° 22′ West Longitude   850 Feet Altitude

	Y. R.	Jan.	Feb.	Mar.	Apr.	May	Jun.	Jul.	Aug.	Sep.	Oct.	Nov.	Dec.	Yr.
Mean	22B	0.3	0.6	14.7	31.5	46.0	55.7	64.2	60.7	52.0	40.4	24.9	8.2	33.3
Mn. Max.	22B	11.7	12.8	21.9	41.6	55.4	62.9	73.3	69.4	59.6	47.0	30.9	16.8	42.4
Mn. Min.	22B	−11.1	−11.7	1.4	21.4	36.5	48.6	55.1	52.0	44.5	33.7	18.8	−0.4	24.1
H. Max.	29B	44	46	62	82	87	94	97	90	87	76	68	48	97
L. Max.	29B	19	22	33	45	60	75	78	73	69	66	37	10	10
H. Min.	29B	−28	−23	14	14	34	40	49	45	44	29	12	−10	−28
L. Min.	29B	−47	−51	−42	−20	8	27	34	30	36	11	−20	−45	−51
M. D. R.	22B	22.8	24.5	26.5	20.2	18.9	14.3	18.2	17.4	15.1	13.3	12.1	17.2	18.3
Ex. R.	29B	91	97	104	102	79	67	63	60	51	65	88	93	148

ANNAPOLIS ROYAL, NOVA SCOTIA

44° 38′ North Latitude   65° 29′ West Longitude   10 Feet Altitude

	Y. R.	Jan.	Feb.	Mar.	Apr.	May	Jun.	Jul.	Aug.	Sep.	Oct.	Nov.	Dec.	Yr.
Mean	23	23.0	23.4	30.4	40.2	50.0	58.6	63.9	63.0	57.9	49.2	37.9	28.1	43.8
Mn. Max.	23	30.8	31.4	38.4	49.0	60.5	69.3	74.0	73.0	69.0	58.2	44.4	34.5	52.7
Mn. Min.	23	15.3	15.4	22.5	31.4	39.5	48.0	53.8	52.9	46.8	40.3	31.4	21.7	34.9
H. Max.	10	60	58	69	77	86	89	88	86	86	78	71	59	89
L. Max.	10	39	37	49	59	62	74	79	79	75	65	53	47	37
H. Min.	10	1	14	12	25	32	41	49	44	35	32	26	13	49
L. Min.	10	−11	−13	−5	10	25	26	30	36	28	22	15	−13	−13
M. D. R.	23	15.5	16.0	15.9	17.6	21.0	21.3	20.2	20.1	22.2	17.9	13.0	12.8	17.8
Ex. R.	10	71	71	74	67	61	63	58	50	58	56	56	72	102

ATLIN, BRITISH COLUMBIA

59° 35′ North Latitude   133° 38′ West Longitude   2240 Feet Altitude

	Y. R.	Jan.	Feb.	Mar.	Apr.	May	Jun.	Jul.	Aug.	Sep.	Oct.	Nov.	Dec.	Yr.
Mean	14	−1.6	6.7	18.4	30.9	42.2	49.6	52.7	50.9	43.9	35.6	22.0	14.3	30.5
High Mn.	8	16.2	18.1	23.6	33.7	46.2	51.8	54.8	53.8	46.2	38.8	27.7	21.4	—
Low Mn.	8	−18.5	−3.4	10.1	26.1	41.1	47.4	50.0	49.0	41.1	29.2	5.6	7.3	—
Mn. Max.	14	4.6	14.2	27.2	39.4	51.0	60.3	62.8	59.7	50.9	40.8	26.6	19.4	38.1
Mn. Min.	14	−7.8	−0.9	9.6	22.4	33.3	38.8	42.6	42.0	36.9	30.3	17.4	9.2	22.8
H. Max.	22	45	46	50	62	76	84	86	81	73	61	56	46	86
L. Max.	22	20	32	37	42	56	64	63	64	55	46	36	17	17
H. Min.	22	7	0	27	17	33	33	40	40	30	24	11	0	40
L. Min.	22	−54	−53	−39	−24	18	25	32	28	16	−3	−28	−58	−58
M. D. R.	14	12.4	15.1	17.6	17.0	17.7	21.5	20.2	17.7	14.0	10.5	9.2	4.6	15.3
Ex. R.	22	99	99	89	86	94	109	118	109	89	64	84	104	144

BANFF, ALBERTA

51° 25′ North Latitude   115° 30′ West Longitude   4521 Feet Altitude

	Y. R.	Jan.	Feb.	Mar.	Apr.	May	Jun.	Jul.	Aug.	Sep.	Oct.	Nov.	Dec.	Yr.
Mean	20	13.4	16.2	23.0	36.5	45.1	51.7	56.8	54.4	46.7	38.7	24.3	19.3	35.5
High Mn.	20	23.4	24.9	34.2	42.4	52.0	56.0	62.8	59.0	50.9	44.6	35.9	26.1	—
Low Mn.	20	−4.2	6.2	14.6	29.0	40.3	47.1	53.5	50.2	41.1	32.6	1.7	9.7	—
Mn. Max.	20	22.3	26.6	34.5	37.4	57.5	64.8	71.3	68.3	58.3	48.2	31.6	26.5	46.4
Mn. Min.	20	4.5	5.8	11.6	25.6	32.8	38.6	42.3	40.5	35.1	29.2	17.0	12.1	24.6
H. Max.	33	50	54	62	77	83	90	93	89	82	73	58	49	93
L. Max.	33	19	32	38	49	67	72	78	74	65	50	37	31	19
H. Min	33	−4	−10	12	22	28	34	38	43	28	22	16	−1	−10
L. Min.	33	−48	−47	−40	−14	12	21	28	27	2	−5	−41	−54	−54
M. D. R.	20	17.8	20.8	22.9	11.8	24.7	26.2	29.0	27.8	23.2	19.0	14.6	14.4	21.8
Ex. R.	33	98	101	102	91	71	69	65	62	80	78	99	103	147

BARKERVILLE, BRITISH COLUMBIA

53° 2′ North Latitude   121° 35′ West Longitude   4180 Feet Altitude

	Y. R.	Jan.	Feb.	Mar.	Apr.	May	Jun.	Jul.	Aug.	Sep.	Oct.	Nov.	Dec.	Yr.
Mean	36B	15.9	18.7	25.7	35.0	43.7	49.9	54.1	53.4	45.4	37.1	25.7	19.8	35.3
High Mn.	36B	26.4	27.1	33.6	49.5	50.6	54.9	59.7	61.5	52.6	43.6	35.1	26.0	37.6
Low Mn.	36B	−9.0	4.6	16.9	28.7	38.2	45.8	49.7	47.5	40.2	27.2	5.2	11.3	30.8
Mn. Max.	36B	23.1	26.8	35.4	44.3	56.0	61.9	62.3	66.3	56.3	45.7	32.3	27.6	45.3
Mn. Min.	36B	10.1	11.0	16.3	24.2	32.9	38.3	41.8	41.1	34.9	29.4	18.1	14.8	26.1
H. Max.	40B	46	50	62	82	86	86	88	93	76	73	66	58	93
L. Max.	40B	21	26	37	51	58	67	72	67	58	51	37	36	21
H. Min.	40B	10	4	21	22	29	36	36	36	30	25	12	10	36
L. Min.	40B	−44	−48	−25	−8	6	24	28	24	8	−5	−27	−32	−48
M. D. R.	36B	13.0	15.8	19.1	20.1	23.1	23.6	20.5	25.2	21.4	16.3	14.2	12.8	19.2
Ex. R.	40B	90	98	87	90	92	110	60	69	68	78	93	90	141

BELLE ISLE, NEWFOUNDLAND

51° 52′ North Latitude   55° 24′ West Longitude   426 Feet Altitude

	Y. R.	Jan.	Feb.	Mar.	Apr.	May	Jun.	Jul.	Aug.	Sep.	Oct.	Nov.	Dec.	Yr.
Mean	20B	9.4	11.6	19.4	27.2	35.0	42.4	50.8	52.5	46.5	38.0	27.7	16.0	31.4
High Mn.	20B	17.9	27.7	26.4	31.8	38.6	48.4	56.8	59.7	54.0	41.1	32.6	22.0	—
Low Mn.	20B	−6.3	−0.7	12.6	22.4	31.1	37.2	46.3	47.1	42.2	33.8	21.7	7.4	—
Mn. Max.	20B	14.5	16.1	24.2	31.7	39.2	47.4	56.2	57.9	51.5	42.0	31.9	20.5	36.1
Mn. Min.	20B	4.4	6.9	14.7	22.7	30.8	37.4	45.3	47.2	41.4	33.8	23.5	11.5	26.4
H. Max.	20B	40	39	43	56	59	69	70	71	68	57	48	40	71
L. Min.	20B	−27	−26	−18	−10	12	22	28	31	27	17	−6	−25	−27
M. D. R.	20B	10.1	9.2	9.5	9.0	8.4	10.0	10.9	10.7	10.1	8.2	8.4	9.0	9.7
Ex. R.	20B	67	65	61	66	47	47	42	40	41	40	54	65	98

CHARLOTTETOWN, PRINCE EDWARD ISLAND
46° 14′ North Latitude   63° 10′ West Longitude   38 Feet Altitude

	Y. R.	Jan.	Feb.	Mar.	Apr.	May	Jun.	Jul.	Aug.	Sep.	Oct.	Nov.	Dec.	Yr.
Mean	50B	17.3	14.7	26.0	31.1	47.6	57.7	65.3	64.9	57.5	47.3	36.2	24.8	41.3
High Mn.	50B	25.6	24.6	34.2	42.5	53.8	62.4	69.9	68.7	62.3	55.4	41.3	32.0	—
Low. Mn.	50B	8.0	8.3	16.9	28.6	41.6	53.2	60.5	61.4	53.9	42.9	29.7	16.0	—
Mn. Max.	50B	25.6	25.5	33.0	43.0	55.9	62.2	73.1	72.3	64.6	53.6	41.8	31.2	48.8
Mn. Min.	50B	9.0	3.8	19.0	29.3	39.2	49.3	57.5	57.5	50.4	40.9	30.7	18.4	33.8
H. Max.	53B	52	49	58	74	81	87	91	92	87	82	63	59	92
L. Max.	39B	34	35	31	52	61	71	77	77	70	53	49	39	31
H. Min.	39B	1	8	16	28	35	46	55	53	44	35	26	15	55
L. Min.	53B	−27	−23	−16	2	22	32	37	42	34	26	3	−18	−27
M. D. R.	50B	16.6	21.7	14.0	13.7	16.7	12.9	15.6	14.8	14.2	12.7	11.1	12.8	15.0
Ex. R.	53B	79	72	74	72	59	55	54	50	5 3	56	60	77	119

CHESTERFIELD INLET, NORTHWEST TERRITORIES
63° 25′ North Latitude   92° 30′ West Longitude   48 Feet Altitude

	Y. R.	Jan.	Feb.	Mar.	Apr.	May	Jun.	Jul.	Aug.	Sep.	Oct.	Nov.	Dec.	Yr.
Mean	8B	−26.5	−22.4	−16.4	2.5	21.1	39.2	47.2	44.6	37.2	22.0	0.3	−18.2	10.9
High Mn.	8B	−20.4	−16.9	−4.1	7.7	28.2	40.6	51.6	50.2	40.5	28.6	5.6	−5.7	51.6
Low Mn.	8B	−33.8	−36.2	−30.0	−3.7	15.9	30.0	45.6	44.4	34.8	13.2	−2.2	−26.7	−36.2
Mn. Max.	8B	−19.7	−17.8	−10.9	9.2	26.5	43.9	54.7	49.3	41.3	25.3	7.7	−12.8	16.4
Mn. Min.	8B	−33.3	−26.9	−22.0	−4.2	15.6	34.5	39.6	39.9	33.1	18.7	−7.1	−23.6	5.8
H. Max.	8B	8	17	20	37	44	76	84	75	66	44	32	21	84
L. Max.	8B	−17	−16	−2	20	34	46	67	62	51	37	18	−1	−17
H. Min.	8B	−42	−42	−34	−20	11	28	35	36	26	11	−24	−32	36
L. Min.	8B	−51	−50	−52	−38	−10	21	30	26	18	−17	−33	−42	−52
M. D. R.	8B	13.6	9.1	11.1	13.4	10.9	9.4	15.1	9.4	8.2	6.6	14.8	10.8	10.6
Ex. R.	8B	59	67	72	75	54	55	54	49	48	61	65	63	136

CHURCHILL, MANITOBA
58° 30′ North Latitude   94° 00′ West Longitude   55 Feet Altitude

	Y. R.	Jan.	Feb.	Mar.	Apr.	May	Jun.	Jul.	Aug.	Sep.	Oct.	Nov.	Dec.	Yr.
Mean	18B	−20.2	−15.6	−3.0	22.4	32.5	42.8	55.5	52.6	42.3	27.3	7.9	−9.0	19.6
High Mn.	22B	−10.5	−8.2	9.7	25.8	39.0	47.8	60.2	57.9	48.0	37.9	19.1	−1.7	21.6
Low Mn.	22B	−33.7	−30.1	−14.3	1.9	17.9	36.2	47.7	48.2	37.0	17.5	0.7	−21.9	15.4
Mn. Max.	18B	−12.3	−8.5	4.1	31.6	40.0	54.8	66.8	61.8	50.7	33.1	12.4	−4.3	27.5
Mn. Min.	18B	−27.8	−26.6	−21.0	7.6	20.7	31.5	40.3	38.2	31.1	16.4	−2.7	−21.4	7.2
H. Max.	16B	32	29	40	61	80	82	88	82	82	60	45	39	88
L. Max.	16B	−12	0	17	32	38	67	71	69	53	39	20	4	−12
H. Min.	16B	−35	−30	−22	−11	17	31	40	38	37	20	−6	−28	40
L. Min.	16B	−57	−52	−52	−28	−14	13	22	24	15	−17	−38	−45	−57
M. D. R.	18B	15.5	18.1	25.1	24.0	19.3	23.3	26.5	23.6	19.6	16.7	15.1	17.1	20.3
Ex. R.	16B	89	81	92	89	94	69	66	58	67	77	83	84	145

DAWSON, YUKON TERRITORY

64° 3' North Latitude   139° 25' West Longitude   1052 Feet Altitude

	Y. R.	Jan.	Feb.	Mar.	Apr.	May	Jun.	Jul.	Aug.	Sep.	Oct.	Nov.	Dec.	Yr.
Mean	29B	-22.4	-11.8	4.4	27.6	46.3	56.8	59.3	54.3	41.6	26.2	1.2	-11.2	22.7
High Mn.	24	0.8	4.3	15.1	38.3	51.5	60.0	62.6	58.8	46.0	33.1	12.8	3.0	28.0
Low Mn.	24	-43.2	-26.2	-6.7	17.8	41.8	52.5	52.3	51.1	36.4	16.8	-9.5	-51.3	18.6
Mn. Max.	29B	-15.9	-4.1	16.3	40.3	58.9	70.5	72.3	67.1	51.5	32.7	7.0	-5.4	32.6
Mn. Min.	29B	-28.9	-19.4	-7.4	14.9	33.8	43.1	46.3	41.5	31.8	19.6	-4.5	-17.1	12.8
H. Max.	29B	30	45	52	69	85	91	95	88	· 78	68	47	39	95
L. Max.	29B	-12	-3	29	49	65	75	76	72	58	38	13	-35	-35
H. Min.	29B	-15	-23	-10	9	27	38	42	37	26	13	-14	-20	42
L. Min.	29	-68	-59	-47	-33	9	25	29	17	8	-22	-48	-63	-68
M. D. R.	29B	13.0	15.3	23.7	25.4	25.1	27.4	26.0	25.6	19.7	13.1	11.5	11.7	19.8
Ex. R.	29B	98	104	99	60	76	66	66	71	70	90	95	102	163

EDMONTON, ALBERTA

53° 33' North Latitude   113° 30' West Longitude   2158 Feet Altitude

	Y. R.	Jan.	Feb.	Mar.	Apr.	May	Jun.	Jul.	Aug.	Sep.	Oct.	Nov.	Dec.	Yr.
Mean	38	5.5	10.5	23.4	40.5	51.0	57.2	61.1	59.2	50.2	41.1	24.7	14.3	36.5
High Mn.	38	21.9	23.7	36.6	48.8	57.3	61.9	66.4	63.6	55.4	47.4	39.5	25.0	40.9
Low Mn.	38	-13.7	-10.4	8.5	27.5	43.6	52.4	57.8	55.9	45.1	29.1	0.4	-6.8	31.5
Mn. Max.	30	15.6	21.1	34.9	52.9	54.4	70.1	73.7	76.6	62.9	53.2	33.3	24.7	48.2
Mn. Min.	30	-3.8	0.1	11.9	28.6	38.1	44.4	48.8	46.4	37.8	30.3	15.6	7.3	25.6
H. Max.	46	56	62	72	84	90	94	98	93	87	81	68	60	98
L. Max.	46	29	29	39	52	71	74	78	77	74	52	44	34	29
H. Min.	46	-8	-10	5	26	30	43	45	43	32	24	13	0	-10
L. Min.	46	-57	-57	-40	-15	10	25	29	26	12	-15	-44	-45	-57
M. D. R.	30	19.4	21.0	23.0	24.3	16.3	25.7	24.9	30.2	25.1	22.9	17.7	17.4	22.6
Ex. R.	46	113	119	112	99	80	49	49	51	62	67	88	79	155

FORT CHIMO, QUEBEC

58° 10' North Latitude   68° 15' West Longitude   50 Feet Altitude

	Y. R.	Jan.	Feb.	Mar.	Apr.	May	Jun.	Jul.	Aug.	Sep.	Oct.	Nov.	Dec.	Yr.
Mean	4	-16.5	-16.4	-0.7	14.3	31.5	43.2	50.6	51.2	46.2	30.5	14.6	-5.7	20.2
H. Max.	4	23	34	46	57	59	80	88	82	71	55	37	33	88
L. Min.	4	-42	-43	-38	-22	3	18	29	27	26	1	-18	-29	-43
Ex. R.	4	65	77	84	79	56	62	59	55	45	54	55	62	131

FORT CHIPEWYAN, ALBERTA

58° 42′ North Latitude   111° 10′ West Longitude   714 Feet Altitude

	Y.R.	Jan.	Feb.	Mar.	Apr.	May	Jun.	Jul.	Aug.	Sep.	Oct.	Nov.	Dec.	Yr.
Mean	43B	-12.7	-6.9	4.9	26.6	42.3	52.9	59.4	55.8	44.4	32.5	14.4	-18.0	26.0
High Mn.	43B	1.68	2.35	1.75	3.04	1.94	3.31	9.52	4.43	2.93	5.30	2.28	3.20	—
Low Mn.	43B	.02	0.03	0.09	T	T	0.02	0.21	0.36	0.27	0.20	0.10	0.05	—
Mn. Max.	43B	-3.6	3.2	15.6	37.3	52.3	63.4	69.3	65.3	53.1	39.8	20.0	6.4	35.2
Mn. Min.	43B	-21.8	-17.0	-5.9	15.9	32.3	42.4	49.4	46.3	35.7	25.2	8.7	-10.0	16.8
H. Max.	43B	45	46	49	69	83	90	93	89	79	66	56	49	93
L. Max.	28	2	2	21	42	56	69	76	73	61	49	29	15	2
H. Min.	28	-16	-10	-21	12	31	39	42	37	30	21	8	-19	42
L. Min.	43B	-58	-56	-54	-32	-14	16	23	23	10	-9	-33	-54	-58
M. D. R.	43B	18.2	20.2	21.5	21.4	20.0	21.0	19.9	19.0	17.4	14.6	11.3	16.4	18.4
Ex. R.	43B	103	102	103	101	97	74	70	66	69	75	89	103	151

FORT CONGER, NORTHWEST TERRITORIES

81° 44′ North Latitude   64° 45′ West Longitude

	Y.R.	Jan.	Feb.	Mar.	Apr.	May	Jun.	Jul.	Aug.	Sep.	Oct.	Nov.	Dec.	Yr.
Mean	3B	-37.0	-42.7	-23.9	-11.7	16.1	32.7	37.0	34.3	14.5	-8.5	-26.2	-29.9	-3.8
Mn. Max.	3B	-24.0	-16.4	-6.2	3.0	29.2	41.8	43.4	42.2	24.5	7.7	-9.4	-9.3	10.5
Mn. Min.	3B	-48.7	-54.4	-42.2	-31.2	0.6	22.2	32.6	25.0	0.8	-22.0	-38.4	-41.8	-16.4
H. Max.	3B	-10	-5	20	14	36	53	50	48	30	14	-1	6	53
L. Max.	3B	-18	-10	-7	7	32	40	48	42	27	9	-3	-10	-18
H. Min.	3B	-51	-15	-47	-37	1	23	30	30	1	-24	-43	-43	30
L. Min.	3B	-58	-62	-49	-42	-13	13	29	15.6	-10.4	-31.1	-46	-52	-62
M. D. R.	3B	24.7	38.0	36.0	34.2	28.6	19.6	10.8	17.2	23.7	29.7	29.0	32.5	26.9
Ex. R.	3B	48	57	69	56	49	40	21	32.4	40.4	45.1	45.0	46.0	115

FORT GEORGE, QUEBEC

53° 50′ North Latitude   79° 05′ West Longitude   320 Feet Altitude

	Y.R.	Jan.	Feb.	Mar.	Apr.	May	Jun.	Jul.	Aug.	Sep.	Oct.	Nov.	Dec.	Yr.
Mean	4	-9.7	-11.1	0.0	23.5	35.2	49.3	57.0	53.7	42.9	33.8	24.7	3.5	25.2
H. Max.	4	25	25	36	64	75	81	90	84	70	55	44	34	90
L. Max.	4	15	10	18	41	52	68	74	65	59	38	35	11	10
H. Min.	4	-36	-30	-18	-5	23	31	39	35	40	25	27	-15	40
L. Min.	4	-49	-49	-46	-19	1	25	32	31	25	17	-10	-37	—49
Ex. R.	4	74	74	82	83	74	56	58	53	45	38	54	71	139

FORT GOOD HOPE, NORTHWEST TERRITORIES
66° 25′ North Latitude   128° 53′ West Longitude   214 Feet Altitude

	Y. R.	Jan.	Feb.	Mar.	Apr.	May	Jun.	Jul.	Aug.	Sep.	Oct.	Nov.	Dec.	Yr.
Mean	19B	-31.6	-26.1	-12.3	14.5	35.1	56.3	61.2	53.0	38.7	16.6	-15.2	-25.0	13.8
High Mn.	12	-9.8	-1.0	6.8	24.7	43.4	60.2	65.0	57.8	43.9	28.2	1.6	-7.7	—
Low Mn.	12	-35.7	-33.2	-17.8	3.9	31.3	47.1	52.6	47.6	33.9	14.8	-15.6	-42.6	—
Mn. Max.	12	-12.9	-8.3	2.5	27.2	49.7	66.8	72.4	65.1	47.9	28.3	1.6	-11.6	27.4
Mn. Min.	12	-32.9	-28.1	-21.9	-0.1	25.9	41.3	46.7	40.8	30.3	13.7	-14.7	-29.6	6.0
H. Max.	31B	42	44	41	65	80	95	95	93	87	69	34	38	95
L. Max.	31B	-10	-2	18	39	58	75	75	76	51	38	6	-12	-12
H. Min.	31B	-43	-46	-41	-10	20	36	40	32	21	6	-30	-32	40
L. Min.	31B	-69	-64	-57	-42	-13	22	28	19	5	-27	-55	-79	-79
M. D. R.	12	20.0	19.8	24.4	27.3	23.8	25.5	25.7	24.3	17.6	14.6	16.3	18.0	21.4
Ex. R.	31B	111	118	98	107	93	73	67	74	82	96	89	117	174

FORT HOPE, ONTARIO
51° 33′ North Latitude   87° 49′ West Longitude   1100 Feet Altitude

	Y. R.	Jan.	Feb.	Mar.	Apr.	May	Jun.	Jul.	Aug.	Sep.	Oct.	Nov.	Dec.	Yr.
Mean	30B	-8.7	-5.4	8.5	29.2	42.6	55.8	61.5	57.8	48.0	36.0	18.8	1.5	28.8
High Mn.	30B	1.2	5.4	21.4	40.2	48.9	64.0	66.2	61.9	54.4	42.6	27.5	11.7	—
Low Mn.	30B	-20.6	-15.8	0.8	18.0	30.2	49.8	58.4	53.8	40.2	32.3	9.6	-5.0	—
Mn. Max.	30B	2.2	6.8	22.0	41.3	54.7	68.8	73.0	69.2	58.0	44.2	26.0	11.4	39.8
Min. Mn.	30B	-19.6	-17.5	-5.0	17.0	30.5	42.9	50.0	46.4	38.0	27.9	11.6	-8.4	17.8
H. Max.	30B	38	42	55	80	87	95	93	99	89	83	56	42	99
L. Max.	14	9	23	32	46	66	81	79	75	66	60	34	28	9
H. Min.	14	-29	-35	-18	6	22	35	44	41	34	18	2	-14	44
L. Min.	30B	-54	-53	-49	-27	-7	24	27	27	16	-5	-38	-39	-54
M. D. R.	30B	21.8	24.3	27.0	24.3	24.2	25.9	23.0	22.8	20.0	16.3	14.4	19.8	22.0
Ex. R.	30B	92	95	104	107	94	71	66	72	73	88	94	81	143

FORT VERMILION, ALBERTA
58° 27′ North Latitude   116° 3′ West Longitude   950 Feet Altitude

	Y. R.	Jan.	Feb.	Mar.	Apr.	May	Jun.	Jul.	Aug.	Sep.	Oct.	Nov.	Dec.	Yr.
Mean	22B	-14.3	-5.6	7.8	30.2	47.0	54.9	60.0	56.8	45.6	32.0	10.3	-4.1	26.7
Mn. Max.	22B	-2.2	8.8	23.2	45.0	61.1	69.6	74.3	70.8	59.3	43.0	20.8	6.5	40.0
Mn. Min.	22B	-26.3	-19.9	-7.6	15.4	32.8	40.2	45.7	42.8	31.8	21.0	-0.3	-14.6	13.4
H. Max.	19B	48	49	62	75	93	98	92	92	86	76	60	49	98
L. Max.	19B	7	16	37	49	76	78	81	70	71	59	33	14	7
H. Min.	19B	-32	-37	-14	16	28	37	38	38	26	19	6	-38	38
L. Min.	19B	-76	-71	-49	-38	-20	16	20	23	-4	-22	-47	-64	-76
M. D. R.	22B	24.1	28.7	30.8	29.6	28.3	29.4	28.6	28.0	27.5	22.0	21.1	21.1	26.6
Ex. R.	19B	124	120	111	113	113	82	72	69	90	98	54	113	174

FREDERICTON, NEW BRUNSWICK
45° 55′ North Latitude   66° 40′ West Longitude   164 Feet Altitude

	Y. R.	Jan.	Feb.	Mar.	Apr.	May	Jun.	Jul.	Aug.	Sep.	Oct.	Nov.	Dec.	Yr.
Mean	52	12.9	14.9	25.7	38.5	50.9	60.2	65.9	64.1	55.9	44.9	32.5	18.8	40.4
High Mn.	52	22.1	21.8	35.1	44.6	56.6	64.4	70.4	68.2	60.6	53.2	36.8	27.8	—
Low Mn.	52	4.0	8.5	16.0	34.5	46.4	55.3	62.8	59.2	52.0	41.2	24.5	8.4	—
Mn. Max.	52	23.6	26.4	36.0	48.9	62.5	72.1	77.2	74.9	66.6	54.7	40.4	28.1	50.9
Mn. Min.	52	2.2	3.3	15.5	28.1	39.4	48.2	54.6	53.2	45.2	35.1	24.6	9.6	29.9
H. Max.	42	55	53	65	83	92	96	96	95	92	82	68	58	96
L. Max.	42	33	34	43	56	65	80	84	82	73	60	50	38	33
H. Min.	42	-11	-8	7	23	39	41	49	47	38	29	18	3	49
L. Min.	42	-34	-35	-27	-5	24	27	38	35	25	13	-16	-31	—35
M. D. R.	52	21.4	23.1	20.5	20.8	23.1	23.9	22.6	21.7	21.4	19.6	15.8	18.5	21.0
Ex. R.	42	89	88	92	88	68	69	58	60	67	69	84	89	131

HALIFAX, NOVA SCOTIA
44° 39′ North Latitude   63° 35′ West Longitude   88 Feet Altitude

	Y. R.	Jan.	Feb.	Mar.	Apr.	May	Jun.	Jul.	Aug.	Sep.	Oct.	Nov.	Dec.	Yr.
Mean	50	23.0	23.0	30.4	39.4	49.3	57.8	64.8	64.5	58.3	48.7	38.8	28.3	43.8
High Mn.	50	30.2	29.2	38.1	42.8	53.4	62.5	68.7	67.8	62.4	57.8	43.4	34.2	—
Low Mn.	50	14.4	13.6	23.6	33.4	44.5	53.6	59.6	61.1	55.0	45.3	32.5	20.2	—
Mn. Max.	50	31.7	31.4	37.9	47.7	58.5	67.8	74.1	73.5	67.5	57.0	45.8	35.7	52.4
Mn. Min.	50	14.4	14.5	22.8	31.2	40.0	47.8	55.1	55.5	49.1	40.5	31.8	20.9	35.3
H. Max.	53	55	50	70	82	90	94	99	93	88	86	67	58	99
L. Max.	33	39	38	45	58	66	74	81	74	73	62	52	46	33
H. Min.	33	6	11	20	29	34	43	50	51	40	33	28	14	51
L. Min.	53	-17	-21	-10	12	25	32	40	39	29	21	9	-14	-21
M. D. R.	50	17.3	15.9	15.1	16.5	18.5	20.0	19.0	18.0	18.4	16.5	14.0	14.8	17.1
Ex. R.	53	72	71	80	70	65	62	59	54	59	65	58	72	120

HARRINGTON HARBOUR, QUEBEC
50° 40′ North Latitude   59° 19′ West Longitude   30 Feet Altitude

	Y. R.	Jan.	Feb.	Mar.	Apr.	May	Jun.	Jul.	Aug.	Sep.	Oct.	Nov.	Dec.	Yr.
Mean	17	8.3	9.3	18.5	28.3	38.0	46.5	53.5	54.7	49.3	39.8	28.1	16.8	32.6
High Mn.	17	18.2	19.7	27.3	32.3	41.5	49.9	59.6	58.2	51.2	43.7	35.4	26.2	35.0
Low Mn.	17	-1.4	0.2	6.0	24.2	33.6	40.3	49.4	47.4	40.7	35.0	18.0	5.2	28.9
Mn. Max.	17	15.7	17.2	26.8	35.7	43.4	51.4	58.8	59.4	53.5	44.2	33.8	24.1	38.7
Mn. Min.	17	-2.9	-1.2	9.0	22.6	31.7	39.7	47.6	48.4	41.8	33.0	21.9	8.8	25.9
H. Max.	16	44	41	48	53	64	85	79	76	76	62	56	46	85
L. Max.	16	28	28	34	37	48	60	64	64	58	48	40	34	28
H. Min.	16	-10	1	12	22	32	40	48	44	38	32	18	7	48
L. Min.	16	-40	-35	-16	-7	21	30	36	28	20	8	-1	-21	-40
M. D. R.	17	18.6	18.4	17.8	13.1	11.7	11.7	11.2	11.0	11.7	11.2	11.9	15.3	12.8
Ex. R.	16	84	76	64	60	43	55	43	48	56	54	57	67	125

HEBRON, LABRADOR

58° 15′ North Latitude   62° 30′ West Longitude   60 Feet Altitude

	Y. R.	Jan.	Feb.	Mar.	Apr.	May	Jun.	Jul.	Aug.	Sep.	Oct.	Nov.	Dec.	Yr.
Mean	18	-5.7	-5.1	5.8	18.3	31.5	39.9	47.1	48.1	40.9	31.2	19.8	4.2	23.0
Mn. Max.	18	1.0	1.9	14.0	26.2	38.8	48.0	55.8	56.3	47.3	36.3	24.8	10.2	30.1
Mn. Min.	18	-12.5	-12.1	-2.4	10.4	24.1	32.0	38.5	39.9	34.5	26.1	14.7	-1.8	16.0
H. Max.	18	56	48	43	53	59	72	83	84	81	57	46	37	84
L. Min.	18	-42	-42	-36	-20	-7	14	25	26	19	5	-20	-29	-42
M. D. R.	18	13.5	13.0	16.4	15.8	14.7	16.0	17.3	16.4	12.8	10.2	10.1	12.0	14.1
Ex. R.	18	98	90	79	73	66	58	58	58	62	52	66	66	126

HERSCHEL ISLAND, NORTHWEST TERRITORIES

69° 30′ North Latitude   139° 15′ West Longitude   10 Feet Altitude

	Y. R.	Jan.	Feb.	Mar.	Apr.	May	Jun.	Jul.	Aug.	Sep.	Oct.	Nov.	Dec.	Yr.
Mean	7	-22.0	-12.3	-12.1	2.1	19.2	35.5	44.1	41.3	31.3	16.0	-6.1	-14.5	10.6
Mn. Max.	7	-16.1	-3.9	-4.7	9.4	25.2	41.0	50.6	46.5	37.5	20.3	2.6	-8.0	16.7
Mn. Min.	7	-28.0	-20.7	-19.5	-5.2	13.1	30.0	37.6	36.0	25.1	11.8	-15.0	-21.0	3.7
H. Max.	7	29	32	38	33	49	63	69	64	56	49	34	28	69
L. Min.	7	-52	-51	-43	-29	-11	12	29	24	8	-17	-32	-43	-52
M. D. R.	7	11.9	16.8	14.8	14.6	12.1	11.0	13.0	10.5	12.4	8.5	17.6	13.0	13.0
Ex. R.	7	81	83	81	62	60	51	40	40	48	66	66	71	121

JONES SOUND, NORTHWEST TERRITORIES

76° 40′ North Latitude   86° 30′ West Longitude

	Y. R.	Jan.	Feb.	Mar.	Apr.	May	Jun.	Jul.	Aug.	Sep.	Oct.	Nov.	Dec.	Yr.
Mean	3B	-33.2	-20.2	-25.6	-10.5	13.1	34.2	40.0	18.7	14.8	-1.8	-14.4	-22.7	-0.6
Mn. Max.	3B	-27.0	-14.0	-18.4	-2.4	20.0	38.8	45.3	20.5	18.9	4.1	-8.0	-15.5	5.2
Mn. Min.	3B	-39.5	-26.7	-32.6	-18.8	6.3	29.5	34.7	16.9	10.8	-7.6	-21.8	-29.7	-6.5
H. Max.	3B	4.6	35.2	13.8	24.3	34.9	54.0	55.9	46.0	37.4	26.6	17.6	29.3	55.9
L. Max.	3B	-12.6	9.5	5.9	14.7	32.2	46.4	51.4	22.5	22.6	12.4	11.5	-1.5	-12.6
H. Min.	3B	-45.4	-44.9	-48.6	-32.3	-7.6	22.6	35.2	20.5	1.4	-19.3	-31.7	-35.9	35.2
L. Min.	3B	-60.5	-53.9	-51.9	-38.9	-12.8	14.4	30.2	-20.2	-5.8	-23.6	-35.0	-51.5	-60.5
M. D. R.	3B	12.5	12.7	14.2	16.4	13.7	9.3	10.6	3.6	8.1	11.7	13.8	14.2	11.7
Ex. R.	3B	65.1	89.1	65.7	63.2	47.7	39.6	25.7	66.2	43.2	50.2	52.6	80.8	116.4

KAMLOOPS, ALBERTA

50° 41′ North Latitude   120° 29′ West Longitude   1245 Feet Altitude

	Y. R.	Jan.	Feb.	Mar.	Apr.	May	Jun.	Jul.	Aug.	Sep.	Oct.	Nov.	Dec.	Yr.
Mean	34B	21.8	26.8	37.9	49.6	57.7	64.5	69.8	68.3	58.6	47.6	35.6	27.2	47.1
High Mn.	34B	33.8	38.4	46.5	61.3	63.2	68.6	78.1	75.8	62.8	52.1	46.0	37.4	50.2
Low Mn.	34B	-3.1	14.5	30.3	45.7	53.6	59.8	65.0	62.3	51.1	41.2	15.5	15.3	42.9
Mn. Max.	34B	27.6	33.8	47.5	61.3	70.5	76.7	83.3	81.3	69.9	56.2	41.2	31.5	56.7
Mn. Min.	34B	16.0	19.8	28.3	37.8	44.9	52.3	56.4	55.3	47.2	38.9	29.9	23.0	37.5
H. Max.	34B	56	63	70	92	100	101	103	101	93	88	72	59	103
L. Max.	33	32	42	53	68	78	76	90	86	69	62	50	40	32
H. Min.	33	20	24	28	33	39	52	52	51	41	31	24	24	52
L. Min.	34B	-31	-27	-6	13	26	35	42	35	24	16	-22	-25	-31
M. D. R.	34B	11.6	14.0	19.2	23.5	25.6	24.4	26.9	26.0	22.7	17.3	11.3	8.5	19.2
Ex. R.	34B	87	90	76	79	74	66	61	66	69	72	94	84	134

LAKE HARBOUR, NORTHWEST TERRITORIES
62° 52′ North Latitude   69° 58′ West Longitude

	Y. R.	Jan.	Feb.	Mar.	Apr.	May	Jun.	Jul.	Aug.	Sep.	Oct.	Nov.	Dec.	Yr.
Mean	11B	-13.7	-10.8	-2.6	11.9	10.7	37.9	44.2	43.1	35.1	25.2	12.0	-2.7	15.8
High Mn.	11B	-4.3	-5.0	1.1	21.5	36.9	45.0	47.8	44.4	39.2	31.4	23.9	13.0	17.7
Low Mn.	11B	-24.4	-16.5	-13.6	6.2	18.1	32.4	41.6	41.7	34.5	19.1	1.8	-14.3	13.5
Mn. Max.	10B	-7.7	-2.9	3.8	20.0	32.8	45.0	51.0	49.2	40.4	29.9	18.1	4.8	23.7
Mn. Min.	10B	-20.3	-18.8	-10.2	3.8	21.9	32.9	37.2	37.0	31.8	20.4	5.9	-8.4	11.2
H. Max.	11B	27	48	59	46	50	69	68	66	57	44	38	42	69
L. Max.	11B	3	-3	8	23	38	43	59	61	45	35	27	14	-3
H. Min.	11B	-27	-24	-17	0	23	31	34.	34	28	16	3	-25	34
L. Min.	11B	-45	-50	-43	-27	-8	22	25	30	22	-3	-23	-37	-50
M. D. R.	10B	12.6	15.9	14.0	16.2	10.9	12.1	13.8	12.2	8.6	9.5	12.2	13.2	12.5
Ex. R.	11B	72	98	102	73	58	47	43	36	35	47	61	79	119

MASSETT, BRITISH COLUMBIA
53° 58′ North Latitude   132° 9′ West Longitude   30 Feet Altitude

	Y. R.	Jan.	Feb.	Mar.	Apr.	May	Jun.	Jul.	Aug.	Sep.	Oct.	Nov.	Dec.	Yr.
Mean	23B	35.3	36.9	38.9	42.7	48.7	53.2	57.8	58.2	53.2	46.7	40.6	38.1	46.0
High Mn.	23B	40.4	40.8	44.9	48.2	57.3	59.2	65.7	62.0	56.7	49.6	44.0	45.3	49.4
Low Mn.	23B	24.0	31.8	34.0	38.3	42.1	49.6	50.6	54.4	50.0	44.0	37.6	32.0	43.6
Mn. Max.	17	42.1	43.5	46.7	49.6	56.8	61.9	65.6	66.8	61.2	53.9	46.6	45.3	53.3
Mn. Min.	17	29.6	31.0	32.2	35.6	40.4	45.5	50.6	51.0	45.9	39.4	34.1	33.5	39.1
H. Max.	27B	60	52	64	69	76	80	83	84	75	68	66	60	84
L. Max.	27B	38	41	40	45	55	59	63	60	58	54	49	45	38
H. Min.	27B	29	31	30	34	40	45	52	53	48	37	32	32	53
L. Min.	27B	-2	9	16	22	27	32	39	38	31	17	12	9	-2
M. D. R.	17	12.5	12.5	14.5	14.0	16.4	16.4	15.0	15.8	15.3	14.5	12.5	11.8	14.2
Ex. R.	27B	62	43	24	47	49	48	44	46	44	51	54	51	86

MEDICINE HAT, ALBERTA
50° 5′ North Latitude   110° 45′ West Longitude   2144 Feet Altitude

	Y. R.	Jan.	Feb.	Mar.	Apr.	May	Jun.	Jul.	Aug.	Sep.	Oct.	Nov.	Dec.	Yr.
Mean	30	11.3	13.5	26.5	44.9	54.7	62.2	67.9	66.5	55.9	45.7	29.2	20.7	41.6
High Mn.	30	26.7	26.6	45.0	54.7	62.0	68.6	73.5	70.6	63.1	51.8	42.7	31.3	44.7
Low Mn.	30	-8.1	-9.4	8.3	37.4	48.5	55.0	61.4	61.3	46.7	40.5	2.0	-1.2	37.0
Mn. Max.	30	21.7	23.2	37.9	58.4	68.0	75.6	82.1	80.5	69.7	58.6	40.0	30.6	53.9
Mn. Min.	30	0.8	3.7	15.0	31.3	41.4	48.9	53.8	51.5	42.0	32.7	18.4	10.7	29.2
H. Max.	44	56	64	84	96	99	107	108	103	94	93	76	68	108
L. Max.	44	30	36	43	62	75	83	86	83	76	68	54	41	30
H. Min.	44	-7	-5	11	29	33	47	48	48	37	30	22	4	48
L. Min.	44	-50	-51	-38	-16	12	30	36	31	18	-10	-36	-30	-51
M. D. R.	30	20.9	19.5	22.9	27.1	26.6	26.7	28.3	29.0	27.7	25.9	21.6	19.9	24.7
Ex. R.	44	106	115	122	112	87	77	72	72	76	103	112	98	159

MISTASSINI POST, QUEBEC

50° 15′ North Latitude　　　73° 55′ West Longitude　　　1255 Feet Altitude

	Y. R.	Jan.	Feb.	Mar.	Apr.	May	Jun.	Jul.	Aug.	Sep.	Oct.	Nov.	Dec.	Yr.
Mean	12B	-5.8	-3.0	10.2	27.9	41.0	53.9	60.6	56.8	47.8	35.1	20.1	2.5	28.9
High Mn.	12B	3	5	20	33	48	60	67	61	53	42	25	8	—
Low Mn.	12B	-12	-9	0	18	37	48	56	52	43	30	17	-7	—
Mn. Max.	12B	6.3	11.2	24.0	40.0	53.7	66.9	71.5	67.2	57.8	44.4	27.8	12.6	40.3
Mn. Min.	12B	-18.0	-16.0	5.2	17.5	30.5	42.2	49.3	46.8	39.0	29.7	14.7	-6.6	19.4
H. Max.	12B	41	36	57	67	86	91	95	87	83	73	49	37	95
L. Max.	12B	20	22	36	47	59	74	76	77	63	51	35	25	20
H. Min.	12B	-41	-32	-11	1	20	29	43	38	30	18	1	-24	43
L. Min.	12B	-54	-49	-42	-26	2	13	24	24	16	10	-29	-56	-56
M. D. R.	12B	24.3	27.2	18.8	22.5	23.2	24.7	22.2	20.4	18.8	14.7	13.1	19.2	20.9
Ex. R.	12B	95	85	99	93	84	78	71	63	67	63	78	93	151

MONTREAL, QUEBEC

45° 30′ North Latitude　　　73° 35′ West Longitude　　　187 Feet Altitude

	Y. R.	Jan.	Feb.	Mar.	Apr.	May	Jun.	Jul.	Aug.	Sep.	Oct.	Nov.	Dec.	Yr.
Mean	50	13.0	14.5	25.6	41.3	55.1	64.7	69.5	66.8	58.7	46.6	33.1	19.6	42.4
High Mn.	50	22.1	27.2	33.9	48.6	62.7	69.2	76.2	70.7	64.6	52.4	39.0	29.8	45.4
Low Mn.	50	4.3	6.0	13.5	35.5	48.2	59.7	64.8	61.0	53.4	39.9	24.1	8.6	38.4
Mn. Max.	50	20.9	22.1	32.7	49.2	64.1	73.4	77.9	74.9	66.4	53.4	38.9	26.2	50.0
Mn. Min.	50	5.0	6.9	18.5	33.3	46.0	56.0	61.2	58.8	50.9	39.8	27.3	12.9	34.7
H. Max.	43	53	51	68	83	89	94	95	96	90	80	68	59	96
L. Max.	43	34	30	39	56	67	80	84	80	72	58	46	32	30
H. Min.	43	-4	6	13	31	40	53	56	55	46	34	21	5	56
L. Min.	43	-27	-27	-15	2	23	37	46	43	32	20	-18	-25	-27
M. D. R.	50	15.9	15.2	14.2	15.9	18.1	17.4	16.7	16.1	15.5	13.6	11.6	13.3	15.3
Ex. R.	43	60	78	83	81	66	57	49	53	58	60	86	84	123

MOOSE FACTORY, ONTARIO

51° 16′ North Latitude　　　80° 56′ West Longitude　　　30 Feet Altitude

	Y. R.	Jan.	Feb.	Mar.	Apr.	May	Jun.	Jul.	Aug.	Sep.	Oct.	Nov.	Dec.	Yr.
Mean	33	-4.4	-2.0	9.9	28.0	42.4	54.2	61.2	58.5	51.1	39.2	22.3	4.6	30.4
High Mn.	33	4.8	9.9	20.8	36.8	50.8	60.7	67.7	64.7	60.8	46.2	29.9	13.8	32.8
Low Mn.	33	-13.8	-13.0	-3.5	17.2	34.9	50.1	54.7	53.3	44.5	31.9	14.3	-9.2	26.7
Mn. Max.	33	7.4	10.6	23.6	39.6	53.0	66.2	73.0	69.3	61.0	47.2	29.4	14.0	41.2
Mn. Min.	33	-16.2	-14.6	-3.8	16.5	31.8	42.1	49.4	47.7	41.2	31.1	15.2	-4.7	19.6
H. Max.	38B	43	44	61	75	95	96	97	96	91	84	64	50	97
L. Max.	38B	11	20	23	44	57	77	80	76	67	53	40	26	11
H. Min.	38B	-30	-20	-12	5	27	33	43	44	39	27	16	-11	44
L. Min.	38B	-54	-48	-48	-29	-11	23	30	29	20	-3	-39	-43	-54
M. D. R.	33	23.6	25.2	27.4	23.1	21.2	24.1	23.6	21.6	19.8	16.1	14.2	18.7	21.6
Ex. R.	38B	97	92	109	104	106	73	67	67	71	87	103	93	151

NORWAY HOUSE, MANITOBA

54° 5′ North Latitude 98° 5′ West Longitude 720 Feet Altitude

	Y. R.	Jan.	Feb.	Mar.	Apr.	May	Jun.	Jul.	Aug.	Sep.	Oct.	Nov.	Dec.	Yr.
Mean	21B	-9.7	-5.9	5.6	35.4	45.3	55.5	62.3	59.1	48.7	35.8	16.7	-1.1	28.1
Mn. Max.	21B	1.8	5.4	20.9	41.7	56.8	66.4	72.0	68.3	56.8	42.4	23.7	7.4	38.6
Mn. Min.	21B	-21.2	-17.2	-3.8	19.2	33.8	44.5	52.6	49.9	40.6	29.2	9.8	-9.9	19.8
H. Max.	21B	47	43	50	75	88	89	88	90	80	75	57	38	90
L. Max.	21B	0	14	20	43	64	68	76	76	64	49	31	17	0
H. Min.	21B	-14	-12	-1	24	28	35	40	35	30	20	2	-11	40
L. Min.	21B	-54	-53	-34	-12	10	20	23	23	16	-10	-18	-36	-54
M. D. R.	21B	23.0	22.6	24.7	22.5	23.0	21.9	19.4	18.4	16.2	13.2	13.9	17.3	18.8
Ex. R.	21B	101	96	84	87	78	69	65	67	64	85	75	74	144

PARRY SOUND, ONTARIO

45° 19′ North Latitude 80° 0′ West Longitude 635 Feet Altitude

	Y. R.	Jan.	Feb.	Mar.	Apr.	May	Jun.	Jul.	Aug.	Sep.	Oct.	Nov.	Dec.	Yr.
Mean	50	13.6	14.1	23.7	39.1	51.6	61.8	67.2	64.8	57.6	46.2	33.3	20.6	41.2
High Mn.	50	25.8	24.0	35.6	47.7	58.9	72.0	76.7	69.6	64.0	54.8	39.6	31.4	—
Low Mn.	50	7.0	1.1	7.4	32.8	45.2	56.4	62.0	59.7	52.2	39.2	26.8	12.8	—
Mn. Max.	50	24.7	25.0	34.2	49.4	62.6	72.9	77.7	75.2	67.6	54.8	40.5	29.4	51.2
Mn. Min.	50	2.5	3.2	13.2	28.8	40.6	50.6	56.7	54.3	47.6	37.7	26.1	11.9	31.1
H. Max.	50	54	58	71	83	90	97	100	99	90	84	69	56	100
L. Max.	40	25	32	42	54	63	77	85	77	75	60	50	36	25
H. Min.	40	-11	-8	18	23	41	45	53	47	40	29	20	5	53
L. Min.	50	-38	-38	-27	-3	16	31	37	35	24	9	-20	-39	-39
M. D. R.	50	22.2	21.8	21.0	20.6	22.0	22.3	21.0	20.9	20.0	17.1	14.4	17.5	20.1
Ex. R.	50	92	96	98	86	74	66	63	64	66	75	89	95	139

PONDS INLET, NORTHWEST TERRITORIES

72° 43′ North Latitude 78° 30′ West Longitude 13 Feet Altitude

	Y. R.	Jan.	Feb.	Mar.	Apr.	May	Jun.	Jul.	Aug.	Sep.	Oct.	Nov.	Dec.	Yr.
Mean	5B	-28.4	-29.7	-24.4	5.7	23.4	39.0	42.4	40.8	30.2	13.5	-5.1	-21.6	7.2
High Mn.	5B	-22.1	-26.4	-11.8	17.8	32.3	45.9	48.6	44.2	30.3	14.3	-3.2	14.3	—
Low Mn.	5B	-33.5	-32.9	-36.9	-2.9	17.2	34.7	38.9	37.2	30.2	12.4	-10.4	-25.8	—
Mn. Max.	5B	-23.0	-22.8	-16.7	17.1	31.4	46.6	49.3	46.7	34.7	18.1	0.6	-15.6	13.9
Mn. Min.	5B	-33.9	-36.6	-32.1	-5.7	15.5	31.4	35.5	34.9	25.8	8.9	-10.8	-27.6	0.4
Mn. Max.	5B	-33.9	-36.6	-32.1	5.7	15.5	31.4	35.5	34.9	25.8	8.9	-10.8	-27.6	0.4
H. Max.	5B	6	12	34	58	66	73	77	66	54	36	35	10	77
L. Max.	5B	-10	0	-18	27	35	49	52	54	41	32	26	0	-18
H. Min.	5B	-40	-48	-36	-17	3	25	33	32	17	-8	-27	-33	33
L. Min.	5B	-52	-49	-50	-40	-10	15	28	26	9	-16	-32	-46	-52
M. D. R.	5B	10.9	13.8	15.4	22.8	16.0	15.2	13.8	11.8	8.9	9.2	11.4	12.0	13.5
Ex. R.	5B	58	61	84	98	76	58	49	40	45	52	67	56	129

PORT ARTHUR, ONTARIO

48° 27' North Latitude   89° 12' West Longitude   644 Feet Altitude

	Y. R.	Jan.	Feb.	Mar.	Apr.	May	Jun.	Jul.	Aug.	Sep.	Oct.	Nov.	Dec.	Yr.
Mean	40	6.3	8.2	19.9	35.6	47.0	57.0	62.8	59.8	53.0	42.0	28.0	14.3	36.2
High Mn.	40	16.7	20.0	33.7	43.2	53.6	62.4	70.3	63.7	58.5	49.7	36.7	25.1	—
Low Mn.	40	-7.7	-1.2	7.0	28.1	37.5	52.6	57.8	56.8	48.8	35.4	19.7	3.8	—
Mn. Max.	40	16.6	19.1	30.7	44.5	57.1	67.5	73.5	70.5	62.4	50.1	35.5	23.2	45.9
Mn. Min.	40	-4.0	-2.6	9.1	26.7	37.0	46.5	52.2	49.0	43.7	33.8	20.4	5.4	26.4
H. Max.	40	48	52	70	78	89	91	99	94	89	78	69	51	99
L. Max.	39	23	27	32	42	60	74	79	75	71	58	42	34	23
H. Min.	39	-19	-15	1	23	35	40	50	45	35	28	22	-6	50
L. Min.	40	-40	-39	-30	-6	16	20	36	33	20	5	-22	-34	-37
M. D. R.	40	20.6	21.7	21.6	17.8	20.1	21.0	21.3	21.5	18.7	16.3	15.1	17.8	19.5
Ex. R.	40	88	91	100	84	73	71	63	61	69	73	91	85	136

PORT AUX BASQUES, NEWFOUNDLAND

48° 27' North Latitude   89° 12' West Longitude   644 Feet Altitude

	Y. R.	Jan.	Feb.	Mar.	Apr.	May	Jun.	Jul.	Aug.	Sep.	Oct.	Nov.	Dec.	Yr.
Mean	10	20.5	17.5	24.1	33.7	40.9	48.6	56.3	58.3	52.7	44.3	35.4	27.5	38.3
High Mn.	10	25.1	25.4	33.1	37.4	43.4	50.3	59.2	62.5	54.4	46.5	39.9	33.6	—
Low Mn.	10	12.7	7.8	16.8	30.3	38.9	45.8	53.6	53.0	51.6	40.7	32.0	21.2	—
Mn. Max.	10	25.9	23.6	29.7	38.7	46.8	54.4	62.0	63.7	58.2	49.4	39.5	32.0	43.7
Mn. Min.	10	15.1	11.4	18.5	28.8	35.0	42.9	50.7	52.9	47.3	39.2	31.3	23.0	33.0
H. Max.	19B	46	40	52	60	70	73	80	80	69	62	56	50	80
L. Max.	19B	32	30	34	38	54	56	66	66	64	52	44	38	30
H. Min.	19B	14	12	16	22	32	38	50	47	42	34	26	18	50
L. Min.	19B	-10	-14	-10	8	22	30	39	37	32	24	14	2	-14
M. D. R.	10	10.8	12.2	11.2	9.9	11.8	11.5	11.3	10.8	10.9	10.2	8.2	9.0	10.7
Ex. R.	19B	56	54	62	52	48	43	41	43	37	38	42	48	94

PORT NELSON MANITOBA

57° 3' North Latitude   92° 36' West Longitude   49 Feet Altitude

	Y. R.	Jan.	Feb.	Mar.	Apr.	May	Jun.	Jul.	Aug.	Sep.	Oct.	Nov.	Dec.	Yr.
Mean	19	-18.8	-14.0	-0.2	21.5	34.6	48.0	55.7	53.4	43.7	28.4	10.5	-10.1	21.0
High Mn.	14	-9.8	-3.0	9.6	21.6	41.0	53.8	62.3	58.0	49.9	38.0	16.3	1.4	23.0
Low Mn.	14	-22.5	-25.0	-13.3	9.3	23.6	39.2	50.6	48.6	41.6	20.0	3.5	-22.2	18.1
Mn. Max.	19	-11.2	-5.5	11.3	31.9	42.8	58.5	67.4	54.1	52.5	34.9	18.0	3.0	29.8
Mn. Min.	19	-26.4	-22.5	-11.7	11.1	26.6	38.0	44.0	42.7	34.9	21.9	3.0	-17.0	12.0
H. Max.	13	36	29	49	60	87	92	91	91	82	78	44	33	92
L. Max.	13	4	4	14	37	49	71	80	72	64	43	28	0	0
H. Min.	13	-36	-34	-21	-6	18	30	37	44	30	20	-14	-19	44
L. Min.	13	-55	-52	-44	-35	-11	20	28	26	17	-13	-32	-50	-55
M. D. R.	19	15.2	17.0	0.4	20.8	16.2	20.5	23.4	11.4	17.6	13.0	15.0	20.0	17.8
Ex. R.	13	91	81	93	95	98	72	63	65	65	91	76	83	147

PRINCE ALBERT, SASKATCHEWAN
53° 10′ North Latitude   105° 38′ West Longitude   1432 Feet Altitude

	Y.R.	Jan.	Feb.	Mar.	Apr.	May	Jun.	Jul.	Aug.	Sep.	Oct.	Nov.	Dec.	Yr.
Mean	51	-4.7	0.7	14.2	36.7	49.7	58.2	62.7	59.6	50.0	38.4	19.7	5.8	32.6
High Mn.	41	12.7	14.2	32.0	44.5	57.7	64.7	67.1	64.4	55.7	45.4	30.3	16.6	35.5
Low Mn.	41	-26.0	-13.5	1.5	23.3	42.6	50.3	58.4	55.2	42.3	31.4	1.1	-13.0	27.6
Mn. Max.	30	5.3	11.3	26.2	48.7	62.6	71.0	74.2	71.7	61.7	49.2	27.4	15.1	43.7
Mn. Min.	30	-17.1	-13.9	-2.1	23.6	35.2	45.1	49.8	46.0	37.1	27.4	9.5	-4.5	20.2
H. Max.	43	55	55	68	86	95	96	95	94	90	85	66	52	96
L. Max.	43	10	20	26	45	67	74	78	76	70	60	32	22	10
H. Min.	43	-30	-12	-8	20	33	48	46	43	32	24	9	-14	48
L. Min.	43	-66	-70	-44	-23	2	17	33	22	14	-8	-41	-56	-70
M. D. R.	30	22.4	25.2	28.3	25.1	27.4	25.9	24.4	25.7	24.6	21.8	16.9	19.6	23.5
Ex. R.	43	121	125	112	109	93	79	62	72	76	93	107	108	166

PRINCE GEORGE, BRITISH COLUMBIA
53° 55′ North Latitude   122° 41′ West Longitude   1867 Feet Altitude

	Y.R.	Jan.	Feb.	Mar.	Apr.	May	Jun.	Jul.	Aug.	Sep.	Oct.	Nov.	Dec.	Yr.
Mean	12	12.6	18.4	28.8	40.2	48.4	55.6	59.3	58.4	49.6	40.9	29.6	16.1	38.2
Mn. Max.	12	22.5	30.6	40.8	54.2	63.4	70.2	74.7	74.2	64.0	52.6	38.0	24.5	50.8
Mn. Min.	12	2.8	6.2	16.9	26.3	33.5	40.9	43.9	42.7	35.1	29.2	21.1	7.7	25.5
H. Max.	15B	50	55	67	81	89	92	95	91	84	84	61	55	95
L. Max.	15B	22	34	42	59	68	79	79	82	70	62	51	32	22
H. Min.	15B	6	4	12	20	30	36	44	38	31	22	10	8	44
L. Min.	15B	-56	-43	-35	-13	12	24	28	28	6	-1	-22	-43	-56
M. D. R.	12	19.7	24.4	23.9	27.9	29.9	29.3	30.8	31.5	28.9	23.4	16.9	16.8	25.3
Ex. R.	15B	106	98	102	94	77	68	67	63	78	85	83	98	151

QU'APPELLE, SASKATCHEWAN
50° 30′ North Latitude   103° 47′ West Longitude   2115 Feet Altitude

	Y.R.	Jan.	Feb.	Mar.	Apr.	May	Jun.	Jul.	Aug.	Sep.	Oct.	Nov.	Dec.	Yr.
Mean	38	-0.4	2.1	16.1	37.8	50.1	59.1	63.5	61.5	51.7	40.0	22.2	8.7	34.5
High Mn.	38	17.7	18.3	36.0	49.3	59.3	64.4	70.1	68.0	59.6	46.2	38.4	20.1	39.4
Low Mn.	38	-14.2	-9.7	1.3	26.7	43.6	53.0	57.6	56.8	46.2	28.0	0.7	-7.0	30.6
Mn. Max.	30	8.5	11.2	25.7	49.1	62.4	70.8	75.9	73.3	64.0	51.5	30.4	18.5	45.1
Mn. Min.	30	-9.7	-7.2	6.2	25.5	37.3	48.4	51.7	48.9	39.9	30.2	13.3	2.8	23.9
H. Max.	45	50	50	76	88	92	100	102	100	92	86	65	49	102
L. Max.	45	20	27	29	45	71	75	78	78	74	51	34	26	20
H. Min.	56	-16	-12	-4	26	37	42	50	44	30	24	18	-8	50
L. Min.	45	-48	-50	-45	-24	8	25	30	27	10	-14	-30	-41	-50
M. D. R.	30	18.2	18.4	19.5	23.6	25.1	22.4	24.2	24.2	24.1	21.3	17.1	15.7	21.2
Ex. R.	45	98	100	121	112	84	75	72		82	100	95	90	152

QUEBEC, QUEBEC

46° 48′ North Latitude   71° 13′ West Longitude   296 Feet Altitude

	Y.R.	Jan.	Feb.	Mar.	Apr.	May	Jun.	Jul.	Aug.	Sep.	Oct.	Nov.	Dec.	Yr.
Mean	50	9.7	11.5	22.3	36.4	50.9	61.3	66.7	63.6	55.6	43.5	29.7	15.6	38.5
High Mn.	50	17.0	24.4	30.5	41.3	58.0	65.8	72.5	68.2	60.4	49.4	34.3	26.8	—
Low Mn.	50	2.3	3.4	11.8	30.5	45.1	55.5	62.6	58.6	49.7	37.7	21.9	3.9	—
Mn. Max.	50	17.7	19.6	30.3	44 3	60.5	71.1	76.5	72.5	63.9	50.5	35.3	22.4	47.1
Mn. Min.	50	1.6	3.3	14.4	28.5	41.4	51.4	57.0	54.6	47.2	36.6	24.1	8.9	29.9
H. Max.	52	51	49	64	80	91	92	96	97	88	77	67	54	97
L. Max.	43	29	28	38	51	66	78	82	76	71	52	38	30	28
H. Min.	43	−11	−4	9	26	36	46	52	48	40	30	19	0	52
L. Min.	52	−34	−32	−22	0	21	31	39	37	27	14	−20	−32	−34
M. D. R.	50	16.1	16.3	15.9	15.8	19.1	19.7	19.5	17.9	16.7	13.9	11.2	13.5	17.2
Ex. R.	52	85	81	86	80	70	61	57	60	61	63	87	86	131

ST. JOHNS, NEWFOUNDLAND

47° 34′ North Latitude   52° 42′ West Longitude   125 Feet Altitude

	Y.R.	Jan.	Feb.	Mar.	Apr.	May	Jun.	Jul.	Aug.	Sep.	Oct.	Nov.	Dec.	Yr.
Mean	50	23.4	22.0	27.6	35.0	43.2	51.4	59.1	59.1	53.8	45.3	37.2	29.2	40.5
High Mn.	50	31.2	31.9	34.5	41.5	49.0	58.7	67.8	65.4	57.4	50.0	43.0	34.8	44.4
Low Mn.	50	12.1	12.5	18.4	26.9	37.9	44.4	53.3	55.1	49.0	41.3	31.0	21.5	37.8
Mn. Max.	50	30.5	29.1	34.1	41.4	51.3	60.5	68.0	67.9	61.4	51.8	43.2	35.3	47.9
Mn. Min.	50	16.4	14.8	21.1	28.6	34.9	42.3	50.3	51.9	46.1	38.7	31.3	23.0	33.3
H. Max.	52B	59	56	63	72	81	87	90	92	84	75	66	60	92
L. Max.	42B	40	32	40	48	58	67	68	65	62	57	48	38	32
H. Min.	42B	10	12	18	26	34	38	49	49	44	34	30	18	49
L. Min.	52B	−19	−21	−7	−1	20	28	34	32	29	22	6	−4	−21
M. D. R.	50	14.1	14.3	13.0	12.8	16.4	18.2	17.7	16.0	15.3	13.1	11.9	12.3	14.6
Ex. R.	52B	78	77	70	73	61	59	56	60	55	53	60	64	113

SOUTHWEST POINT, QUEBEC

49° 23′ North Latitude   63° 43′ West Longitude   30 Feet Altitude

	Y.R.	Jan.	Feb.	Mar.	Apr.	May	Jun.	Jul.	Aug.	Sep.	Oct.	Nov.	Dec.	Yr.
Mean	50	12.3	13.1	21.2	31.1	40.1	49.8	56.8	56.4	49.4	40.3	30.7	20.0	35.1
High Mn.	50	23.1	23.6	29.4	37.5	45.6	53.4	61.6	62.5	54.2	46.7	36.3	28.7	37.5
Low Mn.	50	4.3	4.1	13.4	24.4	35.5	45.1	52.5	49.8	43.2	26.0	14.3	14.3	32.1
Mn. Max.	50	19.9	20.5	27.2	36.1	45.5	55.0	62.5	61.6	54.7	45.5	35.7	26.3	40.9
Mn. Min.	50	4.7	5.8	15.2	26.0	34.7	44.7	51.2	51.2	44.0	35.1	25.7	13.8	29.3
H. Max.	53	47	48	48	71	78	85	79	80	73	68	57	52	85
L. Max.	48	28	28	31	39	49	59	65	64	55	46	39	33	28
H. Min.	48	1	10	13	24	32	41	52	48	38	32	22	8	52
L. Min.	53	−40	−35	−20	−3	19	26	34	28	20	8	−1	−39	−40
M. D. R.	50	15.2	14.7	12.0	10.1	10.8	10.3	11.3	10.4	10.7	10.4	10.0	12.5	11.6
Ex. R.	53	87	81	68	74	59	59	45	52	53	60	58	91	125

43° 40′ North Latitude 79° 24′ West Longitude 379 Feet Altitude

	Y. R.	Jan.	Feb.	Mar.	Apr.	May	Jun.	Jul.	Aug.	Sep.	Oct.	Nov.	Dec.	Yr.
Mean	80	22.2	21.6	29.5	41.8	53.2	63.2	68.7	66.9	59.6	47.8	36.8	26.5	44.8
High Mn.	80	32.7	30.3	38.9	49.8	61.2	72.4	77.8	72.0	67.8	55.7	43.0	36.1	49.8
Low Mn.	80	12.7	10.2	18.4	34.2	46.5	58.4	61.1	60.8	54.2	42.3	27.5	17.2	40.6
Mn. Max.	80	29.3	29.2	36.8	50.0	62.6	73.0	78.6	76.5	68.7	55.9	43.0	32.7	53.0
Mn. Min.	80	15.2	14.1	22.2	33.6	43.7	53.3	58.8	57.3	50.5	39.8	30.6	20.3	36.6
H. Max.	87	58	54	75	90	93	97	103	102	97	86	70	61	103
L. Max.	87	33	34	40	52	65	76	82	77	73	60	49	39	34
H. Min.	87	11	10	17	32	40	50	59	54	46	35	27	18	59
L. Min.	87	−26	−28	−15	11	24	28	38	39	27	19	−2	−21	−28
M. D. R.	80	14.1	15.1	14.6	16.4	18.9	19.7	19.8	19.2	18.2	16.1	12.4	12.4	16.4
Ex. R.	87	84	82	90	79	69	69	65	63	70	67	72	82	131

VANCOUVER, BRITISH COLUMBIA
49° 17′ North Latitude 123° 5′ West Longitude 136 Feet Altitude

	Y. R.	Jan.	Feb.	Mar.	Apr.	May	Jun.	Jul.	Aug.	Sep.	Oct.	Nov.	Dec.	Yr.
Mean	28	35.6	38.3	42.2	47.6	53.9	59.0	63.3	62.3	56.4	49.4	42.7	38.3	49.1
High Mn.	28	40.8	42.2	45.7	50.6	56.4	61.3	66.1	62.8	57.5	53.0	44.6	42.7	50.3
Low Mn.	28	27.3	34.6	39.4	44.9	51.2	55.7	60.5	59.8	54.1	44.2	39.5	33.9	47.2
Mn. Max.	28	39.6	43.3	48.9	55.9	62.7	68.3	73.4	71.7	64.7	55.6	47.3	42.1	56.1
Mn. Min.	28	31.7	33.3	35.6	39.4	45.1	49.8	53.3	52.9	48.2	43.2	38.1	34.6	42.1
H. Max.	29	56	58	65	79	82	92	91	92	82	73	63	58	92
L. Max.	29	44	46	53	61	68	72	77	79	69	58	52	46	44
H. Min.	29	29	31	36	36	42	47	50	51	44	39	38	32	51
L. Min.	29	2	10	15	27	33	36	43	39	30	23	10	8	2
M. D. R.	28	7.9	10.0	13.3	16.5	17.6	18.5	20.1	18.8	16.5	12.4	9.2	7.5	14.0
Ex. R.	29	54	48	50	52	49	56	48	53	52	50	53	50	90

VICTORIA, BRITISH COLUMBIA
48° 24′ North Latitude 123° 19′ West Longitude 228 Feet Altitude

	Y. R.	Jan.	Feb.	Mar.	Apr.	May	Jun.	Jul.	Aug.	Sep.	Oct.	Nov.	Dec.	Yr.
Mean	43	38.6	40.4	43.6	48.4	53.0	57.0	59.9	59.9	56.0	50.4	44.6	41.0	49.4
High Mn.	43	43.3	45.1	48.6	51.2	56.0	59.8	65.5	62.6	59.9	54.4	50.2	45.1	50.8
Low Mn.	43	29.5	34.0	38.8	45.0	50.0	54.4	57.4	49.5	52.8	47.5	37.2	36.7	47.3
Mn. Max.	43	42.6	45.1	49.9	56.1	60.9	65.3	68.9	68.6	63.8	56.2	48.8	44.6	55.9
Mn. Min.	43	34.6	35.6	37.4	40.8	45.2	48.8	50.9	51.2	48.1	44.5	40.3	37.4	42.9
H. Max.	43	56	58	68	75	84	95	92	88	85	74	63	58	95
L. Max.	33	47	47	52	59	62	69	68	71	67	58	52	49	47
H. Min.	33	34	37	38	40	42	48	50	50	47	44	40	36	50
L. Min.	43	−2	6	17	24	30	36	37	38	30	28	14	12	−2
M. D. R.	43	8.0	9.5	12.5	15.3	15.7	16.5	18.0	17.4	15.7	11.7	8.5	7.2	13.0
Ex. R.	43	58	52	51	51	54	59	55	50	55	46	49	46	97

WHITE RIVER, ONTARIO

48° 35′ North Latitude　　　85° 16′ West Longitude　　　1244 Feet Altitude

	Y. R.	Jan.	Feb.	Mar.	Apr.	May	Jun.	Jul.	Aug.	Sep.	Oct.	Nov.	Dec.	Yr.
Mean	30	0.4	1.1	13.6	34.2	46.4	56.8	60.5	57.0	50.2	36.4	23.7	7.8	32.3
High Mn.	30	10.1	12.1	27.3	40.6	54.3	64.6	68.1	63.3	55.9	48.4	31.8	17.4	—
Low Mn.	30	−13.4	−9.7	2.1	21.2	34.3	51.7	55.9	52.9	42.3	30.7	16.2	−4.0	—
Mn. Max.	30	14.6	16.3	28.9	48.6	60.2	71.7	74.8	70.3	61.9	46.4	31.9	19.5	45.4
Mn. Min.	30	−13.8	−14.1	−1.8	19.7	32.7	41.9	46.2	43.8	38.5	26.3	15.5	−4.0	19.2
H. Max.	42B	44	45	60	79	93	95	97	91	91	80	69	54	97
L. Max.	42B	19	2	32	46	64	76	79 /	74	65	54	36	30	2
H. Min.	42B	−34	−31	−17	12	30	42	42	36	30	22	8	−18	42
L. Min.	42B	−58	−60	−50	−30	−11	18	24	21	14	−2	−43	−59	−60
M. D. R.	30	28.4	30.4	30.7	28.9	27.5	29.8	28.6	26.5	23.4	20.1	16.4	23.5	26.2
Ex. R.	42B	104	105	110	109	104	77	73	70	77	82	112	113	157

WINNIPEG, MANITOBA

49° 53′ North Latitude　　　97° 7′ West Longitude　　　760 Feet Altitude

	Y. R.	Jan.	Feb.	Mar.	Apr.	May	Jun.	Jul.	Aug.	Sep.	Oct.	Nov.	Dec.	Yr.
Mean	40	−3.4	0.6	15.3	37.8	52.1	62.4	66.6	64.1	54.0	40.9	21.7	6.0	34.8
High Mn.	40	11.0	22.9	34.8	47.9	60.1	68.4	72.2	69.5	61.1	51.0	34.7	25.9	40.4
Low Mn.	40	−16.2	−14.8	3.2	27.1	39.7	56.6	60.6	59.3	47.3	32.5	6.9	−14.7	29.0
Mn. Max.	40	6.2	10.8	26.0	49.0	64.5	74.4	78.1	75.3	65.2	51.1	29.7	15.5	45.5
Mn. Min.	40	−14.7	−11.8	2.5	26.4	38.9	50.0	54.2	50.7	41.8	30.5	12.1	−3.8	23.0
H. Max.	43	42	46	73	90	95	100	98	103	99	86	71	49	103
L. Max.	43	20	20	29	49	74	79	81	81	76	61	38	23	20
H. Min.	43	−26	−13	2	24	33	43	51	45	34	29	18	−14	51
L. Min.	43	−46	−46	−36	−13	11	21	36	30	17	−3	−33	−42	−46
M. D. R.	40	20.9	22.6	23.5	19.6	25.6	24.4	23.9	24.6	23.4	20.6	17.6	19.3	22.5
Ex. R.	43	88	92	109	103	84	79	62	73	82	89	104	91	149

PRECIPITATION DATA

ABITIBI, QUEBEC

	Y. R.	Jan.	Feb.	Mar.	Apr.	May	Jun.	Jul.	Aug.	Sep.	Oct.	Nov.	Dec.	Yr.
Mean	29B	1.76	1.40	2.08	1.22	2.63	2.41	2.62	2.64	2.58	2.91	2.14	1.99	26.38
Max.	29B	3.40	3.26	4.95	5.61	4.97	5.92	6.53	5.45	5.39	5.82	4.08	5.55	38.97
Min.	29B	0.80	0.40	0.45	0.09	0.10	0.35	0.38	1.00	0.16	1.43	0.00	1.06	18.96
Wet Yr.	29B	2.10	1.55	2.05	3.61	2.26	1.83	5.19	4.64	5.39	4.77	2.48	3.10	38.97
Dry Yr.	29B	0.80	2.15	0.90	0.96	3.41	2.00	1.34	1.19	0.79	2.07	2.03	1.32	18.96
Mn. Sn.	22	17.3	14.0	19.3	4.6	2.0	T	—	T	T	2.4	12.5	18.7	90.8
Max. Sn.	28	27.0	21.5	49.5	18.0	10.0	T	—	T	2.0	20.0	30.5	41.8	—
Pr. Das.	10	8.0	6.6	6.9	6.7	6.0	5.3	6.7	6.8	6.6	7.0	8.6	9.1	84.3

ANNAPOLIS ROYAL, NOVA SCOTIA

	Y. R.	Jan.	Feb.	Mar.	Apr.	May	Jun.	Jul.	Aug.	Sep.	Oct.	Nov.	Dec.	Yr.
Mean	10B	3.59	3.33	3.86	3.57	2.23	3.06	3.60	3.32	3.10	3.94	4.24	5.30	43.14
Max.	10B	7.54	5.45	6.58	7.20	4.51	4.98	7.18	5.94	7.92	9.09	6.21	9.08	48.24
Min.	10B	1.80	1.24	2.42	1.31	1.06	1.27	1.27	1.19	1.40	0.62	2.51	3.23	38.90
Wet Yr.	10B	2.45	3.78	3.04	1.31	2.23	3.22	4.30	2.59	7.92	6.78	6.21	4.41	48.24
Dry Yr.	10B	2.67	5.45	6.58	2.66	1.62	3.14	4.58	2.81	2.05	0.62	2.93	3.79	38.90
Mn. Sn.	10B	18.2	18.2	11.0	3.9	—	—	—	—	—	0.2	4.4	23.4	79.3
Max. Sn.	10B	44.0	26.8	36.0	9.5	—	—	—	—	—	1.0	13.8	67.0	—
Pr. Das.	10B	13	10	10	10	9	10	10	10	8	12	13	14	139

ATLIN, BRITISH COLUMBIA

	Y. R.	Jan.	Feb.	Mar.	Apr.	May	Jun.	Jul.	Aug.	Sep.	Oct.	Nov.	Dec.	Yr.
Mean	18	0.93	0.87	0.62	0.31	0.41	0.81	1.04	0.93	1.25	1.25	1.28	1.24	10.94
Max.	23B	1.65	2.18	2.12	1.19	1.06	1.98	2.11	1.82	3.46	2.70	3.67	3.10	14.43
Min.	23B	0.33	0.05	0.05	0.06	0.13	0.15	0.15	0.16	0.13	0.46	0.21	0.28	6.73
Wet Yr.	21	0.50	1.10	0.36	0.54	0.19	0.91	1.70	0.80	3.46	1.27	1.98	1.62	14.43
Dry Yr.	21	0.58	0.85	0.75	0.10	0.23	0.15	1.18	0.40	0.53	0.46	0.65	0.58	6.73
Mn. Sn.	18	8.7	8.2	5.0	2.4	0.7	0.1	—	0.2	1.8	7.4	9.0	10.6	54.1
Max. Sn.	18	16.5	21.5	17.6	11.0	4.5	2.5	—	2.5	9.8	26.0	26.5	30.3	79.8
Pr. Das.	10	8.4	6.6	4.9	3.4	5.5	5.8	7.4	7.3	9.1	9.1	10.2	9.4	87.1

BANFF, ALBERTA

	Y. R.	Jan.	Feb.	Mar.	Apr.	May	Jun.	Jul.	Aug.	Sep.	Oct.	Nov.	Dec.	Yr.
Mean	23	1.43	0.79	1.27	1.16	2.38	3.02	2.48	2.39	1.71	1.19	1.80	1.06	20.68
Max.	23	3.94	2.47	4.00	2.48	7.63	6.05	5.70	5.47	2.71	1.87	4.88	3.42	30.59
Min.	23	0.22	0.20	0.19	0.32	0.63	0.51	0.46	0.59	0.59	0.17	0.30	0.05	14.58
Wet Yr.	23	1.75	0.55	1.37	0.54	7.63	5.12	3.14	2.91	2.71	1.72	1.68	1.47	30.59
Dry Yr.	23	0.77	0.40	0.19	0.32	2.98	1.91	0.89	2.26	0.54	1.95	0.87	1.50	14.58
Mn. Sn.	23	13.8	7.5	11.6	7.8	6.3	1.3	T	0.1	2.3	4.7	14.1	9.9	79.4
Max. Sn.	33	39.4	24.7	38.7	21.7	29.7	6.6	3.0	1.6	17.8	12.7	37.6	31.5	—
Pr. Das.	10	10.1	8.1	11.7	10.4	13.3	12.7	11.0	11.4	10.3	10.7	7.8	9.7	127.2

BARKERVILLE, BRITISH COLUMBIA

	Y. R.	Jan.	Feb.	Mar.	Apr.	May	Jun.	Jul.	Aug.	Sep.	Oct.	Nov.	Dec.	Yr.
Mean	37B	3.33	2.63	2.63	2.21	2.52	3.48	3.21	3.21	3.69	3.14	3.43	3.54	37.02
Max.	37B	9.30	5.20	6.47	5.45	4.34	5.91	7.92	8.50	7.74	6.32	5.28	6.67	49.54
Min.	37B	0.77	0.46	0.70	0.30	0.58	1.35	0.16	0.56	T	0.51	0.92	1.10	20.61
Wet Yr.	37B	2.50	3.33	5.75	2.99	2.29	4.75	4.52	3.72	7.06	5.25	4.43	2.95	49.54
Dry Yr.	37B	2.31	2.90	2.20	0.80	2.18	1.95	0.16	1.75	0.99	1.77	2.30	1.30	20.61
Mn. Sn.	37B	31.8	24.2	23.4	15.9	5.3	0.9	—	0.1	2.6	11.8	27.2	33.5	176.7
Max. Sn.	37B	75.0	52.0	57.5	37.0	13.2	4.0	—	2.0	8.0	38.3	50.9	59.0	—
Pr. Das.	10	16.2	11.8	16.0	12.5	14.1	16.6	14.9	14.3	13.1	14.9	14.6	14.6	173.6

BELLE ISLE, NEWFOUNDLAND

	Y. R.	Jan.	Feb.	Mar.	Apr.	May	Jun.	Jul.	Aug.	Sep.	Oct.	Nov.	Dec.	Yr.
Mean	10	2.17	2.06	3.50	2.71	2.56	5.37	4.96	5.97	5.66	6.04	3.87	2.72	47.59
Max.	10	3.10	3.31	6.47	6.35	6.20	8.24	9.34	11.48	8.48	10.04	15.96	6.66	58.56
Min.	10	0.00	0.00	0.40	0.01	0.14	0.11	0.76	1.45	1.71	1.82	1.12	0.95	27.41
Wet Yr.	10	3.10	2.06	4.01	1.50	2.14	5.30	2.71	6.21	8.48	7.01	15.96	0.08	58.56
Dry Yr.	10	2.57	3.31	1.43	0.01	0.14	0.11	0.76	2.37	3.18	3.78	6.65	3.10	27.41
Mn. Sn.	10	17.0	17.9	21.7	12.8	1.6	0.4	—	—	1.5	3.0	10.1	17.3	103.3
Max. Sn.	10	31.0	29.0	39.6	26.0	6.5	3.0	—	—	12.1	7.0	26.5	26.0	—
Pr. Das.	15B	6	5	7	6	4	4	5	5	6	5	4	4	61

CHARLOTTETOWN, PRINCE EDWARD ISLAND

	Y. R.	Jan.	Feb.	Mar.	Apr.	May	Jun.	Jul.	Aug.	Sep.	Oct.	Nov.	Dec.	Yr.
Mean	50B	3.60	3.13	3.17	2.90	2.69	2.69	3.09	3.36	3.39	4.30	3.78	3.80	39.90
Max.	50B	7.62	6.37	6.34	6.10	5.85	5.37	8.97	8.44	8.75	10.38	8.00	7.25	56.43
Min.	46B	1.10	0.88	1.48	0.82	0.40	0.47	0.81	0.94	0.60	0.76	0.50	1.41	18.50
Wet Yr.	50B	3.29	3.19	6.24	3.55	2.94	3.86	1.09	5.30	8.75	8.10	4.23	5.89	56.43
Dry Yr.	50B	2.47	2.15	1.47	1.97	0.60	1.77	0.70	3.13	0.78	0.68	1.21	1.57	18.50
Mn. Sn.	50B	22.8	19.9	15.1	9.8	0.9	—	—	—	—	0.4	7.6	19.1	95.6
Max. Sn.	50B	59.0	53.8	31.4	27.0	7.5	—	—	—	—	13.8	26.1	43.8	—
Pr. Das.	10	11.9	9.8	11.7	11.1	11.1	10.9	10.9	11.3	11.3	11.8	13.9	13.0	138.7

CHESTERFIELD INLET, NORTHWEST TERRITORIES

	Y. R.	Jan.	Feb.	Mar.	Apr.	May	Jun.	Jul.	Aug.	Sep.	Oct.	Nov.	Dec.	Yr.
Mean	3B	—	0.23	0.15	0.15	0.75	1.15	6.86	4.24	5.78	0.44	0.50	0.60	—

CHURCHILL, MANITOBA

	Y. R.	Jan.	Feb.	Mar.	Apr.	May	Jun.	Jul.	Aug.	Sep.	Oct.	Nov.	Dec.	Yr.
Mean	18	0.62	0.98	1.11	0.99	0.97	1.98	1.79	2.51	3.60	1.27	1.16	0.86	17.85
Max.	18	1.90	3.40	2.40	3.10	2.40	5.74	3.66	8.49	5.15	2.50	3.50	1.40	—
Min.	18	0.10	0.05	0.41	0.29	0.37	0.10	0.25	0.28	0.82	0.34	0.30	0.30	—
Mn. Sn.	18	6.2	9.8	10.8	8.4	2.0	1.2	—	T	2.7	· 6.9	11.6	8.6	68.2
Max. Sn.	18	19.0	34.0	24.0	31.0	4.0	3.0	—	T	17.0	22.0	35.0	14.0	—

DAWSON, YUKON TERRITORY

	Y. R.	Jan.	Feb.	Mar.	Apr.	May	Jun.	Jul.	Aug.	Sep.	Oct.	Nov.	Dec.	Yr.
Mean	29	0.83	0.71	0.53	0.57	0.91	1.22	1.54	1.42	1.46	1.14	1.16	1.00	12.49
Max.	24B	1.97	1.65	1.76	1.70	2.00	2.66	3.32	2.51	3.52	4.09	3.75	4.16	17.75
Min.	24B	T	0.15	0.00	0.13	0.19	0.25	0.06	0.07	0.37	0.10	0.22	0.08	9.22
Wet Yr.	24B	1.53	0.34	0.88	0.23	1.06	0.85	1.93	1.28	2.34	4.09	2.60	0.62	17.75
Dry Yr.	24B	T	0.95	0.20	0.25	1.04	1.73	1.37	1.59	1.21	0.10	0.70	0.08	9.22
Mn. Sn.	29	8.3	7.1	5.3	4.0	0.7	0.2	—	—	1.3	8.3	11.5	10.0	56.7
Max. Sn.	29	19.7	16.5	17.6	16.8	4.2	5.0	—	1.0	10.0	38.3	37.5	20.9	—
Pr. Das.	10	8.9	7.2	6.0	3.7	8.1	12.1	10.6	11.2	10.3	8.8	11.0	9.9	107.8

EDMONTON, ALBERTA

	Y. R.	Jan.	Feb.	Mar.	Apr.	May	Jun.	Jul.	Aug.	Sep.	Oct.	Nov.	Dec.	Yr.
Mean	38	0.87	0.64	0.67	0.82	1.81	3.13	3.39	2.40	1.39	0.73	0.69	0.77	17.31
Max.	38	2.49	2.33	1.93	2.60	7.67	8.53	11.13	6.43	4.32	2.28	3.57	3.21	27.81
Min.	38	0.05	T	T	0.01	0.19	T	0.15	0.17	T	T	T	T	8.16
Wet Yr.	38	0.78	2.18	1.93	2.60	2.71	3.77	3.91	4.18	3.16	1.16	0.18	1.25	27.81
Dry Yr.	38	0.05	T	0.07	1.17	.22	1.30	1.85	1.15	1.45	0.08	0.51	0.31	8.16
Mn. Sn.	30	7.0	6.7	6.2	3.6	1.3	T	—	T	0.7	3.5	6.7	6.8	42.5
Max. Sn.	30	24.1	23.3	19.3	14.0	15.0	1.2	—	1.0	10.8	16.0	35.5	32.1	—
Pr. Das.	10	11.8	8.6	10.7	7.6	10.0	12.6	13.2	14.0	7.4	7.8	6.6	8.6	118.9

FORT CHIMO, QUEBEC

	Y. R.	Jan.	Feb.	Mar.	Apr.	May	Jun.	Jul.	Aug.	Sep.	Oct.	Nov.	Dec.	Yr.
Mean	4	0.77	0.86	1.82	1.43	1.76	3.98	4.34	4.32	3.62	3.52	1.57	0.62	28.61

FORT CHIPEWYAN, ALBERTA

	Y. R.	Jan.	Feb.	Mar.	Apr.	May	Jun.	Jul.	Aug.	Sep.	Oct.	Nov.	Dec.	Yr.
Mean	43B	0.68	0.54	0.68	0.69	0.83	1.36	2.31	1.63	1.22	0.91	0.94	0.80	12.59
Max.	43B	1.68	2.35	1.75	3.04	1.94	3.31	9.52	4.43	2.93	5.30	2.28	3.20	17.09
Min.	43B	0.02	0.03	0.09	T	T	0.02	0.21	0.36	0.27	0.20	0.10	0.05	5.69
Wet Yr.	43B	0.71	1.74	1.20	0.83	0.91	0.92	0.86	3.67	0.45	2.39	2.21	1.20	17.09
Dry Yr.	43B	0.75	0.13	0.30	0.20	1.03	0.02	0.94	0.95	0.57	0.20	0.10	0.50	5.69
Mn. Sn.	43B	6.8	5.4	6.5	4.4	1.6	0.1	—	—	0.1	4.6	8.8	8.0	46.3
Max. Sn.	43B	16.8	23.5	17.5	13.0	10.0	1.5	—	—	6.2	22.5	22.1	32.0	—
Pr. Das.	10	5.4	4.0	5.1	2.5	6.2	6.8	9.1	10.0	8.6	5.6	5.6	4.4	73.3

FORT CONGER, NORTHWEST TERRITORIES

	Y. R.	Jan.	Feb.	Mar.	Apr.	May	Jun.	Jul.	Aug.	Sep.	Oct.	Nov.	Dec.	Yr.
Mean	3B	0.42	0.13	0.44	0.17	0.40	0.18	0.66	0.38	0.35	0.24	0.20	0.30	3.88
Max.	3B	0.57	0.15	0.61	0.20	0.58	0.26	1.01	0.81	0.47	0.24	0.29	0.39	4.52
Min.	3B	0.24	0.11	0.28	0.14	0.23	0.11	0.32	0.15	0.23	0.23	0.11	0.30	3.44
Wet Yr.	3B	0.57	0.11	0.28	0.20	0.23	0.26	1.01	0.81	0.47	0.24	0.11	0.23	4.52
Dry Yr.	3B	0.24	0.15	0.61	0.14	0.58	0.11	0.32	0.15	0.23	0.23	0.29	0.39	3.44

FORT GEORGE, BRITISH COLUMBIA

	Y. R.	Jan.	Feb.	Mar.	Apr.	May	Jun.	Jul.	Aug.	Sep.	Oct.	Nov.	Dec.	Yr.
Mean	12	2.02	0.88	1.50	0.88	1.14	1.55	1.45	1.94	1.66	1.93	1.56	1.68	18.19
Max.	12	3.99	2.15	4.48	2.80	2.22	2.95	3.25	3.03	4.04	3.84	6.00	4.05	24.73
Min.	12	0.15	0.10	0.37	0.02	0.38	0.49	0.37	0.67	0.04	0.47	0.42	0.43	14.87
Wet Yr.	12	0.75	0.60	2.70	0.53	1.27	2.95	1.18	1.71	1.04	3.84	6.00	2.16	24.73
Dry Yr.	12	1.90	0.44	0.37	0.75	1.27	1.56	0.37	3.03	2.36	0.62	1.76	0.45	14.87
Pr. Das.	6B	4.0	2.5	3.0	1.0	5.6	6.6	9.1	9.0	10.0	6.5	8.5	0.0	65.8

FORT GOOD HOPE, NORTHWEST TERRITORIES

	Y. R.	Jan.	Feb.	Mar.	Apr.	May	Jun.	Jul.	Aug.	Sep.	Oct.	Nov.	Dec.	Yr.
Mean	21	0.48	0.52	0.60	0.54	0.66	1.02	1.39	1.63	1.11	1.04	0.73	0.53	10.24
Max.	21	1.39	1.93	1.55	1.23	1.77	2.31	2.60	3.45	2.51	2.63	2.87	1.82	15.14
Min.	21	0.03	0.02	0.01	0.03	T	0.25	0.16	0.08	0.23	0.27	0.17	0.10	7.73
Wet Yr.	21	1.39	0.45	0.31	0.44	1.02	2.33	1.64	2.97	2.51	0.86	0.73	0.49	15.14
Dry Yr.	21	0.10	0.07	0.30	0.22	1.10	0.66	2.01	1.20	0.42	0.79	0.47	0.39	7.73
Mn. Sn.	21	4.8	5.2	6.0	5.4	4.4	0.5	—	0.3	4.0	8.5	7.2	5.2	51.5
Max. Sn.	21	13.9	16.1	15.5	12.3	14.4	5.8	—	3.5	19.1	22.1	28.7	18.2	76.3
Pr. Das.	21	8.8	7.1	6.7	6.4	7.6	9.9	9.8	11.4	10.6	7.8	9.0	8.3	103.4

FORT HOPE, ONTARIO

	Y. R.	Jan.	Feb.	Mar.	Apr.	May	Jun.	Jul.	Aug.	Sep.	Oct.	Nov.	Dec.	Yr.
Mean	20B	0.90	0.45	0.90	0.49	1.12	1.69	2.78	1.93	2.45	1.07	1.11	0.94	15.83
Max.	20B	2.00	1.60	2.10	1.72	2.47	3.87	8.25	3.50	5.22	2.05	2.33	2.10	24.83
Min.	20B	0.20	0.00	0.18	0.00	0.18	0.25	0.30	0.15	0.51	0.20	0.00	0.10	11.51
Wet Yr.	20B	0.20	0.30	1.22	1.72	1.78	1.25	8.25	2.69	2.52	1.10	2.10	1.70	24.83
Dry Yr.	20B	1.97	0.18	0.90	0.40	0.70	1.35	0.30	1.98	1.22	1.22	0.89	0.40	11.51
Mn. Sn.	20B	8.9	6.5	9.6	4.9	3.0	0.1	—	—	2.6	4.6	10.0	8.2	58.4
Max. Sn.	15	20.0	16.0	21.0	10.0	8.0	1.0	—	—	7.2	9.0	23.3	19.5	—
Pr. Das.	10	7.6	8.1	9.0	4.8	6.5	9.5	10.2	14.1	10.8	9.5	10.0	9.8	109.9

FORT VERMILION, ALBERTA

	Y. R.	Jan.	Feb.	Mar.	Apr.	May	Jun.	Jul.	Aug.	Sep.	Oct.	Nov.	Dec.	Yr.
Mean	22	0.60	0.33	0.49	0.71	1.03	1.86	2.14	2.05	1.39	0.74	0.52	0.42	12.28
Max.	22	1.70	0.78	1.70	1.70	2.43	5.55	4.49	3.80	3.43	1.56	1.40	0.85	17.09
Min.	22	0.13	0.03	0.00	0.05	0.00	0.17	0.41	0.42	0.13	0.13	0.05	0.05	8.87
Wet Yr.	22	1.70	0.25	0.10	1.38	1.05	0.57	2.50	3.80	0.68	0.23	0.05	0.85	17.09
Dry Yr.	22	0.70	0.47	0.70	0.80	0.16	0.66	1.74	1.75	0.79	0.25	0.80	0.05	8.87
Mn. Sn.	22	6.0	3.3	4.8	3.3	0.9	0.1	—	—	0.5	2.7	4.6	4.2	30.4
Max. Sn.	22	17.0	7.8	17.0	9.5	4.8	2.7	—	—	9.1	14.8	14.0	8.5	—
Pr. Das.	10	4.8	3.3	3.7	2.8	5.7	9.1	8.5	10.2	5.6	5.0	3.9	3.8	66.4

FREDERICTON, NEW BRUNSWICK

	Y. R.	Jan.	Feb.	Mar.	Apr.	May	Jun.	Jul.	Aug.	Sep.	Oct.	Nov.	Dec.	Yr.
Mean	52	4.14	3.33	3.93	2.72	3.12	3.68	3.49	3.93	3.52	3.87	3.93	3.48	43.4
Max.	52	8.34	6.07	7.58	4.89	9.08	8.01	7.82	8.84	10.95	10.62	6.80	6.51	54.62
Min.	52	1.50	0.95	0.66	1.24	0.68	1.71	1.18	1.05	0.48	0.85	1.45	1.64	33.01
Wet Yr.	52	3.00	2.60	4.70	3.12	2.60	7.57	4.85	5.72	4.05	7.07	4.60	4.74	54.62
Dry Yr.	52	6.62	2.75	1.13	1.24	1.94	2.43	1.76	1.60	5.25	0.86	3.57	3.86	33.01
Mn. Sn.	52	18.2	24.6	23.6	17.2	7.0	0.2	—	—	—	0.6	8.6	8.6	100.0
Max. Sn.	52	59.2	41.0	33.5	24.5	3.0	—	—	—	—	3.0	26.4	52.0	—
Pr. Das.	10	11.6	10.6	11.1	9.6	10.4	12.8	12.3	10.6	10.0	11.2	9.8	11.8	131.8

HALIFAX, NOVA SCOTIA

	Y. R.	Jan.	Feb.	Mar.	Apr.	May	Jun.	Jul.	Aug.	Sep.	Oct.	Nov.	Dec.	Yr.
Mean	50	5.59	4.52	5.02	4.50	4.17	3.70	3.90	4.53	3.55	5.25	5.40	5.39	55.52
Max.	50	10.12	8.74	10.29	8.53	8.82	6.97	9.04	10.66	6.87	15.02	10.25	10.25	67.69
Min.	50	1.73	0.97	0.30	1.26	0.67	1.09	1.05	1.31	1.01	0.75	1.94	2.78	43.66
Wet Yr.	50	9.48	6.96	4.25	8.21	3.32	5.07	5.36	2.69	3.93	8.62	5.21	4.59	67.69
Dry Yr.	50	4.05	3.92	4.27	3.48	4.26	3.80	1.41	2.51	1.83	2.93	7.64	3.56	43.66
Mn. Sn.	50	20.4	20.2	13.0	5.8	0.6	—	—	—	—	0.2	3.0	1.39	77.1
Max. Sn.	50	55.9	43.9	32.3	22.8	8.0	—	—	—	—	3.5	18.6	33.4	—
Pr. Das.	10	15.7	13.2	14.4	14.0	13.3	14.4	13.4	13.3	11.7	12.9	13.9	16.4	166.6

HARRINGTON HARBOUR, QUEBEC

	Y. R.	Jan.	Feb.	Mar.	Apr.	May	Jun.	Jul.	Aug.	Sep.	Oct.	Nov.	Dec.	Yr.
Mean	17	3.66	2.68	2.44	1.80	2.73	2.45	3.52	3.08	1.86	2.13	2.04	2.69	31.08
Max.	17B	5.81	5.50	4.38	3.31	4.19	5.36	5.21	5.89	3.98	10.01	3.28	8.30	39.55
Min.	17B	0.51	0.21	0.44	0.19	0.03	0.20	0.93	0.26	0.64	0.40	0.30	0.49	15.09
Wet Yr.	17	3.91	2.60	1.08	1.60	2.56	3.37	5.21	5.89	1.30	10.01	0.88	1.14	39.55
Dry Yr.	17	2.40	0.49	0.44	0.34	2.40	0.30	1.30	2.22	0.64	0.92	1.24	2.40	15.09
Mn. Sn.	17	23.6	20.2	12.0	5.2	1.1	0.6	T	—	T	0.1	5.2	18.9	86.9
Max. Sn.	17	48.0	55.0	34.0	12.7	7.4	9.6	T	—	T	1.0	17.4	83.0	—
Pr. Das.	10	9.0	7.2	8.7	8.4	7.9	8.2	8.0	8.5	6.3	6.3	8.7	8.8	96.0

HEBRON, LABRADOR

	Y. R.	Jan.	Feb.	Mar.	Apr.	May	Jun.	Jul.	Aug.	Sep.	Oct.	Nov.	Dec.	Yr.
Mean	15	0.95	0.67	0.86	1.10	1.56	2.15	2.70	2.71	3.34	1.56	1.10	0.60	19.30
Pr. Das.	15	9	8	10	11	12	12	12	12	12	10	9	8	125

JONES SOUND, NORTHWEST TERRITORIES

	Y. R.	Jan.	Feb.	Mar.	Apr.	May	Jun.	Jul.	Aug.	Sep.	Oct.	Nov.	Dec.	Yr.
Pr. Das.	4B	3.8	9.2	7.0	11.8	13.8	12.5	11.2	13.0	14.0	16.3	7.8	8.2	128.6

KAMLOOPS, ALBERTA

	Y. R.	Jan.	Feb.	Mar.	Apr.	May	Jun.	Jul.	Aug.	Sep.	Oct.	Nov.	Dec.	Yr.
Mean	34B	0.92	0.72	0.34	0.40	0.94	1.33	1.08	1.10	0.96	0.61	0.93	1.02	10.35
Max.	31	2.71	2.48	1.10	1.36	2.51	3.12	3.50	3.73	2.34	1.41	2.52	4.18	13.49
Min.	31	0.40	0.00	0.01	0.00	0.00	0.12	0.11	0.00	0.12	0.00	0.07	0.12	5.50
Wet Yr.	20	1.64	0.28	0.14	0.35	0.67	2.18	1.24	0.89	0.86	0.35	0.71	4.18	13.49
Dry Yr.	20	0.40	0.79	0.71	0.48	0.28	0.11	0.50	0.25	0.26	0.13	0.58	1.01	5.50
Mn. Sn.	34B	8.2	5.5	1.5	T	—	—	—	—	—	0.3	5.3	13.3	34.1
Max. Sn.	34B	19.3	24.4	10.7	1.2	—	—	—	—	—	2.7	23.3	39.2	—
Pr. Das.	10	8.6	5.9	5.4	6.4	6.6	8.8	6.1	7.7	5.9	6.7	6.9	10.1	85.1

LAKE HARBOUR, NORTHWEST TERRITORIES

	Y. R.	Jan.	Feb.	Mar.	Apr.	May	Jun.	Jul.	Aug.	Sep.	Oct.	Nov.	Dec.	Yr.
Mean	8B	1.36	0.95	0.97	1.18	1.06	0.47	0.89	0.74	1.19	2.20	2.62	1.80	15.43
Max.	8B	2.10	2.10	1.90	2.10	2.10	1.14	2.61	2.51	1.98	4.20	5.96	6.60	24.22
Min.	8B	0.23	T	0.18	0.17	0.35	0.01	0.14	0.19	0.15	0.32	1.06	0.60	7.74
Wet Yr.	8B	1.50	1.40	0.70	0.60	1.11	0.33	0.32	0.28	1.22	4.20	5.96	6.06	24.22
Dry Yr.	8B	0.42	T	0.26	0.32	0.35	0.11	0.71	0.19	1.28	0.50	3.00	0.60	7.74
Mn. Sn.	10B	13.6	9.5	8.9	11.4	7.2	1.7	T	0.6	4.1	14.3	22.7	18.0	112.0
Max. Sn.	10B	21.0	21.0	17.0	23.0	10.8	5.0	T	4.0	10.0	38.0	57.0	66.0	—
Pr. Das.	8B	5.6	4.3	5.2	5.2	7.3	5.7	8.9	7.2	6.1	8.1	9.2	5.5	78.3

MASSETT, BRITISH COLUMBIA

	Y. R.	Jan.	Feb.	Mar.	Apr.	May	Jun.	Jul.	Aug.	Sep.	Oct.	Nov.	Dec.	Yr.
Mean	23B	5.79	4.04	3.42	4.97	3.99	2.46	2.80	2.65	3.88	6.18	7.37	6.37	53.92
Max.	23B	15.48	16.90	5.99	13.40	16.35	6.40	6.50	8.35	10.65	14.48	18.51	10.77	82.46
Min.	23B	0.40	0.80	0.00	1.24	0.86	0.00	0.20	0.41	0.39	2.35	1.35	1.60	35.00
Wet Yr.	23B	8.20	3.50	2.15	8.80	16.35	6.40	0.35	2.65	2.75	10.15	11.65	9.51	82.46
Dry Yr.	23B	2.36	5.71	4.44	2.07	1.60	0.65	6.50	2.80	1.17	2.35	1.35	4.00	35.00
Mn. Sn.	17	13.9	5.8	6.9	1.7	T	—	—	—	—	T	2.3	8.1	38.7
Max. Sn.	17	53.0	21.0	29.0	9.0	1.0	—	—	—	—	1.0	15.0	47.0	—
Pr. Das.	10	19.0	15.1	19.2	19.0	16.4	12.3	12.0	15.0	14.9	21.2	22.2	20.9	207.2

MEDICINE HAT, ALBERTA

	Y. R.	Jan.	Feb.	Mar.	Apr.	May	Jun.	Jul.	Aug.	Sep.	Oct.	Nov.	Dec.	Yr.
Mean	34	0.58	0.62	0.58	0.66	1.78	2.64	1.80	1.44	1.03	0.64	0.67	0.59	13.03
Max.	34	1.72	1.51	1.31	3.00	6.29	5.75	4.86	5.65	3.84	3.48	3.11	2.94	22.28
Min.	34	0.00	0.00	0.02	T	0.13	0.00	0.09	0.00	0.00	T	0.00	0.00	6.72
Wet Yr.	34	1.12	1.13	1.17	0.87	3.32	2.60	3.79	4.60	1.66	0.80	0.31	0.91	22.28
Dry Yr.	34	0.00	0.00	0.32	0.80	1.41	1.53	0.78	0.11	0.19	0.79	0.51	0.28	6.72
Mn. Sn.	34	5.5	5.7	5.1	2.4	0.6	T	—	—	0.4	1.1	6.0	4.3	31.1
Max. Sn.	44	19.2	19.0	22.5	22.6	20.3	T	—	—	7.9	28.2	21.0	12.9	—
Pr. Das.	10	8.3	7.3	8.2	6.6	5.9	7.9	6.4	5.2	5.1	5.3	4.3	7.2	77.7

MISTASSINI POST, QUEBEC

	Y. R.	Jan.	Feb.	Mar.	Apr.	May	Jun.	Jul.	Aug.	Sep.	Oct.	Nov.	Dec.	Yr.
Mean	12B	2.36	2.09	1.65	2.18	2.54	3.60	3.74	3.05	2.94	2.76	2.06	2.89	31.86
Max.	12B	4.31	3.41	3.40	4.26	3.84	6.44	5.94	4.19	4.60	4.44	3.11	3.75	37.21
Min.	12B	0.55	0.32	0.52	0.85	1.21	1.62	0.88	1.38	1.37	1.38	0.61	1.39	23.88
Wet Yr.	12B	2.78	1.92	1.66	4.26	2.49	2.10	5.92	3.49	2.20	3.53	3.11	3.75	37.21
Dry Yr.	12B	0.55	3.07	1.59	0.89	1.59	4.20	1.38	2.93	1.70	1.38	2.07	2.53	23.88
Mn. Sn.	12B	22.0	18.3	10.8	5.1	0.6	—	—	—	T	2.1	11.5	19.9	90.3
Max. Sn.	12B	38.1	31.8	17.1	21.8	2.4	—	—	—	T	9.0	26.3	31.7	—
Pr. Das.	10	9.5	9.1	9.2	7.7	12.2	11.9	15.9	16.5	14	14	12.4	10.0	142.4

MONTREAL, QUEBEC

	Y. R.	Jan.	Feb.	Mar.	Apr.	May	Jun.	Jul.	Aug.	Sep.	Oct.	Nov.	Dec.	Yr.
Mean	50	3.75	3.17	3.52	2.51	3.03	3.48	3.70	3.46	3.54	3.28	3.47	3.74	40.65
Max.	50	6.84	6.22	6.60	6.10	6.94	8.62	7.72	8.08	7.82	7.77	7.65	8.72	52.22
Min.	50	1.74	0.49	0.81	0.48	0.11	0.90	0.96	1.23	0.88	0.42	1.44	1.12	29.23
Wet Yr.	50	5.59	6.13	4.77	1.46	3.11	4.33	7.41	3.14	3.62	2.25	7.65	2.76	52.22
Dry Yr.	50	3.65	4.32	0.81	1.44	2.32	2.59	1.01	2.46	2.57	1.75	2.30	4.01	29.23
Mn. Sn.	50	28.5	24.4	24.4	5.5	T	—	—	—	—	0.8	12.3	23.7	119.6
Max. Sn.	50	62.7	46.3	46.4	29.8	1.0	—	—	—	0.1	7.8	36.1	53.2	—
Pr. Das.	10	16.7	13.2	12.8	13.1	11.6	12.0	11.8	10.0	12.4	12.9	14.3	15.2	156.0

MOOSE FACTORY, ONTARIO

	Y. R.	Jan.	Feb.	Mar.	Apr.	May	Jun.	Jul.	Aug.	Sep.	Oct.	Nov.	Dec.	Yr.
Mean	33	1.26	0.91	1.14	1.03	1.76	2.22	2.39	3.27	2.89	1.80	1.11	1.17	20.95
Max.	33	3.80	2.05	2.36	3.73	5.27	5.76	5.04	6.91	4.87	3.64	2.85	3.50	29.09
Min.	—	0.20	0.20	0.05	0.15	0.15	0.29	0.26	1.16	0.72	T	0.20	0.20	14.88
Wet Yr.	33	1.90	0.85	2.41	3.73	5.27	2.87	2.83	1.16	2.00	2.75	1.42	1.90	29.09
Dry Yr.	33	0.80	0.65	1.70	0.38	0.71	1.30	1.76	3.00	2.32	1.10	0.41	0.75	14.88
Mn. Sn.	33	12.6	9.1	10.3	5.5	3.0	0.4	—	—	T	2.8	7.7	11.0	62.4
Max. Sn.	33	38.0	20.5	22.0	25.3	21.0	4.0	—	—	0.6	13.4	24.5	35.0	—
Pr. Das.	10	3.5	4.3	3.2	2.0	4.0	5.8	6.6	7.1	5.3	4.5	2.7	5.1	54.1

NORWAY HOUSE, MANITOBA

	Y. R.	Jan.	Feb.	Mar.	Apr.	May	Jun.	Jul.	Aug.	Sep.	Oct.	Nov.	Dec.	Yr.
Mean	21B	0.69	0.73	1.03	0.72	1.31	2.23	2.45	2.63	2.76	0.84	1.12	0.82	17.33
Max.	21	1.28	2.90	4.29	2.50	3.60	4.16	4.76	6.32	3.87	2.53	3.80	2.10	22.80
Min.	21	0.00	0.00	T	T	T	0.49	0.28	0.33	0.18	0.00	0.03	T	10.54
Wet Yr.	21B	0.60	2.90	1.30	0.80	0.85	2.54	2.70	6.32	3.25	0.34	1.20	T	22.80
Dry Yr.	21B	0.00	0.30	T	1.00	0.00	1.69	3.37	1.88	0.30	0.80	0.90	0.30	10.54
Mn. Sn.	21B	6.9	7.3	9.5	4.9	2.6	T	T	0.0	0.9	2.4	10.1	8.0	52.6
Max. Sn.	21B	12.8	29.0	42.9	25.0	9.8	0.4	T	—	9.0	8.5	28.0	21.0	—
Pr. Das.	10	6.0	7.0	4.0	7.0	6.6	10.2	9.8	11.8	8.6	10.2	16.0	0.0	97.2

PARRY SOUND, ONTARIO

	Y. R.	Jan.	Feb.	Mar.	Apr.	May	Jun.	Jul.	Aug.	Sep.	Oct.	Nov.	Dec.	Yr.
Mean	50	3.98	2.98	2.76	2.25	2.95	2.46	2.66	2.85	3.49	3.91	4.09	4.54	38.92
Max.	50	7.75	5.60	7.21	4.62	6.06	5.47	7.90	5.46	8.43	7.10	7.88	8.16	50.30
Min.	50	1.76	0.46	0.18	0.53	0.44	0.70	0.23	0.63	0.48	0.57	1.39	1.44	30.42
Wet Yr.	50	3.92	4.24	3.51	1.84	3.33	3.44	7.90	4.08	3.54	4.66	3.86	5.98	50.30
Dry Yr.	50	1.86	2.34	0.54	1.82	0.95	2.85	2.22	4.07	3.83	3.40	3.64	2.90	30.42
Mn. Sn.	50	32.5	23.3	14.6	3.3	0.6	—	—	—	T	1.3	14.1	32.2	121.9
Max. Sn.	50	73.0	54.0	35.8	19.0	9.7	—	—	—	0.6	12.4	42.9	65.8	—
Pr. Das.	10	16.0	13.7	12.0	10.1	9.0	9.5	8.6	8.5	12.5	13.8	15.1	16.6	145.4

PONDS INLET, NORTHWEST TERRITORIES

	Y. R.	Jan.	Feb.	Mar.	Apr.	May	Jun.	Jul.	Aug.	Sep.	Oct.	Nov.	Dec.	Yr.
Mean	4	—	—	—	—	0.23	0.41	1.21	0.62	0.44	—	—	—	—

PORT ARTHUR, ONTARIO

	Y. R.	Jan.	Feb.	Mar.	Apr.	May	Jun.	Jul.	Aug.	Sep.	Oct.	Nov.	Dec.	Yr.
Mean	40	0.70	0.63	0.88	1.54	2.03	2.75	3.62	2.86	3.14	2.22	1.30	0.86	22.53
Max.	40	1.95	2.02	2.76	3.15	4.10	6.94	9.21	6.77	7.54	5.27	4.29	3.21	29.35
Min.	50	0.22	0.04	0.05	0.07	0.28	0.50	1.39	0.35	1.08	0.37	0.13	0.02	14.93
Wet Yr.	40	1.95	0.08	1.32	3.15	3.47	3.03	2.41	5.54	5.11	2.40	0.13	0.76	29.35
Dry Yr.	40	0.33	0.78	0.99	0.68	1.42	1.17	1.45	2.22	1.78	2.71	0.37	1.03	14.93
Mn. Sn.	40	6.9	6.0	7.5	3.3	0.4	—	—	—	—	0.6	5.0	6.6	36.3
Max. Sn.	40	19.5	20.2	27.6	15.8	3.8	—	—	—	—	7.1	18.6	27.3	—
Pr. Das.	10	6.4	5.8	7.9	7.3	6.5	11.5	10.5	8.7	10.4	10.5	6.7	7.2	99.4

PORT AUX BASQUES, NEWFOUNDLAND

	Y. R.	Jan.	Feb.	Mar.	Apr.	May	Jun.	Jul.	Aug.	Sep.	Oct.	Nov.	Dec.	Yr.
Mean	10	6.43	3.96	3.96	3.59	3.59	4.16	4.42	5.03	4.38	4.74	3.78	5.12	53.16
Max.	10	9.10	6.08	6.88	4.92	6.58	6.07	7.64	7.28	6.09	7.77	5.69	6.93	59.79
Min.	10	2.35	2.08	2.49	1.69	2.27	1.55	1.58	1.83	2.12	1.91	1.76	2.25	44.72
Wet Yr.	10	5.31	6.08	2.49	4.09	3.03	5.53	7.64	5.11	5.59	4.14	5.69	5.09	59.79
Dry Yr.	10	4.71	4.76	5.25	3.90	2.27	3.57	3.72	4.31	3.77	2.07	2.27	4.12	44.72
Mn. Sn.	10	43.6	26.5	24.7	8.0	0.9	—	—	—	—	1.0	8.6	30.3	143.6
Max. Sn.	10	75.2	42.1	58.9	21.7	4.2	—	—	—	—	3.4	17.3	58.9	—
Pr. Das.	10	23.5	19.4	17.0	15.9	14.5	15.2	14.3	14.3	16.6	18.0	19.6	24.1	212.4

PORT NELSON MANITOBA

	Y. R.	Jan.	Feb.	Mar.	Apr.	May	Jun.	Jul.	Aug.	Sep.	Oct.	Nov.	Dec.	Yr.
Mean	19B	0.84	0.46	0.88	1.07	0.94	1.92	1.96	2.60	2.08	1.19	1.08	1.13	16.15
Max.	13B	1.68	1.18	1.61	2.60	2.08	4.40	3.61	4.90	2.82	1.73	2.77	1.81	19.31
Min.	13B	0.15	0.05	0.10	0.20	0.05	0.51	0.35	0.62	0.78	0.28	0.19	0.05	8.78
Wet Yr.	13B	0.52	1.18	1.61	1.97	2.08	1.72	2.56	1.20	2.82	1.45	0.70	1.50	19.31
Dry Yr.	13B	0.49	0.10	0.10	2.60	0.10	0.91	0.35	0.79	1.32	0.31	1.23	0.48	8.78
Mn. Sn.	13B	6.1	4.5	6.3	6.2	3.6	2.2	T	T	1.7	6.8	11.2	7.8	56.4
Max. Sn.	13B	16.8	11.8	16.1	22.5	10.1	8.0	1.0	T	9.3	17.3	27.7	18.1	94.9
Pr. Das.	10	4.2	6.0	9.2	5.6	5.5	8.5	7.6	10.8	10.3	8.4	9.6	7.0	92.7

PRINCE ALBERT, SASKATCHEWAN

	Y. R.	Jan.	Feb.	Mar.	Apr.	May	Jun.	Jul.	Aug.	Sep.	Oct.	Nov.	Dec.	Yr.
Mean	41	0.76	0.60	0.86	0.88	1.48	2.67	2.17	2.27	1.39	0.79	0.87	0.66	15.40
Max.	41	2.00	2.15	2.71	3.37	4.87	7.36	5.31	8.01	3.27	1.97	3.06	2.10	29.88
Min.	41	T	0.04	T	T	0.01	0.34	0.17	T	0.09	0.04	0.02	0.04	7.40
Wet Yr.	41	1.96	0.04	1.84	1.03	1.97	4.36	4.86	8.01	2.31	1.53	1.16	0.81	29.88
Dry Yr.	41	0.81	0.45	0.31	0.40	0.69	0.34	1.37	0.69	0.79	0.16	1.21	0.18	7.40
Mn. Sn.	30	8.2	6.8	7.7	4.4	1.6	—	—	—	0.7	2.3	8.7	8.0	48.4
Max. Sn.	30	20.0	21.5	24.5	13.8	9.5	—	—	—	8.0	9.0	30.6	26.1	—
Pr. Das.	10	9.1	5.1	8.0	6.8	7.8	12.3	10.5	10.3	7.1	6.0	5.6	7.5	85.8

PRINCE GEORGE, BRITISH COLUMBIA

	Y. R.	Jan.	Feb.	Mar.	Apr.	May	Jun.	Jul.	Aug.	Sep.	Oct.	Nov.	Dec.	Yr.
Mean	12	1.82	0.98	1.50	0.93	1.14	1.46	1.25	1.94	1.67	1.93	1.56	1.68	17.90
Max.	12	3.99	2.15	4.48	2.80	2.22	2.95	3.25	3.03	4.04	3.84	6.00	4.05	24.73
Min.	12	0.15	0.10	0.60	0.02	0.38	0.49	0.37	0.67	0.04	0.47	0.43	0.43	14.87
Wet Yr.	12	0.75	0.60	2.70	0.53	1.27	2.95	1.18	1.71	1.04	3.84	6.00	2.16	24.73
Dry Yr.	12	1.90	0.44	0.37	0.75	1.27	1.56	0.37	3.02	2.36	0.62	1.76	0.45	14.87
Mn. Sn.	12	16.2	8.0	8.6	0.2	—	—	—	—	—	2.5	9.5	15.9	60.9
Max. Sn.	12	39.3	21.5	27.0	2.0	—	—	—	—	—	17.5	56.0	40.5	—
Pr. Das.	10	6.0	4.5	5.6	3.5	6.2	10.0	8.0	10.0	9.2	9.1	8.0	6.9	87.1

QU'APPELLE, SASKATCHEWAN

	Y. R.	Jan	Feb.	Mar.	Apr.	May	Jun.	Jul.	Aug.	Sep.	Oct.	Nov.	Dec.	Yr.
Mean	38	0.77	0.79	1.03	1.13	2.25	3.46	2.76	2.00	1.58	1.07	0.91	0.75	18.59
Max.	38	2.28	2.85	4.11	3.59	6.95	7.19	7.25	5.03	5.39	3.35	2.51	3.11	26.54
Min.	38	0.05	0.12	0.05	0.17	0.23	0.32	0.50	0.30	0.08	T	0.12	0.03	10.14
Wet Yr.	38	1.10	0.34	2.24	1.25	3.15	4.10	2.13	2.99	5.39	2.78	0.15	0.92	26.54
Dry Yr.	38	0.40	0.80	0.50	1.58	1.99	0.32	2.34	0.72	0.14	0.12	0.65	0.58	10.14
Mn. Sn.	30	6.9	8.1	9.6	6.7	3.1	T	—	—	1.0	4.5	8.4	7.1	55.4
Max. Sn.	30	22.8	28.5	41.1	34.0	20.3	0.7	—	—	8.5	28.2	19.5	31.1	—
Pr. Das.	10	8.4	7.1	8.9	8.0	8.1	12.1	9.7	10.0	9.1	7.9	5.9	6.1	101.3

QUEBEC, QUEBEC

	Y. R.	Jan.	Feb.	Mar.	Apr.	May	Jun.	Jul.	Aug.	Sep.	Oct.	Nov.	Dec.	Yr.
Mean	50	3.75	3.14	3.22	2.40	3.16	3.94	4.07	3.92	4.01	3.47	3.55	3.43	42.06
Max.	50	6.58	6.22	6.17	6.57	6.93	9.23	8.14	9.58	9.43	6.99	7.09	6.70	53.79
Min.	50	1.10	0.98	0.42	0.70	0.27	1.18	0.53	1.35	0.84	0.93	0.90	1.13	32.12
Wet Yr.	50	3.11	39.6	1.44	1.89	4.96	7.60	7.98	2.82	9.43	3.33	2.88	4.39	53.79
Dry Yr.	50	2.36	2.42	1.78	1.54	3.13	2.99	2.59	1.35	4.66	3.67	2.86	2.77	32.12
Mn. Sn.	50	31.6	26.0	20.4	7.0	0.6	—	—	—	—	1.5	14.2	25.4	126.7
Max. Sn.	50	61.3	51.5	51.7	30.5	6.0	—	—	—	—	8.1	40.0	61.7	—
Pr. Das.	10	16.5	13.3	13.1	12.3	12.3	13.8	14.0	10.8	13.0	13.6	13.9	15.6	162.2

ST. JOHNS, NEWFOUNDLAND

	Y. R.	Jan.	Feb.	Mar.	Apr.	May	Jun.	Jul.	Aug.	Sep.	Oct.	Nov.	Dec.	Yr.
Mean	50	5.38	5.07	4.51	4.24	3.56	3.55	3.73	3.58	3.77	5.40	6.06	4.92	53.77
Max.	50B	11.38	12.84	8.84	8.79	7.10	7.83	7.72	9.76	11.42	13.11	12.27	14.05	69.05
Min.	50B	2.65	1.30	0.50	0.90	1.58	1.01	1.79	0.62	1.17	0.94	2.38	1.76	42.74
Wet Yr.	50	9.44	5.86	6.15	8.08	2.16	4.27	3.69	4.39	3.16	7.11	8.37	6.37	69.05
Dry Yr.	50	5.91	2.85	4.49	3.57	2.43	2.68	4.61	1.90	0.28	4.08	4.75	5.19	42.74
Mn. Sn.	50	24.7	26.2	15.8	7.3	1.5	—	—	—	—	0.3	4.1	16.4	96.3
Max. Sn.	50	77.8	109.0	60.0	26.5	14.8	—	—	—	—	6.5	19.4	56.0	—
Pr. Das.	10	14.2	13.0	13.1	16.0	13.6	11.8	13.5	12.4	13.8	16.0	15.5	16.4	169.3

SOUTHWEST POINT, QUEBEC

	Y. R.	Jan.	Feb.	Mar.	Apr.	May	Jun.	Jul.	Aug.	Sep.	Oct.	Nov.	Dec.	Yr.
Mean	50	2.26	2.51	2.31	1.80	1.83	2.47	2.95	3.09	3.53	2.67	3.58	2.90	31.90
Max.	44B	5.70	5.23	5.65	7.92	5.22	6.66	8.70	7.75	5.51	9.85	4.54	5.10	48.59
Min.	44B	0.54	0.27	0.30	T	0.05	0.40	0.43	0.76	0.70	0.54	0.49	0.32	15.83
Wet Yr.	44B	3.40	5.23	5.65	4.82	2.46	1.46	4.84	4.11	2.46	6.46	3.40	4.30	48.59
Dry Yr.	44B	0.69	0.45	0.31	0.28	0.05	1.32	1.82	2.01	2.26	1.34	4.41	0.89	15.83
Mn. Sn.	50	19.4	14.6	12.4	6.0	0.4	T	—	—	T	0.4	5.7	15.4	74.3
Pr. Das.	10	56.0	49.0	40.5	26.4	3.5	0.6	—	—	0.3	4.0	28.0	44.0	—
Max. Sn.	50	12.0	9.9	10.4	10.1	12.0	10.5	11.4	10.8	9.1	11.1	9.2	12.0	128.5

TORONTO, ONTARIO

	Y. R.	Jan.	Feb.	Mar.	Apr.	May	Jun.	Jul.	Aug.	Sep.	Oct.	Nov.	Dec.	Yr.
Mean	80	2.72	2.48	2.53	2.46	2.92	2.81	2.88	2.80	2.96	2.43	2.76	2.58	32.33
Max.	80	5.52	5.01	5.66	5.40	9.07	5.81	5.63	8.13	7.69	5.39	5.61	4.90	48.48
Min.	52	0.67	0.29	0.50	0.10	0.39	0.65	0.36	0.00	0.39	0.54	0.11	0.53	24.39
Wet Yr.	80	3.15	3.02	3.49	2.62	2.60	1.90	5.63	7.09	7.69	3.27	3.93	4.09	48.48
Dry Yr.	80	4.04	2.24	1.65	2.34	1.49	1.80	3.35	0.38	1.55	1.42	2.11	4.02	24.39
Mn. Sn.	80	17.0	16.2	10.9	2.5	0.1	—	—	—	T	0.4	4.4	11.6	63.1
Max. Sn.	80	43.6	46.1	62.4	12.9	3.1	—	—	—	T	4.5	19.6	38.0	—
Pr. Das.	10	14.4	14.9	12.3	13.3	12.3	12.3	10.4	9.4	11.2	11.9	12.2	15.4	150.0

VANCOUVER, BRITISH COLUMBIA

	Y. R.	Jan.	Feb.	Mar.	Apr.	May	Jun.	Jul.	Aug.	Sep.	Oct.	Nov.	Dec.	Yr.
Mean	26B	8.40	6.03	4.98	3.29	2.99	2.57	1.23	1.70	4.07	5.65	9.52	8.22	58.65
Max.	17	12.16	10.50	14.55	8.20	5.39	5.40	5.25	5.86	10.37	10.08	12.68	15.88	63.28
Min.	17	3.15	1.21	0.89	1.70	0.31	0.17	0.02	0.36	0.30	2.16	2.63	5.56	40.63
Wet Yr.	17	8.92	1.21	5.20	2.51	1.94	3.06	0.67	2.91	10.37	8.34	7.14	11.01	63.28
Dry Yr.	17	3.15	4.75	3.44	2.63	2.46	0.17	0.02	2.01	5.76	3.26	2.63	10.35	40.63
Mn. Sn.	26B	12.0	7.9	3.6	0.1	—	—	—	—	—	0.2	2.5	3.8	30.1
Max. Sn.	17	26.4	36.5	16.2	1.5	—	—	—	—	—	3.7	27.0	27.0	—
Pr. Das.	10	20.1	15.5	17.9	13.9	10.7	9.4	5.8	6.6	9.3	13.5	19.1	21.1	162.9

VICTORIA, BRITISH COLUMBIA

	Y. R.	Jan.	Feb.	Mar.	Apr.	May	Jun.	Jul.	Aug.	Sep.	Oct.	Nov.	Dec.	Yr.
Mean	43	4.63	3.21	2.37	1.47	1.11	0.87	0.39	0.62	1.78	2.65	5.02	5.58	29.70
Max.	35	8.47	7.03	5.37	5.40	2.83	2.37	1.23	2.26	4.27	5.60	11.50	13.02	51.03
Min.	35	1.55	0.62	0.61	0.21	0.18	0.03	T	0.00	0.32	0.46	0.91	0.59	20.66
Wet Yr.	35	4.56	6.57	3.36	5.40	2.40	1.73	0.95	0.06	1.21	4.61	10.43	9.75	51.03
Dry Yr.	35	5.00	2.39	2.00	1.70	0.54	0.27	0.16	0.37	0.51	1.14	1.79	4.79	20.66
Mn. Sn.	43	6.1	5.3	1.1	T	—	—	—	—	—	T	1.0	1.3	14.8
Max. Sn.	43	30.2	46.4	12.5	0.2	—	—	—	—	—	2.0	13.5	16.7	—
Pr. Das.	10	18.5	15.8	15.8	12.3	7.4	7.1	4.2	5.1	8.6	14.0	18.1	20.9	147.8

WHITE RIVER, ONTARIO

	Y. R.	Jan.	Feb.	Mar.	Apr.	May	Jun.	Jul.	Aug.	Sep.	Oct.	Nov.	Dec.	Yr.
Mean	30	1.63	1.25	1.46	1.52	2.14	2.47	3.12	3.00	2.88	2.44	2.39	1.86	26.16
Max.	30	4.50	4.63	4.09	4.22	4.96	6.15	7.03	6.99	5.73	4.87	5.14	3.86	35.37
Min.	37	0.13	0.14	0.18	0.34	0.16	0.26	0.50	0.73	0.47	0.45	0.38	0.29	16.24
Wet Yr	30	2.80	2.00	1.40	1.29	3.04	4.34	4.57	4.02	2.61	1.94	4.60	2.76	35.37
Dry Yr.	30	1.00	0.80	0.90	1.62	0.84	0.70	1.33	1.77	2.07	1.96	1.75	1.50	16.24
Mn. Sn.	30	16.0	12.4	12.6	7.1	3.1	0.1	—	—	0.5	3.8	15.0	17.3	87.9
Max. Sn.	30	45.0	46.3	39.9	31.0	18.6	1.2	—	—	3.4	21.3	42.0	38.1	—
Pr. Das.	10	14.1	12.1	10.1	8.9	8.9	11.2	11.7	12.9	11.9	12.3	12.2	14.3	140.6

WINNIPEG, MANITOBA

	Y. R.	Jan.	Feb.	Mar.	Apr.	May	Jun.	Jul.	Aug.	Sep.	Oct.	Nov.	Dec.	Yr.
Mean	40	0.74	0.79	1.08	1.50	2.23	3.27	3.04	2.38	1.97	1.48	0.96	0.93	20.37
Max.	40	3.36	1.80	3.00	5.64	6.38	10.07	7.14	4.75	5.49	5.67	3.03	3.99	27.19
Min.	40	0.12	0.10	0.09	0.22	0.03	0.45	0.61	0.13	0.34	0.21	0.10	0.10	13.76
Wet Yr.	40	1.07	2.56	0.98	0.89	6.10	1.77	2.15	2.50	5.67	2.00	0.61	0.89	27.19
Dry Yr.	40	1.10	0.88	0.53	0.22	0.03	2.13	3.27	1.70	1.93	1.36	0.22	0.59	13.76
Mn. Sn.	40	7.4	7.7	8.4	4.4	0.9	T	—	—	0.1	2.1	8.1	8.6	47.7
Max. Sn.	40	33.6	25.2	26.7	14.5	9.6	T	—	—	2.3	15.2	22.8	39.9	—
Pr. Das.	10	8.4	7.9	7.9	7.6	7.4	10.6	9.2	10.4	10.0	9.0	8.5	8.6	105.5

WIND FREQUENCIES

ABITIBI, QUEBEC

	Jan.	Feb.	Mar.	Apr.	May	Jun.	Jul.	Aug.	Sep.	Oct.	Nov.	Dec.	Yr.
North	22.0	21.6	28.1	30.0	31.0	24.4	23.0	16.3	21.1	23.0	19.7	22.8	23.6
Northeast	2.7	1.8	4.6	4.0	4.2	3.0	1.8	1.2	2.7	2.1	2.1	2.8	2.7
East	13.4	14.0	11.8	15.0	12.3	11.1	7.6	6.2	8.7	9.7	13.9	13.9	11.5
Southeast	4.2	2.0	3.9	5.0	3.8	3.0	2.1	2.7	2.3	2.5	3.0	2.8	3.1
South	17.5	18.9	15.6	12.0	16.3	17.0	21.1	22.3	26.4	22.0	18.8	18.9	18.9
Southwest	3.9	2.8	3.4	2.9	3.8	6.4	5.6	10.0	7.6	6.1	6.3	3.6	5.2
West	29.1	32.4	24.1	23.0	20.8	28.0	31.1	31.4	22.4	24.0	24.7	24.6	26.3
Northwest	6.8	6.3	8.5	8.0	7.8	7.0	7.6	9.3	8.4	10.5	11.5	10.4	8.5
Calm	0.4	0.2	0.0	0.1	0.0	0.1	0.1	0.6	0.4	0.1	0.0	0.2	0.2

ANNAPOLIS ROYAL, NOVA SCOTIA

	Jan.	Feb.	Mar.	Apr.	May	Jun.	Jul.	Aug.	Sep.	Oct.	Nov.	Dec.	Yr.
North	15.8	15.8	9.2	13.2	8.9	5.0	5.2	3.2	3.4	6.8	10.4	16.3	9.4
Northeast	5.8	9.7	9.8	11.2	8.5	6.5	3.1	4.5	7.1	4.9	7.8	8.5	7.3
East	10.8	6.9	7.0	9.3	9.5	5.8	5.7	3.2	4.4	7.3	7.4	6.4	7.0
Southeast	1.5	2.8	3.2	2.3	1.5	4.3	2.0	2.0	2.7	0.7	2.6	3.3	2.4
South	3.8	4.3	4.6	4.2	3.6	2.8	2.0	2.7	2.1	3.7	2.2	2.4	3.2
Southwest	2.9	2.4	5.3	5.3	9.0	8.8	5.3	7.3	5.5	7.1	6.5	4.1	5.8
West	22.1	23.1	23.1	24.6	35.1	40.0	37.8	40.0	32.4	33.3	23.4	20.0	29.6
Northwest	9.1	7.6	9.0	12.7	6.5	9.8	11.5	13.2	15.3	10.3	7.7	11.7	10.4
Calm	28.2	27.4	28.8	17.3	17.4	17.0	27.4	24.0	27.1	25.9	32.0	27.3	24.9

ATLIN, BRITISH COLUMBIA

	Jan.	Feb.	Mar.	Apr.	May	Jun.	Jul.	Aug.	Sep.	Oct.	Nov.	Dec.	Yr.
North	7.1	4.8	3.2	1.2	0.3	0.3	0.3	0.6	2.2	3.9	8.9	10.5	36.2
Northeast	12.3	8.0	5.8	2.2	2.2	2.2	2.3	5.0	11.2	11.3	23.3	37.2	10.2
East	4.0	4.3	3.3	3.3	1.7	2.0	1.3	2.1	3.2	3.9	3.8	4.2	3.1
Southeast	17.6	17.7	19.3	28.5	24.0	29.2	31.2	31.3	34.0	31.3	28.0	17.3	25.8
South	5.0	13.2	18.0	30.0	41.1	39.1	38.2	35.0	23.0	23.0	15.7	9.0	24.2
Southwest	1.6	3.3	4.6	9.3	12.9	9.2	8.9	11.3	8.0	7.0	3.5	1.9	6.8
West	1.3	2.8	2.9	2.2	3.9	2.0	3.2	2.2	1.5	1.1	0.3	0.4	2.0
Northwest	23.1	15.8	26.6	11.3	10.6	10.0	9.0	8.6	12.0	13.1	11.8	13.6	13.8
Calm	28.0	30.1	16.3	12.0	3.3	6.0	5.6	3.9	4.9	5.4	4.7	5.9	10.5

267

CHESTERFIELD INLET, NORTHWEST TERRITORIES

	Jan.	Feb.	Mar.	Apr.	May	Jun.	Jul.	Aug.	Sep.	Oct.	Nov.	Dec.	Yr.
North	5.7	7.2	8.8	7.5	11.0	14.5	9.2	13.2	15.8	24.0	14.5	17.1	12.4
Northeast	2.7	6.1	8.5	10.1	14.7	11.0	8.2	19.6	10.8	13.8	6.5	10.0	10.2
East	3.8	2.5	3.8	7.5	6.1	8.7	6.0	13.6	5.6	10.8	5.3	4.3	6.5
Southeast	2.2	5.8	6.2	10.9	15.5	12.3	11.4	8.7	11.1	6.9	3.0	3.3	8.1
South	2.4	2.2	4.2	9.2	2.8	8.3	11.4	9.5	10.8	6.0	1.8	3.5	6.0
Southwest	1.6	2.2	1.2	3.4	2.0	4.4	3.7	6.3	5.6	9.4	5.3	3.3	4.0
West	2.7	1.8	2.6	4.6	1.5	3.5	8.2	4.6	6.5	6.4	7.5	2.4	4.3
Northwest	78.9	71.8	63.5	46.4	46.0	35.6	41.9	23.5	28.5	22.7	56.1	55.9	47.6
Calm	0.0	0.4	1.2	0.4	0.4	1.7	0.0	1.0	5.3	0.0	0.0	0.2	0.9

CHURCHILL, MANITOBA

	Jan.	Feb.	Mar.	Apr.	May	Jun.	Jul.	Aug.	Sep.	Oct.	Nov.	Dec.	Yr.
North	6.5	7.1	3.3	5.8	11.0	11.4	8.0	8.6	8.3	6.0	5.7	6.7	7.4
Northeast	3.3	3.6	5.5	9.3	14.3	21.6	21.6	19.9	13.1	8.3	8.0	2.2	10.8
East	1.1	1.2	3.3	5.8	4.4	8.0	10.2	9.9	11.9	3.6	4.5	0.0	5.3
Southeast	2.2	3.6	4.4	4.7	4.4	9.1	9.1	11.1	10.7	6.0	4.5	4.5	6.2
South	3.3	2.4	3.3	3.5	2.2	3.4	5.7	2.5	7.1	6.0	4.5	5.6	4.1
Southwest	4.3	6.0	6.6	5.8	2.2	4.5	5.7	4.9	8.3	6.0	5.7	9.0	5.7
West	28.3	26.2	22.0	11.6	6.6	5.7	8.0	9.9	10.7	16.7	20.5	29.2	16.3
Northwest	31.5	28.6	28.6	26.7	20.9	10.2	12.5	14.8	19.0	31.0	27.3	24.7	23.0
Calm	19.6	21.4	23.1	26.7	31.1	26.1	19.3	18.5	10.7	16.7	19.3	18.0	21.2

DAWSON, YUKON TERRITORY

	Jan.	Feb.	Mar.	Apr.	May	Jun.	Jul.	Aug.	Sep.	Oct.	Nov.	Dec.	Yr.
North	24.0	27.4	29.7	44.0	43.8	39.9	35.3	30.7	32.0	32.3	36.9	29.0	33.7
Northeast	0.0	0.5	1.0	3.8	2.7	2.0	2.0	2.3	1.3	0.7	0.5	0.5	1.4
East	0.4	0.7	0.7	1.5	2.9	2.0	1.8	1.4	2.3	1.9	1.2	1.2	1.5
Southeast	1.3	2.5	1.3	2.4	1.8	3.0	3.1	4.3	3.3	5.0	2.7	1.2	2.7
South	44.0	41.4	35.1	21.4	21.0	23.0	26.1	30.0	31.3	34.9	38.4	45.0	32.7
Southwest	1.9	2.5	2.3	2.4	1.5	3.5	4.6	2.5	0.3	1.5	1.3	2.3	2.2
West	0.0	0.2	0.3	1.6	0.9	1.1	1.4	0.7	0.5	0.4	0.4	0.0	0.6
Northwest	0.6	0.4	1.2	2.4	4.5	4.5	4.0	3.1	1.7	2.0	1.3	0.5	2.2
Calm	27.8	24.4	28.4	20.5	20.9	21.0	21.7	25.0	27.3	21.3	17.3	20.3	23.0

EDMONTON, ALBERTA

	Jan.	Feb.	Mar.	Apr.	May	Jun.	Jul.	Aug.	Sep.	Oct.	Nov.	Dec.	Yr.
North	9.2	6.5	7.2	5.6	5.5	5.0	5.4	6.3	7.8	7.3	8.5	9.5	7.1
Northeast	13.5	12.4	14.0	15.6	16.8	14.0	16.8	13.2	11.5	11.3	9.9	12.9	13.6
East	5.1	8.1	8.1	9.2	6.8	7.3	6.2	6.5	4.0	4.4	4.0	7.9	6.5
Southeast	7.8	8.5	11.0	16.0	11.3	11.7	10.1	7.8	8.6	7.6	8.0	7.8	9.7
South	6.2	8.2	11.0	7.2	9.5	5.0	8.7	4.8	8.6	6.6	8.5	7.0	7.6
Southwest	16.4	17.5	17.5	15.0	13.2	14.7	15.3	16.5	16.0	16.9	20.1	17.5	16.4
West	11.8	13.4	8.5	6.2	10.0	14.3	11.3	14.2	11.5	15.8	13.1	10.9	11.6
Northwest	23.0	18.5	18.8	23.2	24.0	25.0	23.1	26.0	28.7	27.6	25.4	23.1	23.7
Calm	7.0	6.9	3.9	2.0	2.9	3.0	3.1	4.7	3.3	2.5	2.5	3.4	3.8

FORT CHIPEWYAN, ALBERTA

	Jan.	Feb.	Mar.	Apr.	May	Jun.	Jul.	Aug.	Sep.	Oct.	Nov.	Dec.	Yr.
North	16.8	15.6	21.5	13.3	11.2	9.3	9.2	9.2	10.8	12.8	10.9	15.4	13.0
Northeast	3.7	3.3	5.2	5.5	5.0	3.4	7.2	2.7	4.5	2.5	3.5	4.1	4.2
East	13.9	14.7	19.0	25.5	20.5	15.5	10.3	11.3	10.6	11.8	13.2	13.7	15.0
Southeast	5.7	7.8	6.2	8.7	12.2	6.2	5.6	5.4	7.4	6.6	6.0	5.6	6.9
South	2.7	2.4	2.3	4.5	5.0	6.6	5.4	7.4	6.3	6.0	5.0	2.7	4.7
Southwest	2.9	4.9	2.3	2.8	4.8	4.0	3.6	2.9	3.2	3.1	2.4	1.8	3.4
West	6.5	6.2	4.1	8.2	11.4	8.0	8.6	8.5	6.7	4.8	4.8	6.1	7.0
Northwest	12.3	14.4	13.2	10.2	11.6	14.8	8.8	10.4	11.1	11.3	13.0	12.6	11.9
Calm	35.5	30.7	26.2	21.3	18.3	32.2	41.3	42.2	39.4	41.1	41.2	38.0	33.9

FORT GOOD HOPE, NORTHWEST TERRITORIES

	Jan.	Feb.	Mar.	Apr.	May	Jun.	Jul.	Aug.	Sep.	Oct.	Nov.	Dec.	Yr.
North	3.1	4.4	7.3	12.2	12.1	10.2	7.1	7.7	9.2	4.5	4.3	2.9	7.1
Northeast	6.8	5.5	7.4	8.8	8.4	6.8	1.9	7.4	5.9	4.3	4.5	4.8	6.0
East	29.0	31.6	16.6	18.0	30.0	23.0	16.0	25.5	29.3	36.8	30.0	29.2	26.1
Southeast	2.4	3.4	2.7	3.7	3.5	5.1	6.6	5.5	6.9	7.9	4.3	1.8	4.5
South	6.3	3.9	2.3	2.0	3.4	2.2	4.0	4.0	2.5	2.5	7.0	4.7	3.7
Southwest	8.2	9.2	15.3	15.2	12.6	9.2	15.3	7.7	6.4	10.8	7.0	8.8	10.5
West	19.4	21.9	23.4	28.2	22.0	30.7	33.4	30.5	26.2	22.3	29.2	25.9	26.1
Northwest	4.5	1.9	5.2	5.2	8.2	12.3	10.7	6.3	2.8	3.0	1.5	1.0	5.2
Calm	20.3	18.2	19.8	6.7	1.9	0.5	5.0	5.4	10.8	7.9	12.2	20.9	10.8

FORT HOPE, ONTARIO

	Jan.	Feb.	Mar.	Apr.	May	Jun.	Jul.	Aug.	Sep.	Oct.	Nov.	Dec.	Yr.
North	8.9	9.4	10.3	21.5	23.3	9.9	16.4	14.4	13.5	10.8	9.9	8.4	13.1
Northeast	1.5	2.6	1.9	11.1	12.6	6.8	3.6	3.8	4.9	5.8	3.4	3.1	5.1
East	10.1	9.8	19.7	15.4	17.5	13.0	7.5	5.3	8.5	9.3	6.8	8.6	11.0
Southeast	3.3	1.3	4.2	4.0	3.6	6.8	3.6	1.5	3.3	4.3	3.6	3.3	3.6
South	5.3	9.1	10.6	8.6	10.0	11.1	9.8	11.4	10.9	13.8	12.2	11.4	10.4
Southwest	5.6	4.6	4.8	4.3	3.3	5.2	5.2	11.7	7.2	11.3	8.3	8.4	6.7
West	33.5	26.1	21.6	13.2	8.5	19.2	25.9	29.3	22.7	22.8	28.4	32.3	23.6
Northwest	17.3	20.5	11.1	11.8	7.9	16.2	15.2	7.9	13.5	12.9	14.6	12.5	13.3
Calm	14.5	16.6	15.8	10.1	13.3	11.8	12.8	14.7	15.5	9.0	12.8	12.0	13.2

HALIFAX, NOVA SCOTIA

	Jan.	Feb.	Mar.	Apr.	May	Jun.	Jul.	Aug.	Sep.	Oct.	Nov.	Dec.	Yr.
North	13.4	10.2	10.6	8.7	6.8	4.7	6.0	6.0	8.7	9.7	7.7	11.0	8.6
Northeast	11.8	11.7	17.4	23.3	17.9	10.5	9.0	10.5	14.2	13.7	19.3	12.6	14.3
East	2.6	4.1	4.2	5.0	3.9	5.8	3.6	2.3	2.8	3.1	3.3	2.9	3.8
Southeast	4.4	5.7	7.6	12.8	17.1	15.0	8.0	8.9	9.0	4.8	5.3	7.1	8.8
South	5.3	5.5	8.5	5.8	6.5	9.3	15.8	10.5	5.8	6.3	5.2	4.7	7.4
Southwest	19.2	16.5	17.9	20.3	23.4	33.0	29.9	33.7	24.8	24.5	19.8	13.1	23.0
West	13.6	14.8	9.4	5.6	9.8	10.8	17.0	12.6	13.5	11.4	10.7	12.3	11.8
Northwest	28.7	29.5	24.2	18.0	14.4	10.7	10.2	14.7	20.5	26.0	27.0	34.5	21.5
Calm	1.0	2.0	0.2	0.5	0.2	0.2	0.5	0.8	0.7	0.5	1.7	1.8	0.8

HARRINGTON HARBOUR, QUEBEC

	Jan.	Feb.	Mar.	Apr.	May	Jun.	Jul.	Aug.	Sep.	Oct.	Nov.	Dec.	Yr.
North	22.5	21.1	20.1	20.2	16.5	10.5	17.1	13.2	17.2	18.1	21.9	23.2	18.5
Northeast	10.8	10.9	16.8	21.3	13.9	11.0	11.4	5.2	4.2	5.0	9.3	10.3	10.8
East	5.6	2.5	5.6	14.2	16.0	10.9	9.9	8.1	4.6	7.7	3.5	7.4	8.0
Southeast	1.4	1.1	2.8	3.5	6.3	4.2	5.5	4.4	4.2	3.4	3.3	2.9	3.6
South	6.1	6.4	8.3	8.3	12.2	15.8	8.8	10.3	8.4	5.9	7.7	6.6	8.8
Southwest	8.8	16.3	12.1	10.8	13.7	22.5	21.0	28.3	27.6	16.4	11.5	11.8	16.7
West	19.0	23.1	18.8	12.3	11.9	17.1	18.2	22.1	25.8	27.9	21.8	16.5	19.5
Northwest	25.1	17.7	13.0	8.1	8.7	5.5	7.1	7.2	7.6	15.3	20.0	20.2	13.0
Calm	0.7	0.9	2.5	1.3	0.8	2.5	1.0	1.2	0.4	0.3	1.0	1.1	1.1

HEBRON, LABRADOR

	Jan.	Feb.	Mar.	Apr.	May	Jun.	Jul.	Aug.	Sep.	Oct.	Nov.	Dec.	Yr.
North	5	7	11	16	17	16	14	14	14	14	10	9	12
Northeast	2	3	4	7	9	11	14	11	5	5	8	3	7
East	1	2	3	4	10	14	14	11	10	5	3	2	7
Southeast	0	0	0	1	2	1	3	2	1	2	1	1	1
South	1	1	1	2	2	3	3	4	4	4	2	1	2
Southwest	4	4	4	3	3	3	4	6	7	7	5	3	4
West	59	52	46	35	22	17	17	19	35	38	55	61	38
Northwest	3	3	2	2	3	2	1	2	4	7	5	4	3
Calm	25	28	29	30	32	33	30	31	20	18	11	16	26

JONES SOUND, NORTHWEST TERRITORIES

	Jan.	Feb.	Mar.	Apr.	May	Jun.	Jul.	Aug.	Sep.	Oct.	Nov.	Dec.	Yr.
North	31.1	24.5	26.0	24.0	22.7	18.9	21.9	22.7	41.8	30.7	24.0	26.6	26.3
Northeast	7.5	6.9	3.9	9.2	7.1	3.7	3.2	5.2	11.5	13.2	10.1	6.9	7.4
East	3.9	4.0	4.0	4.6	6.3	1.6	1.1	2.2	6.5	3.6	2.2	2.6	3.6
Southeast	3.4	4.6	7.2	4.0	7.5	9.5	10.6	7.0	2.7	3.9	5.1	4.6	6.0
South	9.0	12.2	7.9	8.4	12.9	19.4	15.7	17.2	2.8	5.4	8.4	7.4	10.6
Southwest	1.0	2.5	1.0	3.4	4.9	9.2	10.9	4.2	2.7	2.7	3.6	2.7	4.1
West	1.2	1.8	1.1	1.2	1.2	2.6	3.6	2.7	3.3	1.2	1.6	1.4	2.0
Northwest	5.4	5.5	5.1	5.9	8.4	6.0	8.6	7.0	17.6	8.1	5.4	6.5	7.5
Calm	37.5	38.0	37.7	39.2	29.0	29.0	24.2	31.5	11.3	31.0	39.5	41.2	32.5

KAMLOOPS, ALBERTA

	Jan.	Feb.	Mar.	Apr.	May	Jun.	Jul.	Aug.	Sep.	Oct.	Nov.	Dec.	Yr.
North	1.9	2.5	2.2	2.1	3.7	3.7	2.9	2.1	2.5	3.0	2.7	1.8	2.7
Northeast	1.2	3.4	3.9	3.7	4.8	4.6	4.2	1.6	4.7	4.0	4.7	3.4	3.8
East	21.1	19.8	26.0	21.5	20.0	19.2	11.4	11.3	14.5	21.0	32.5	26.2	20 5
Southeast	1.7	3.0	5.1	7.0	5.0	8.0	6.8	3.1	4.0	2.2	3.3	1.3	4.2
South	4.3	4.4	7.1	8.2	12.4	11.2	8.8	8.6	7.2	5.8	6.3	8.4	7.6
Southwest	2.3	1.7	2.9	5.5	3.9	4.0	6.0	4.8	4.2	2.9	2.3	1.6	3.5
West	25.1	23.5	25.4	24.5	24.0	21.2	24.0	25.0	20.0	21.2	17.0	24.0	22.7
Northwest	2.4	2.5	3.4	4.8	6.2	6.0	9.0	10.3	4.7	3.5	5.2	1.1	4.9
Calm	40.0	39.2	24.0	22.7	20.0	22.2	27.0	33.2	38.2	36.3	26.0	32.2	30.1

MASSETT, BRITISH COLUMBIA

	Jan.	Feb.	Mar.	Apr.	May	Jun.	Jul.	Aug.	Sep.	Oct.	Nov.	Dec.	Yr.
North	13.1	16.7	10.2	8.6	7.9	6.7	17.6	9.4	10.8	8.5	12.0	13.0	11.2
Northeast	10.9	14.1	11.3	14.0	8.6	6.1	3.2	1.8	4.3	3.6	7.3	12.2	8.1
East	1.8	1.5	1.4	0.5	0.5	1.8	0.5	1.3	0.0	0.0	2.1	1.3	1.1
Southeast	21.0	26.0	23.4	28.6	24.7	20.4	10.6	20.7	28.0	37.0	39.0	28.0	25.6
South	4.1	1.2	0.6	1.7	1.4	4.1	0.2	1.6	3.0	5.9	2.7	3.4	2.6
Southwest	20.0	15.0	18.8	13.0	15.2	15.0	11.9	16.7	20.0	21.0	18.9	16.3	16.8
West	9.0	7.4	11.3	9.6	15.2	12.8	17.6	20.6	8.5	9.3	6.7	7.0	11.2
Northwest	18.5	17.7	23.0	24.0	26.0	32.9	37.5	27.3	25.0	13.4	8.6	16.9	22.5
Calm	1.6	0.4	0.0	0.0	0.5	0.2	0.9	0.6	0.4	1.3	2.7	1.9	2.9

MONTREAL, QUEBEC

	Jan.	Feb.	Mar.	Apr.	May	Jun.	Jul.	Aug.	Sep.	Oct.	Nov.	Dec.	Yr.
North	11.2	9.7	7.6	9.0	7.7	6.3	8.2	10.4	12.4	9.4	8.7	11.3	9.3
Northeast	12.4	14.1	14.2	20.6	17.5	11.4	11.7	9.2	10.8	11.6	16.2	10.4	13.4
East	5.8	6.5	5.7	8.4	6.7	5.2	3.3	5.7	8.0	5.6	5.1	6.2	6.0
Southeast	3.8	4.9	6.1	5.6	6.5	4.0	3.7	4.7	5.2	5.6	5.4	3.9	5.0
South	9.4	6.7	10.4	9.2	8.5	10.2	8.2	10.2	13.0	10.0	7.4	8.5	9.4
Southwest	14.7	14.8	13.2	10.6	13.8	16.0	18.9	17.2	11.8	10.6	16.2	11.7	14.1
West	30.7	29.2	25.7	22.0	25.8	28.1	28.1	26.4	23.2	28.3	25.0	32.0	27.0
Northwest	11.7	13.7	17.0	14.3	13.5	17.8	17.9	15.9	15.3	18.7	16.0	16.0	15.6
Calm	0.3	0.4	0.1	0.2	0.0	0.2	0.0	0.3	0.3	0.2	0.0	0.0	0.2

MOOSE FACTORY, ONTARIO

	Jan.	Feb.	Mar.	Apr.	May	Jun.	Jul.	Aug.	Sep.	Oct.	Nov.	Dec.	Yr.
North	12.2	14.5	20.4	27.0	27.5	21.1	16.5	15.6	13.6	13.3	13.2	12.0	17.3
Northeast	6.7	10.8	17.2	24.7	27.5	34.4	22.0	17.8	12.5	6.7	5.5	4.3	15.9
East	3.3	3.6	3.2	2.2	3.3	3.3	2.2	3.3	4.5	3.3	4.4	2.2	3.2
Southeast	3.3	2.4	3.2	2.2	2.2	2.2	1.1	2.2	4.5	3.3	3.3	2.2	2.7
South	10.0	8.4	8.6	7.9	8.8	10.0	11.0	11.1	11.4	12.2	9.9	12.0	10.1
Southwest	24.4	19.3	14.0	10.1	7.7	11.1	18.7	20.0	21.6	22.2	19.8	29.3	18.2
West	17.8	15.7	12.9	5.6	6.6	6.7	12.1	11.1	13.6	13.3	16.5	15.2	12.2
Northwest	15.6	15.7	11.8	12.4	11.0	5.6	9.9	11.1	11.4	16.7	18.7	15.2	12.9
Calm	6.7	9.6	8.6	7.9	5.5	5.6	6.6	7.8	6.8	8.9	8.8	7.6	7.5

PORT ARTHUR, ONTARIO

	Jan.	Feb.	Mar.	Apr.	May	Jun.	Jul.	Aug.	Sep.	Oct.	Nov.	Dec.	Yr.
North	8.0	7.2	9.5	7.4	7.2	4.9	7.5	5.9	5.0	8.8	8.5	7.5	7.4
Northeast	12.0	16.5	18.3	28.0	28.0	22.9	19.5	14.1	17.2	17.8	11.2	12.7	18.3
East	1.9	3.6	12.5	11.2	12.9	17.1	12.3	12.5	10.0	7.1	4.0	2.1	8.8
Southeast	4.4	4.8	10.7	11.1	13.2	12.8	14.8	12.3	11.2	7.8	4.4	4.6	9.3
South	3.9	5.2	5.8	6.9	7.2	9.0	9.5	10.5	8.4	7.3	3.4	2.7	6.6
Southwest	12.6	9.2	6.8	4.0	3.5	5.9	5.7	5.6	7.3	9.1	11.9	11.2	7.7
West	24.2	19.5	9.9	7.4	5.2	7.3	9.8	13.3	13.9	16.3	25.9	25.0	14.8
Northwest	28.2	29.0	23.0	21.0	17.8	14.2	13.6	21.4	22.6	22.2	26.8	31.4	22.6
Calm	4.8	5.0	3.5	3.0	5.0	5.9	7.3	4.4	4.4	3.6	3.9	2.8	4.5

PORT AUX BASQUES, NEWFOUNDLAND

	Jan.	Feb.	Mar.	Apr.	May	Jun.	Jul.	Aug.	Sep.	Oct.	Nov.	Dec.	Yr.
North	6.3	6.2	4.8	6.8	4.2	2.5	3.7	5.0	6.0	6.1	7.3	7.1	5.5
Northeast	10.3	11.7	17.0	21.0	12.3	5.2	4.8	7.6	12.5	12.9	17.8	17.9	12.6
East	5.5	9.7	15.5	22.3	22.3	23.8	26.6	19.2	13.7	10.6	9.2	7.9	15.5
Southeast	5.6	6.7	9.5	11.3	20.2	27.2	23.4	19.0	16.8	9.2	7.2	7.7	13.6
South	4.4	4.4	2.0	1.8	1.5	3.8	3.9	2.9	3.2	2.9	1.8	2.7	2.9
Southwest	9.2	8.1	4.8	5.0	5.0	5.7	6.1	11.5	9.3	9.8	12.8	10.3	8.0
West	17.2	18.0	8.5	8.0	11.0	10.7	8.6	7.6	9.5	8.6	6.8	10.3	10.4
Northwest	40.4	34.3	34.5	22.3	22.1	20.0	19.2	23.7	25.8	37.2	34.7	34.2	29.0
Calm	1.1	0.9	3.4	1.5	1.4	1.1	3.7	3.5	3.2	2.7	2.4	1.9	2.1

PORT NELSON MANITOBA

	Jan.	Feb.	Mar.	Apr.	May	Jun.	Jul.	Aug.	Sep.	Oct.	Nov.	Dec.	Yr.
North	1.6	6.2	13.7	6.6	9.7	14.5	8.6	6.5	8.3	3.6	2.0	1.6	6.8
Northeast	0.6	2.3	11.3	21.0	36.0	37.5	26.8	23.0	17.8	9.0	1.6	2.6	15.8
East	6.2	2.9	5.6	6.6	7.3	14.5	13.3	16.4	12.1	13.9	5.0	5.5	9.1
Southeast	5.3	2.3	4.8	5.3	1.8	2.2	6.4	6.5	6.6	3.2	4.6	3.5	4.4
South	13.9	10.4	7.0	8.2	5.6	6.7	9.6	7.3	11.1	10.3	8.6	11.2	9.4
Southwest	20.0	12.5	8.3	3.9	3.8	6.0	5.9	8.6	8.1	8.7	13.2	12.0	9.2
West	33.6	28.4	17.2	10.8	4.3	6.4	9.7	12.4	13.3	23.0	34.2	42.0	19.5
Northwest	18.2	34.0	30.2	36.4	31.0	12.2	17.3	18.0	22.1	27.0	29.0	21.6	24.8
Calm	0.6	1.2	1.9	1.2	0.5	0.0	2.4	1.3	0.6	1.3	1.6	0.0	1.0

PRINCE ALBERT, SASKATCHEWAN

	Jan.	Feb.	Mar.	Apr.	May	Jun.	Jul.	Aug.	Sep.	Oct.	Nov.	Dec.	Yr.
North	7.6	6.9	9.2	13.0	13.7	13.2	8.0	8.1	10.8	10.0	7.0	8.6	9.8
Northeast	6.6	5.3	6.1	9.7	12.2	6.7	5.3	5.8	5.7	5.8	4.6	5.8	6.6
East	14.9	11.6	15.8	15.7	15.0	15.2	11.8	14.6	14.2	10.5	15.4	10.7	13.8
Southeast	4.8	2.6	6.4	8.9	12.4	12.2	9.2	6.3	6.7	6.9	4.8	3.9	7.1
South	4.9	10.1	12.9	9.0	9.0	8.3	8.2	5.3	8.8	10.5	8.5	6.8	8.5
Southwest	13.6	12.7	11.4	7.0	7.2	7.0	6.4	5.6	7.2	11.1	16.4	13.9	9.9
West	22.1	22.4	16.3	12.2	11.5	13.7	24.3	24.3	20.7	18.6	21.0	27.0	19.5
Northwest	16.7	17.3	11.1	13.0	12.2	13.0	16.2	17.8	16.7	18.8	15.4	15.5	15.3
Calm	8.8	11.1	10.8	11.5	6.8	10.7	10.6	12.2	9.2	7.8	6.9	7.8	9.5

PRINCE GEORGE, BRITISH COLUMBIA

	Jan.	Feb.	Mar.	Apr.	May	Jun.	Jul.	Aug.	Sep.	Oct.	Nov.	Dec.	Yr.
North	11.3	11.3	7.5	4.1	4.1	2.6	0.5	0.3	2.8	0.7	3.9	5.1	4.6
Northeast	1.1	1.5	2.1	1.9	2.2	1.5	0.5	0.3	1.3	2.7	3.9	3.1	1.8
East	0.5	0.0	0.0	0.0	0.3	0.0	0.0	0.3	0.0	0.6	0.0	0.0	0.2
Southeast	2.1	0.3	2.4	1.9	1.9	1.0	1.6	0.3	0.5	3.8	2.9	2.2	1.7
South	25.0	22.0	19.9	23.0	17.5	15.4	15.0	14.8	14.4	22.1	30.0	19.2	19.8
Southwest	12.5	9.1	19.6	18.0	15.8	17.9	23.0	15.9	12.3	17.8	15.1	18.3	16.3
West	0.8	4.7	7.5	4.5	5.7	8.2	10.6	8.1	7.4	3.3	1.8	1.3	5.3
Northwest	2.7	7.1	7.0	7.5	7.6	3.6	2.6	5.7	3.4	6.4	3.4	5.6	5.2
Calm	44.0	44.0	34.0	39.1	44.9	49.8	46.2	54.3	57.9	42.6	39.0	45.2	45.1

QU'APPELLE, SASKATCHEWAN

	Jan.	Feb.	Mar.	Apr.	May	Jun.	Jul.	Aug.	Sep.	Oct.	Nov.	Dec.	Yr.
North	4.7	6.9	7.1	9.2	8.9	8.2	9.5	8.2	7.5	6.0	5.2	4.5	7.3
Northeast	3.7	6.9	7.1	13.2	8.9	8.5	7.2	5.2	7.1	4.5	3.6	4.0	6.6
East	4.0	6.3	9.2	10.7	10.7	11.4	7.8	7.6	7.0	6.0	3.5	4.5	7.5
Southeast	11.3	5.1	11.9	12.0	15.4	16.2	12.9	12.0	11.0	8.0	8.2	6.1	10.9
South	8.5	8.1	11.0	11.5	11.8	9.5	13.5	10.3	16.5	14.7	13.1	8.5	11.4
Southwest	12.1	13.6	14.2	8.2	10.7	11.0	11.9	10.6	10.0	15.3	17.2	14.7	12.4
West	15.5	14.7	14.6	10.7	9.0	9.0	14.4	19.3	15.3	14.8	18.3	19.8	14.6
Northwest	37.1	35.0	23.1	22.5	23.0	23.2	21.2	25.6	22.6	29.1	28.2	34.0	27.0
Calm	3.1	3.4	1.8	2.0	1.6	3.0	1.6	1.2	3.0	1.6	1.7	3.9	2.3

ST. JOHNS, NEWFOUNDLAND

	Jan.	Feb.	Mar.	Apr.	May	Jun.	Jul.	Aug.	Sep.	Oct.	Nov.	Dec.	Yr.
North	5.5	4.3	6.7	9.3	6.5	6.7	3.2	7.4	4.0	4.1	4.3	5.2	5.6
Northeast	7.6	10.4	15.1	23.9	22.0	14.8	12.4	9.7	14.8	11.0	13.8	11.1	13.9
East	2.1	1.6	4.3	5.7	7.9	5.2	7.1	4.8	2.7	1.2	1.2	1.8	3.8
Southeast	11.0	10.2	13.0	12.6	12.5	11.9	11.5	12.2	9.6	9.7	11.2	10.6	11.3
South	4.0	6.1	3.4	7.0	7.8	8.7	10.8	13.1	4.6	5.1	4.7	4.3	6.5
Southwest	28.3	32.5	28.4	21.1	24.5	39.5	38.3	41.7	47.7	39.3	31.0	32.8	33.8
West	6.1	6.5	5.8	3.0	3.8	3.9	8.3	4.8	3.5	4.0	4.2	1.6	4.6
Northwest	33.9	26.2	21.7	16.3	14.6	8.0	7.0	5.9	11.9	23.8	27.8	31.7	19.2
Calm	1.5	2.2	1.6	1.1	0.4	1.3	1.4	0.4	1.2	1.8	1.8	0.9	1.3

SOUTHWEST POINT, QUEBEC

	Jan.	Feb.	Mar.	Apr.	May	Jun.	Jul.	Aug.	Sep.	Oct.	Nov.	Dec.	Yr.
North	18.3	15.6	19.0	16.2	16.4	12.4	12.6	16.7	16.3	18.5	20.6	19.6	16.8
Northeast	11.0	8.2	9.7	13.3	9.9	5.2	6.3	3.8	7.4	7.4	9.6	13.7	8.8
East	6.5	6.5	6.6	7.8	5.2	3.1	2.8	2.3	2.9	4.4	9.0	7.9	5.4
Southeast	6.1	8.2	12.0	20.9	28.5	31.1	31.3	29.0	23.1	13.4	10.8	8.2	18.5
South	7.8	11.2	12.9	9.0	9.5	15.7	14.7	13.9	11.1	10.5	9.7	7.9	11.2
Southwest	4.5	4.5	2.3	2.9	2.3	2.7	4.0	5.5	6.4	4.8	7.6	7.8	4.6
West	8.1	8.9	5.7	3.9	4.2	4.9	5.6	5.5	6.6	10.0	8.3	6.5	6.4
Northwest	33.7	31.8	25.3	18.8	15.7	14.9	12.7	18.0	22.7	27.3	22.6	25.0	22.4
Calm	4.0	5.1	6.5	7.2	8.3	10.0	10.0	7.3	3.5	3.7	1.8	3.4	5.9

TORONTO, ONTARIO

	Jan.	Feb.	Mar.	Apr.	May	Jun.	Jul.	Aug.	Sep.	Oct.	Nov.	Dec.	Yr.
North	10.0	10.4	9.4	9.7	9.7	9.7	10.6	12.7	14.5	11.7	10.8	9.7	10.7
Northeast	11.6	11.5	16.3	16.2	20.3	19.6	15.0	13.4	11.3	13.5	10.3	13.2	14.3
East	6.2	8.8	11.5	16.9	14.2	14.9	12.2	15.4	14.2	13.5	10.2	8.7	12.2
Southeast	5.5	3.6	3.1	3.6	4.5	5.2	4.3	5.8	6.3	3.7	4.5	4.2	4.5
South	6.1	4.1	7.0	7.2	7.0	9.7	11.2	9.9	8.7	7.3	4.6	4.4	7.3
Southwest	23.7	16.7	15.8	15.8	15.6	14.9	20.5	16.0	17.2	15.4	22.2	20.0	17.8
West	25.6	27.7	15.3	13.8	13.2	13.0	12.1	14.2	12.6	21.2	22.5	27.0	18.2
Northwest	11.1	16.5	21.2	16.6	15.0	12.0	13.5	11.8	14.6	13.2	14.6	12.6	14.5
Calm	0.2	0.7	0.4	0.2	0.5	1.0	0.6	0.8	0.6	0.5	0.3	0.2	0.5

VANCOUVER, BRITISH COLUMBIA

	Jan.	Feb.	Mar.	Apr.	May	Jun.	Jul.	Aug.	Sep.	Oct.	Nov.	Dec.	Yr.
North	1.1	1.4	0.5	1.9	1.4	1.8	3.3	2.9	1.3	1.1	1.2	0.8	1.6
Northeast	7.1	9.0	11.0	6.2	3.2	3.0	2.5	1.9	4.7	3.4	7.0	11.6	5.9
East	38.0	31.6	26.3	29.3	23.0	22.2	16.3	16.6	16.5	21.2	34.1	36.4	25.9
Southeast	15.0	11.8	11.1	11.3	13.0	12.2	14.5	14.0	12.2	13.7	10.8	15.3	12.9
South	3.7	3.3	2.6	3.3	4.4	3.2	1.9	2.6	2.5	2.9	3.0	3.2	3.0
Southwest	7.1	5.5	11.3	12.8	15.8	13.0	14.3	11.0	8.0	4.3	4.5	5.1	9.4
West	8.7	10.4	15.0	12.4	12.4	7.8	10.2	10.8	14.2	14.9	8.3	5.5	10.9
Northwest	1.7	8.0	8.6	11.8	10.4	15.2	13.0	14.2	13.9	9.5	4.6	3.4	9.5
Calm	17.6	19.0	13.6	11.0	16.4	21.6	24.0	26.0	26.7	29.0	26.5	18.7	20.9

WHITE RIVER, ONTARIO

	Jan.	Feb.	Mar.	Apr.	May	Jun.	Jul.	Aug.	Sep.	Oct.	Nov.	Dec.	Yr.
North	10.5	13.4	18.2	20.8	24.0	12.3	10.1	6.9	8.8	11.8	11.7	9.7	13.3
Northeast	2.0	3.9	3.5	7.5	5.8	4.7	3.1	2.0	3.3	2.9	3.5	3.2	3.8
East	3.0	1.6	5.3	5.8	7.1	6.8	3.2	2.6	3.7	4.0	4.5	5.3	4.4
Southeast	4.3	3.2	4.6	7.7	6.0	6.3	8.1	8.1	10.7	8.3	6.0	6.2	6.6
South	10.8	10.2	10.8	7.7	11.4	12.5	11.3	13.2	11.7	10.0	12.2	9.4	10.8
Southwest	4.4	5.3	4.6	5.7	7.0	13.3	15.8	13.2	8.5	8.0	9.5	6.3	8.5
West	10.7	9.5	8.5	9.5	12.0	13.9	13.4	15.0	11.0	9.9	9.0	12.3	11.2
Northwest	11.3	9.9	11.2	9.3	9.2	9.2	7.4	7.6	9.0	9.1	16.0	10.6	10.0
Calm	43.0	43.0	33.3	26.0	17.5	21.0	27.6	31.4	33.3	36.0	27.6	37.0	31.4

WINNIPEG, MANITOBA

	Jan.	Feb.	Mar.	Apr.	May	Jun.	Jul.	Aug.	Sep.	Oct.	Nov.	Dec.	Yr.
North	11.3	11.0	17.8	22.8	24.2	17.8	15.5	11.2	11.7	11.5	9.8	8.3	14.4
Northeast	3.0	3.2	5.6	10.2	8.9	8.5	6.6	5.4	7.1	5.6	3.4	2.7	5.8
East	3.8	3.7	6.3	8.0	6.5	8.2	6.3	5.8	8.7	5.6	4.0	4.8	5.9
Southeast	19.0	13.7	13.2	11.0	16.5	21.0	16.5	20.0	20.0	18.2	21.0	15.2	17.2
South	10.5	10.7	11.8	11.4	10.3	11.4	14.6	12.2	10.3	10.0	10.8	12.5	11.4
Southwest	11.2	13.5	11.6	6.2	8.1	8.6	9.8	11.6	11.4	13.3	18.0	16.6	11.7
West	14.3	18.7	14.2	9.7	7.8	8.5	11.5	11.8	12.7	14.9	12.5	14.5	12.6
Northwest	25.0	23.0	16.7	18.2	14.7	13.2	15.6	19.2	17.8	20.6	20.4	24.1	19.0
Calm	1.9	2.5	2.8	2.5	3.0	2.8	3.6	2.8	0.3	0.3	0.4	1.3	2.0

INDEX

INDEX